美国原版经典数学课本

KEY TO RAY'S ALGEBRA

美国中学数学

代数（上下册）[答案]

JOSEPH RAY

上海三联书店

KEY

TO

NEW ELEMENTARY ALGEBRA.

The numbers in parentheses refer to the corresponding numbers of example, under the same Article in the Algebra.

DIVISION.

Remark.—It is presumed no difficulty will be experienced in solving any of the questions in addition, subtraction, or multiplication. We present the operation of a few of the more difficult examples in division.

Article 79.

Note.—The terms in examples 12 and 17, require to be arranged; after which, the operations present no difficulty.

(14)

$$\begin{array}{l|l}
4a^4-5a^2x^2+x^4 & 2a^2-3ax+x^2 \\
\underline{4a^4-6a^3x+2a^2x^2} & (2a^2+3ax+x^2 \\
\quad 6a^3x-7a^2x^2 & \quad \textit{Ans.} \\
\quad \underline{6a^3x-9a^2x^2+3ax^3} & \\
\qquad +2a^2x^2-3ax^3+x^4 & \\
\qquad \underline{2a^2x^2-3ax^3+x^4} &
\end{array}$$

(15)

$$\begin{array}{l|l}
x^4-y^4 & x-y \\
\underline{x^4-x^3y} & (x^3+x^2y+xy^2+y^3 \\
\quad +x^3y & \quad \textit{Ans.} \\
\quad \underline{x^3y-x^2y^2} & \\
\qquad +x^2y^2 & \\
\qquad \underline{x^2y^2-xy^3} & \\
\qquad\quad +xy^3-y^4 & \\
\qquad\quad \underline{xy^3-y^4} &
\end{array}$$

(18)

$$
\begin{array}{l|l}
4x^4-64 & 2x-4 \\
4x^4-8x^3 & (2x^3+4x^2+8x+16 \\
\quad +8x^3 & \qquad Ans. \\
\quad 8x^3-16x^2 & \\
\qquad +16x^2 & \\
\qquad 16x^2-32x & \\
\qquad\quad +32x-64 & \\
\qquad\quad 32x-64 &
\end{array}
$$

(21)

$$
\begin{array}{l|l}
y^3+1 & y+1 \\
y^3+y^2 & (y^2-y+1 \\
\quad -y^2 & \quad Ans. \\
\quad -y^2-y & \\
\qquad +y+1 & \\
\qquad y+1 &
\end{array}
$$

(24)

$$
\begin{array}{l|l}
x^6-3x^4y^2+3x^2y^4-y^6 & x^3-3x^2y+3xy^2-y^3 \\
x^6-3x^5y+3x^4y^2-x^3y^3 & (x^3+3x^2y+3xy^2+y^3, \quad Ans. \\
\quad +3x^5y-6x^4y^2+x^3y^3+3x^2y^4 & \\
\quad 3x^5y-9x^4y^2+9x^3y^3-3x^2y^4 & \\
\qquad +3x^4y^2-8x^3y^3+6x^2y^4 & \\
\qquad 3x^4y^2-9x^3y^3+9x^2y^4-3xy^5 & \\
\qquad\quad +x^3y^3-3x^2y^4+3xy^5-y^6 & \\
\qquad\quad x^3y^3-3x^2y^4+3xy^5-y^6 &
\end{array}
$$

FACTORING.

REMARKS.—In solving the examples in factoring, the pupil should explain why the given quantity can be separated into factors. Thus, $4a^2x^4-9b^2y^6=(2ax^2+3by^3)(2ax^2-3by^3)$, because it is the difference of the squares of two monomials, $2ax^2$ and $3by^3$. Again, x^3+1 can be separated into two factors, because it is the sum of the odd powers of two quantities x and 1, (Art. 94, 5th); and one of the factors is $x+1$.

It is shown in Art. 215, that the *direct* method of resolving a quadratic trinomial into its factors, is to place it equal to zero, and then find the roots of the equation; yet as the *indirect* method explained in Art. 95, presents no difficulty, and is much shorter than the direct method, it should always be taught. Let it be kept distinctly in mind, that the whole difficulty consists in finding two numbers whose *sum* is equal to the coëfficient of the second term, and whose *product* is equal to the third term.

Article 95.

(2) $a^2+7a+12=(a+3)(a+4)$; because $+3+4=7$, and $3\times4=12$.

(3) $x^2-5x+6=(x-2)(x-3)$; because -2 and $-3=-5$, and $-2\times-3=+6$.

(4) $x^2+x-6=(x+3)(x-2)$; because $-2+3=+1$, and $-2\times3=-6$.

(5) $x^2+x-2=(x+2)(x-1)$; because $+2-1=+1$, and $-1\times2=-2$.

(6) $x^2-13x+40=(x-5)(x-8)$; because -5 and $-8=-13$, and $-5\times8=40$.

(7) $x^2-7x-8=(x-8)(x+1)$; because $-8+1=-7$, and $-8\times1=-8$.

(8) $x^2-x-30=(x-6)(x+5)$; because $-6+5=-1$, and $-6\times5=-30$.

(9) $3x^2+12x-15=3(x^2+4x-5)=3(x+5)(x-1)$.

(10) $2abx^2-14abx-60ab=2ab(x^2-7x-30)=2ab(x-10)(x+3)$.

(11) $2x^3-4x^2-30x=2x(x^2-2x-15)=2x(x-5)(x+3)$.

Article 96.

Note.—In performing the operations on the slate or blackboard, a line should be drawn across each canceled factor. We have not the means, except in the case of figures, of representing this by type.

(2) $\dfrac{(x-3)(x^2-1)}{x-1}=\dfrac{(x-3)(x+1)(x-1)}{(x-1)}=(x-3)(x+1)$
$=x^2-2x-3$.

(3) $\dfrac{(z^3+1)(z^2-1)}{z+1}=\dfrac{(z^3+1)(z-1)(z+1)}{z+1}=(z^3+1)(z^3-1)$
$=z^4-z^3+z-1$.

(4) $\dfrac{(x^2-5x+6)(x^2-7x+12)}{x^2-6x+9}=\dfrac{(x-2)(x-3)(\qquad)(x-4)}{(x-3)(x-3)}$
$=(x-2)(x-4)$.

GREATEST COMMON DIVISOR.

Note.—All the examples, Art 106, may be solved by merely separating the quantities into their factors, by the rules for factoring, Arts. 94, 95.

Article 106.

(5) $5a^2+5ax=5a(a+x)$

By omitting the factor $5a$, and dividing a^2-x^2 by the other factor $a+x$, we find there is no remainder; therefore, $a+x$ is the G. C. D.

(6) $x^3-a^2x=x(x^2-a^2)$

$$\begin{array}{l|l} x^3-a^3 & x^2-a^2 \\ \underline{x^3-a^2x} & (x \\ a^2x-a^3 & \\ a^2(x-a) & \end{array}$$

After dividing, we find the first remainder contains a factor a^2 not contained in x^2-a^2; hence, it is not a factor of the G. C. D., and should be omitted. See Note 3.

$$\begin{array}{l|l} x^2-a^2 & x-a,\ \text{G. C. D.} \\ \underline{x^2-ax} & (x+a \\ ax-a^2 & \\ \underline{ax-a^2} & \end{array}$$

(7) $x^3-c^2x=x(x^2-c^2)$

$$\begin{array}{l|l} x^2+2cx+c^2 & x^2-c^2 \\ \underline{x^2-c^2} & (1 \\ 2cx+2c^2 & \\ 2c(x+c) & \end{array}$$

$$\begin{array}{l|l} x^2-c^2 & x+c,\ \text{G. C. D.} \\ \underline{x^2+cx} & (x-c \\ -cx-c^2 & \\ \underline{-cx-c^2} & \end{array}$$

(8) x^2+5x+6

$$\begin{array}{l|l} x^2+5x+6 & x^2+2x-3 \\ \underline{x^2+2x-3} & (1 \\ 3x+9 & \\ 3(x+3) & \end{array}$$

$$\begin{array}{l|l} x^2+2x-3 & x+3,\ \text{G. C. D.} \\ \underline{x^2+3x} & (x-1 \\ -x-3 & \\ \underline{-x-3} & \end{array}$$

(9)

$$\begin{array}{l|l} 6a^2+11ax+3x^2 & 6a^2+7ax-3x^2 \\ \underline{6a^2+7ax-3x^2} & (1 \\ 4ax+6x^2; & \end{array}$$

by factoring this, we get $2x(2a+3x)$

$$\begin{array}{l|l} 6a^2+7ax-3x^2 & 2a+3x \end{array}$$

By completing this division, we find there is no remainder hence, $2a+3x$ is the G. C. D.

(10)
$$a^4-x^4 \quad |\underline{a^3+a^2x-ax^2-x^3}$$
$$\underline{a^4+a^3x-a^2x^2-ax^3} \quad (a-x$$
$$-a^3x+a^2x^2+ax^3-x^4$$
$$\underline{-a^3x-a^2x^2+ax^3+x^4}$$
$$2a^2x^2-2x^4; \text{ then, by factoring,}$$
$$2x^2(a^2-x^2)$$
$$a^3+a^2x-ax^2-x^3 \quad |\underline{a^2-x^2}$$

By completing the division, we find there is no remainder; hence, a^2-x^2 is the G. C. D.

(11)
$$a^3-a^2x+3ax^2-3x^3 \quad |\underline{a^2-5ax+4x^2}$$
$$\underline{a^3-5a^2x+4ax^2} \quad (a+4x$$
$$+4a^2x-ax^2-3x^3$$
$$\underline{4a^2x-20ax^2+16x^3}$$
$$+19ax^2-19x^3; \text{ by factoring this, we get}$$
$$19x^2(a-x)$$

By dividing $a^2-5ax+4x^2$ by $a-x$, we find there is no remainder; hence, $a-x$ is the G. C. D.

(12) $a^2x^4-a^2y^4=a^2(x^4-y^4)$: $x^5+x^3y^2=x^3(x^2+y^2)$.

By the principle of Note 3, neither of the factors a^2 or x^3, can form factors of the G. C. D.; then, by dividing x^4-y^4 by x^2+y^2, we find there is no remainder; hence, the latter quantity is the required G. C. D.

(13)
$$a^{13}-x^{13} \quad |\underline{a^5-x^5}$$
$$\underline{a^{13}-a^8x^5} \quad (a^8+a^3x^5$$
$$+a^8x^5-x^{13}$$
$$\underline{a^8x^5-a^3x^{10}}$$
$$+a^3x^{10}-x^{13}$$
$$x^{10}(a^3-x^3)$$

$$a^5-x^5 \quad |\underline{a^3-x^3}$$
$$\underline{a^5-a^2x^3} \quad (a^2$$
$$a^2x^3-x^5$$
$$x^3(a^2-x^2)$$
$$a^3-x^3 \quad |\underline{a^2-x^2}$$
$$\underline{a^3-ax^2} \quad (a$$
$$+ax^2-x^3$$
$$x^2(a-x)$$

By dividing a^2-x^2 by $a-x$, we find there is no remainder hence, $a-x$ is the G. C. D. sought.

LEAST COMMON MULTIPLE.

NOTE.—The pupil should be reminded, that the operation of finding the L. C. M. in algebra, involves precisely the same principles as in arithmetic.

(4)

$a-x$	$4a^2(a-x)$	$6ax^4(a^2-x^2)$
$2a$	$4a^2$	$6ax^4(a+x)$
	$2a$	$3x^4(a+x)$

$(a-x)\times 2a\times 2a\times 3x^4(a+x)=12a^2x^4(a^2-x^2)$, *Ans.*

(5)

$x-y$	$10a^2x^2(x-y)$	$15x^5(x+y)$	$12(x^2-y^2)$
$x+y$	$10a^2x^2$	$15x^5(x+y)$	$12(x+y)$
2	$10a^2x^2$	$15x^5$	12
3	$5a^2x^2$	$15x^5$	6
$5x^2$	$5a^2x^2$	$5x^5$	2
	a^2	x^3	2

$(x-y)(x+y)\times 2\times 3\times 5x^2\times a^2\times x^3\times 2=60a^2x^5(x^2-y^2)$, *Ans.*

ALGEBRAIC FRACTIONS.

REMARK.—The pupil can experience but little difficulty in solving any of the examples in fractions, if he is well acquainted with the fundamental operations, and factoring. We present solutions of the only examples likely to occasion difficulty.

Article 128.

(10) $\frac{3z^3-24z+9}{4z^3-32z+12}=\frac{3(z^3-8z+3)}{4(z^3-8z+3)}=\frac{3}{4}$, *Ans.*

(11) $\frac{n^2-2n+1}{n^2-1}=\frac{(n-1)(n-1)}{(n+1)(n-1)}=\frac{n-1}{n+1}$, *Ans.*

(12) $\frac{x^3-xy^2}{x^4-y^4}=\frac{x(x^2-y^2)}{(x^2+y^2)(x^2-y^2)}=\frac{x}{x^2+y^2}$ *Ans.*

$$(13)\quad \frac{x^2-y^2}{x^2-2xy+y^2}=\frac{(x+y)(x-y)}{(x-y)(x-y)}=\frac{x+y}{x-y},\ \textit{Ans}$$

$$(14)\quad \frac{x^3-ax^2}{x^2-2ax+a^2}=\frac{x^2(x-a)}{(x-a)(x-a)}=\frac{x^2}{x-a},\ \textit{Ans.}$$

$$(15)\quad \frac{x^2+2x-15}{x^2+8x+15}=\frac{(x+5)(x-3)}{(x+5)(x+3)}=\frac{x-3}{x+3},\ \textit{Ans.}$$

Article 129.

$$(4)\quad \frac{x^3y^2+x^2y^3}{ax^2y+axy^2}=\frac{xy(x^2y+xy^2)}{a(x^2y+xy^2)}=\frac{xy}{a},\ \textit{Ans.}$$

$$(5)\quad \frac{x^2+2x-3}{x^2+5x+6}=\frac{(x+3)(x-1)}{(x+3)(x+2)}=\frac{x-1}{x+2},\ \textit{Ans.}$$

Article 140.

$$(8)\quad \frac{x}{a+x}\times\frac{a^2-x^2}{x^2}\times\frac{a}{a-x}=\frac{x(a+x)(a-x)a}{(a+x)x^2(a-x)}=\frac{a}{x},\ \textit{Ans.}$$

$$(11)\quad c+\frac{cx}{c-x}=\frac{c^2}{c-x};\ \frac{c^2}{c-x}\times\frac{c^2-x^2}{x+1}=\frac{c^2(c+x)(c-x)}{(c-x)(x+1)}=$$

$$\frac{c^2(c+x)}{x+1},\ \textit{Ans.}$$

Article 142.

$$(14)\quad \frac{2x^2}{a^3+x^3}\div\frac{x}{a+x}=\frac{2x^2}{a^3+x^3}\times\frac{a+x}{x}=\frac{2x^2(a+x)}{(a+x)(a^2-ax+x^2)x}=$$

$$\frac{2x}{a^2-ax+x^2},\ \textit{Ans.}$$

Article 144.

(3)

$$\begin{array}{l|l} ax & a-x \\ \hline ax-x^2 & x+\frac{x^2}{a}+\frac{x^3}{a^2}+\ \&c. \\ \hline \quad +x^2 & \\ \quad +x^2-\frac{x^3}{a} & \\ \hline \qquad +\frac{x^3}{a} & \\ \qquad +\frac{x^3}{a}-\frac{x^4}{a^2} & \\ \hline \end{array}$$

(5)

$$\begin{array}{l|l} x+2 & x+1 \\ \hline x+1 & 1+\frac{1}{x}-\frac{1}{x^2}+\ \&c. \\ \hline \quad 1 & \\ \quad 1+\frac{1}{x} & \\ \hline \quad -\frac{1}{x} & \\ \quad -\frac{1}{x}-\frac{1}{x^2} & \\ \hline \end{array}$$

SIMPLE EQUATIONS.

Remark.—The only difficulty pupils will be likely to experience in solving the examples, Art. 154, 155, will be where a fraction whose numerator contains two or more terms, is preceded by the sign minus, as in Ex. 5, Art. 154, or in Ex. 12, &c., Art. 155. This may be obviated by writing the numerator of the fraction in a vinculum when the equation is cleared of fractions, and then proceeding to perform the operations indicated. It will thus be seen, that the effect of the minus sign before a fraction, is to change the sign of each term of the numerator. (See Art. 132.)

QUESTIONS PRODUCING SIMPLE EQUATIONS.

Article 156.

(16) Let $x=$ A's share; then, $2x=$ B's, and $x+2x=42$; from which $x=14$.

(17) Let $x=$ the first part; then, $2x=$ the second, and $3x=$ the third, and $x+2x+3x=48$; from which $x=8$.

(18) Let $x=$ the first part; then, $3x=$ the second, and $3x\times2=6x=$ the third part.
Therefore, $x+3x+6x=60$; from which $x=6$.

(19) Let $x=$ the number of each;
then, $1x$ or $x=$ cost of the apples,
$2x=$ " " lemons,
and $5x=$ " " oranges.
Therefore, $x+2x+5x=56$; from which $x=7$.

(20) Let $x=$ cost of an apple; then, $2x=$ cost of a lemon, $5x=$ cost of all the apples, and $3\times2x=$ cost of all the lemons.
Therefore, $5x+6x=22$; from which $x=2$.

(21) Let $x=$ C's age; then, $2x=$ B's age, and $4x=$ A's age.
Therefore, $x+2x+4x=98$; from which $x-14$

(22) Let $x=$ A's cents; then, $3x=$ B's, $x+\frac{3x}{3}=2x=$ C's, and $3x+2x=5x=$ D's.
Therefore, $x+3x+2x+5x=44$; from which $x=4$.

(24) Let $5x$ and $7x$ represent the numbers, since $5x$ is to $7x$ as 5 is to 7.
Then, $5x+7x=60$; from which $x=5$.
Hence, $5x=25$, and $7x=35$.

(25) Let $2x$, $3x$, and $5x$ represent the parts; then,
$2x+3x+5x=60$; from which $x=6$.
Hence, $2x=12$, $3x=18$, and $5x=30$.

(26) Let $2x$, $3x$, and $5x$ represent the parts; these will evidently fulfill the second condition, since $\frac{1}{2}$ of the first, $\frac{1}{3}$ of the second, and $\frac{1}{5}$ of the third, are each equal to x
Then, $2x+3x+5x=60$; from which $x=6$.
Hence, $2x=12$, $3x=18$, and $5x=30$.

(27) Let $x=$ the number.
Then, $\frac{x}{2}+\frac{x}{3}+\frac{x}{4}=65$; from which $x=60$.
Or, let $12x=$ the number; then, $6x+4x+3x=65$;
from which $x=5$, and $12x=60$.
To avoid fractions, we choose $12x$, because it is a multiple of 2, 3, and 4.

(28) Let $x=$ the number.
Then, $\frac{x}{5}-\frac{x}{7}=4$; from which $x=70$.
By putting $35x$ for the number, we may avoid fractions.

(29) Let $x=$ A's age; then, $2\frac{4}{5}x=$B's.
Therefore, $x+\frac{14x}{5}=76$; or, $\frac{5x}{5}+\frac{14x}{5}=\frac{19x}{5}=76$.
Clearing of fractions, $19x=76\times5$.
Dividing by 19, $x=4\times5=20$, A's age.

(30) Let $x=$ C's share; then, $\frac{3x}{4}=$ B's, and $\frac{3}{5}$ of $\frac{3x}{4}=\frac{9x}{20}=$A's
Therefore, $\frac{9x}{20}+\frac{3x}{4}+x=440$; from which $x=200$.

(31) Let $3x=$ distance from A to B; then, $5x=$ distance from B to C; also, $\frac{3x}{3}+5x=6x$, and $\frac{6x}{3}=2x=$ distance from C to D.
Therefore, $3x+5x+2x=120$; from which $x=12$.
Hence, $3x=36$, and $5x=60$.

(32) Let $3x=$ capital.

Then, $3x-\frac{3x}{3}=2x=$ capital at close of 1st year;

$2x+\frac{2}{5}$ of $2x=2x+\frac{4x}{5}=\frac{14x}{5}=$ cap. close 2d year:

$\frac{14x}{5}-\frac{1}{7}$ of $\frac{14x}{5}=\frac{14x}{5}-\frac{2x}{5}=\frac{12x}{5}=$ cap. 3d year.

Therefore, $\frac{12x}{5}=1236$; from which $3x=1545$.

(33) Let $x=$ rent last year.

Then, $x+\frac{5x}{100}=168$; whence, $x=160$.

(34) Let $x=$ the less part; then, $x+6=$the greater.
Therefore, $x+x+6=32$; whence, $x=13$.

(35) Let $x=$ votes of unsuccessful candidate.
Then, $x+50=$ votes of successful candidate.
Therefore, $x+x+50=256$; whence, $x=103$.

(36) Let $x=$ A's; then, $x+100=$B's;
and $x+100+270=x+370=$ C's.
Therefore, $x+x+100+x+370=1520$;
from which $x=350$.

(37) Let $x=$ number of women;
then, $x+4=$ " men,
and $2x+4+10=2x+14=$ number of children.
Therefore, $x+x+4+2x+14=90$; whence, $x=18$.

(38) Let $x=$ number of yards cut off;
then, $x-9=$ number of yards remaining.
Therefore, $x+x-9=45$; whence, $x=27$.

(39) Let $x=$the number; then, $7x-20=20-x$;
from which $x=5$.

(40) Let $x=$each daughter's share; then, $2x=$ each son's share
$3x=$ what all the daughters will receive;
$4x=$ " both the sons will receive;
Then, $7x-500=$ what the widow will receive.
Therefore, $3x+4x+7x-500=6500$; whence, $x=500$

(41) Let $x=$ the number of days;
then, $20x=$ distance 1st travels,
and $30x=$ " 2d travels.
Therefore, $20x+30x=400$; whence, $x=8$.

(42) Let $x=$ the number of hours.
Then, $3x+30=$ miles B travels,
and $5x=$ miles A travels.
Therefore, $5x=3x+30$; whence, $x=15$.

(43) Let $x=$ time past noon.
Then, $12-x$ time to midnight.
Therefore, $x+\frac{x}{2}+\frac{x}{3}+\frac{2x}{5}=\frac{12-x}{6}$.
Clearing of fractions and reducing, $72x=60$
whence, $x=\frac{5}{6}$ hr. $=50$ min.

(44) Let $x=$ one part; then, $120-x=$ the other
Therefore, $\frac{120-x}{x}=1\frac{1}{2}$ or $\frac{3}{2}$; whence, $x=48$.

(45) Let $x=$ the number.
Then, $\frac{7x+3}{2}-4=15$; whence, $x=5$.

(46) Let $x=$ the number.
Then, $\frac{5x-24}{6}+13=x$; whence, $x=54$.

(47) Let $3x=$ A's capital, then $2x=$B's.
Then, $3x-100=$ A's after losing \$100;
$2x+100=$ B's after gaining \$100.
Therefore, $2x+100-\frac{5}{7}(3x-100)=134$;
whence, $x=262$. Hence, $3x=786$, and $2x=524$.

(48) Let $x=$ his money.
Then, $x-\left(\frac{2x}{3}+3\right)=\frac{x}{5}+7$; whence, $x=75$.

(49) Let $5x=$ annual income of each.
Then, $x=$ what A saves, and $4x=$ what he spends yearly
also, $4x+25=$ what B spends yearly;
and $5x-(4x+25)=x-25=$ what B saves yearly.
Therefore, $5(x-25)=200$; whence, $x=65$.
Hence, $5x=325$.

(50) Let $x=$ the number of pounds.
Then, $\frac{2x}{3}+10=$ lbs. of niter;

$\frac{2x}{23}+1=$ lbs. of sulphur; $\frac{x}{3}-17=$ lbs. of charcoal.

Therefore, $\frac{2x}{3}+10+\frac{2x}{23}+1+\frac{x}{3}-17=x$.

By omitting $\frac{2x}{3}+\frac{x}{3}$ on the right, and its equivalent x on the left, and reducing, we find $\frac{2x}{23}-6=0$;

whence, $2x=6\times 23$, and $x=3\times 23=69$.

(51) Let $x=$ cost of harness; then, $3x=$ cost of horse, $4x\times 2\frac{2}{3}=\frac{32x}{3}$; therefore, $\frac{32x}{3}-19=$ the cost of chaise.

Hence, $x+3x+\frac{32x}{3}-19=245$.

Transposing and reducing, $\frac{44x}{3}=264$;

whence, $44x=264\times 3$, and $x=6\times 3=18$.

(52) Let $3x$ and $4x$ represent the numbers.
Then, $3x+4 : 4x+4 :: 5 : 6$.
Whence, $6(3x+4)=5(4x+4)$; whence, $x=2$.
Hence, $3x=6$, and $4x=8$.

(53) Let $x=$ the number of years.
Then, $25+x : 30+x :: 8 : 9$;
whence, $9(25+x)=8(30+x)$;
whence, by reducing, $x=15$.

(54) Let $x=$ the number of hours. Then, since the 1st fills the cistern in $1\frac{1}{3}$ hours, it fills $\frac{1}{1\frac{1}{3}}=\frac{3}{4}$ of it in 1 hour, and in x hours it will fill $\frac{3x}{4}$ part of it.

In like manner, the 2d pipe fills $\frac{1}{3\frac{1}{3}}=\frac{3}{10}$ of the cistern in 1 hour, and in x hours it will fill $\frac{3x}{10}$ part of it. Also, the 3d pipe fills $\frac{1}{5}$ in 1 hr., and in x hours $\frac{x}{5}$ of it.

Therefore, $\frac{3x}{4}+\frac{3x}{10}+\frac{x}{5}=1$, or the whole of the cistern; whence, $x=\frac{4}{5}$ hour $=48$ min.

(55) Let $x=$ the number of days.

Then, the 1st does $\frac{1}{7}$ of it in 1 day, and in x days $\frac{x}{7}$.

In like manner, the 2d does $\frac{1}{6}$ in 1 day, and in x days $\frac{x}{6}$

The 3d does $\frac{1}{9}$ in 1 day, and in x days $\frac{x}{9}$.

Therefore, $\frac{x}{7}+\frac{x}{6}+\frac{x}{9}=1$, or the whole; whence, $x=2\frac{20}{53}$.

Or, $\frac{1}{7}+\frac{1}{6}+\frac{1}{9}=\frac{53}{126}=\frac{1}{x}$, whence, $x=2\frac{20}{53}$

(56) Let $3x=$ money, $3x-\frac{3x}{3}=2x$.

Then, $2x+50-\frac{1}{10}(2x+50)+37=100$;
whence, $x=10$; hence, $3x=30$.

(57) Let $5x=$ yearly salary;
$5x-\frac{2}{5}$ of $5x=3x$; and $3x-\frac{1}{3}$ of $3x=2x$.

Then, $2x-\frac{2x}{5}=120$; whence, $x=75$, and $5x=375$.

(58) Let $x=$ value of suit of clothes.

Then, $80+x=$ yearly wages; and $\frac{80+x}{12}=$monthly wages.

Therefore, $7\left(\frac{80+x}{12}\right)=x+35$; whence, $x=28$.

(59) Let $x=$ days it will last the woman.

Then, $\frac{1}{x}=$ part the woman can drink in 1 day.

Since both can drink it in 6 days, they can drink $\frac{1}{6}$ of it in 1 day; and since the man can drink it in 10 days he can drink $\frac{1}{10}$ of it in 1 day.

Therefore, $\frac{1}{6}-\frac{1}{10}=\frac{1}{x}$; whence, $x=15$.

(60) Let $x=$ the distance in miles.

Then, $\frac{x}{15}=$ hours in going from C to L;

and $\frac{x}{10}=$ " in going from L to C.

Therefore, $\frac{x}{15}+\frac{x}{10}=25$. whence, $x=150$

(61) Let $x=$ the whole number of gallons.

Then, $\frac{x}{2}+25=$ gal. of wine; and $\frac{x}{3}-5=$ gal. of water

Therefore, $x=\frac{x}{2}+25+\frac{x}{3}-5$; whence, $x=120$, and $\frac{x}{2}+25=85=$ gal. of wine;

and $\frac{x}{3}-5=35=$ gal. of water.

(62) By representing the four parts by $x-2$, $x+2$, $\frac{1}{2}x$, and $2x$. we at once fulfill the last four conditicns.
Therefore, $x-2+x+2+\frac{1}{2}x+2x=72$.
By adding, $4\frac{1}{2}x=72$; whence, $x=16$.
Then, $x-2=14$; $x+2=18$; $\frac{1}{2}x=8$; and $2x=32$.

(63) Let $x=$ length of each piece.
Then, $3(x-19)+x-17=142$; whence, $x=54$.

(64) Let $x=$ the number of sheep.

Then, $\frac{x}{10}=$ acres plowed; and $\frac{x}{4}=$ acres of pastured.

Therefore, $\frac{x}{10}+\frac{x}{4}=161$; whence, $x=460$.

(65) Let $x=$ greater part; then, $34-x=$ less part.
$18-(34-x)=x-16$.
Therefore, $x-18 : x-16 :: 2 : 3$.
Whence, $3(x-18)=2(x-16)$; whence, $x=22$.

(66) Let $x=$ the number of beggars.
Then, $3x-8=$ his money; also, $2x+3=$ his money.
Therefore, $3x-8=2x+3$; whence, $x=11$.

(67) Let $x=$ number of days, in which B alone could reap it.

Then, $\frac{1}{x}=$ part B could reap in 1 day, and $\frac{6}{x}=$ the part he could reap in 6 days.
Since A can reap it in 20 days, he can reap $\frac{1}{20}$ in 1 day, and in 16 days $\frac{16}{20}$.

Therefore, $\frac{16}{20}+\frac{6}{x}=1$, the whole; whence, $x=30$.

(68) Let $x=$ price of a bushel of barley.

Then, $\frac{4x+90}{9}=$ price of a bushel of oats;

Therefore, $x+3 : \frac{4x+90}{9} :: 8 : 5$.

Whence, $5(x+3)=8\left(\frac{4x+90}{9}\right)$; from which $x=45$.

(69) Let $2x=$ distance from A to B; then,
$3x=$ distance from C to D;
$\frac{2x}{4}+\frac{3x}{2}=2x=$ 3 times the distance from B to C.

Therefore, $\frac{2x}{3}=$ distance from B to C.

Hence, $2x+\frac{2x}{3}+3x=34$; whence, $x=6$.

(70) Let $x=$ the lbs. of rice;
then, $\frac{x+5}{2}=\frac{1}{3}$ the weight of the flour, since $\frac{1}{2}$ of $\frac{2}{3}$ is $\frac{1}{3}$.

and $\frac{3x+15}{2}=$ the weight of the flour;

$\frac{1}{5}\left(\frac{3x+15}{2}+x\right)=\frac{x+3}{2}=$ weight of the water.

Therefore, $x+\frac{3x+15}{2}+\frac{x+3}{2}=15$; whence, $x=2$.

Article 161.

(5) Let $x=$ price of a lb. of coffee, and y of a lb. of sugar.
Then, $5x+3y=79$, (1),
and $3x+5y=73$, (2);
from which $x=11$, and $y=8$.

(6) Let $x=$ price of a horse, and $y=$ price of a cow.
Then, $9x+7y=300$, (1),
and $6x+13y=300$, (2);
from which $x=24$, and $y=12$.

(7) Let x and y represent the numbers.
Then, $\frac{1}{2}x+\frac{1}{3}y=22$, (1),
and $\frac{1}{4}x+\frac{1}{5}y=12$, (2);
from which $x=24$, and $y=30$.

(8) Let x represent the greater, and y the less of the two numbers.
Then, $x+\frac{1}{3}y=37$, (1),
and $y-\frac{1}{4}x=20$, (2);
from which $x=28$, and $y=27$

(9) Let $x=$ value of first horse, and $y=$ value of **second.**
Then, $x+25=2y$, (1), and $y+25=3x$, (2);
from which $x=15$, and $y=20$.

(10) Let $x=$ A's property, and $y=$ B's.
Then, $x+50=y-20$, (1), and $3x+5y=2350$, (2);
from which $x=250$, and $y=320$.

(11) Let $x=$ digit in ten's place, and $y=$ digit in unit's place
Then, $10x+y=$ the number, and $10y+x=$ number inverted

Therefore, $\frac{10x+y}{x+y}=7$, (1), and $\frac{10y+x}{x+y+4}=3$, (2);
from which $x=8$, and $y=4$.

(12) Let $x=$ the numerator, and $y=$ the denominator of the fraction.

Then, $\frac{x+8}{y}=2$, (1), and $\frac{x}{y-5}=3$, (2);
from which $x=6$, and $y=7$.

(13) Let $x=$ A's age, and $y=$ B's.
Then, $x+y+18=2x$, (1), and $x-y-6=y$, (2);
from which $x=30$, and $y=12$.

(14) Let $x=$ the greater, and $y=$ the less of the two numbers

Then, $x+y=37$, (1), and $\frac{4x-3y}{6}=6$, (2);
from which $x=21$, and $y=16$.

(15) Let $x=$ the numerator, and $y=$ the denominator.

Then, $\frac{x-3}{y-3}=\frac{1}{4}$, (1), and $\frac{x+5}{y+5}=\frac{1}{2}$, (2);
from which $x=7$, and $y=19$.

(16) Let $x=$ sum given to A, and $y=$ sum given to B.

Then, $x-\frac{1}{4}x=\frac{3x}{4}=$ A's capital at close of the year;

and $y+\frac{1}{4}y=\frac{5y}{4}=$ B's capital at close of the year.

Then, $x+y=2400$, (1), and $\frac{3x}{4}=\frac{5y}{4}$, (2);
from which $x=1500$, and $y=900$.

(17) Let $x=$ A's, and $y=$ B's.
Then, $x+100=y-100$, (1),
and $2(x-100)=y+100$, (2);
from which $x=500$, and $y=700$.

(18) Let $x=$ the greater, and $y=$ the less of the two numbers.

Then, $5x+7y=198$, (1), and $\frac{x}{5}+\frac{y}{7}=6$, (2);

from which $x=20$, and $y=14$.

(19) Let $x=$ A's age, and $y=$B's.
Then, $x-7$ and $y-7$, represent their ages 7 years ago; and $x+7$ and $y+7$, represent their ages 7 years henoe.
Therefore, $x-7=3(y-7)$, (1), and $x+7=2(y+7)$, (2); from which $x=49$, and $y=21$.

(20) Let $x=$ digit in ten's place, and $y=$ digit in unit's place.
Then, $10x+y=$ the number,
and $10y+x=$ the number inverted.

Therefore, $\frac{10x+y}{x+y}=4$, (1), and $10x+y+27=10y+x$, (2);
from which $x=3$, and $y=6$.

(21) Let $x=$ value of a lb. of the first, and y of the second.
Then, $x+y=20$, (1), and $3x+5y=11(3+5)=88$, (2);
from which $x=6$, and $y=14$.

(22) Let $x=$number of lemons, and y of oranges.
Then, $3x+5y=84$, (1);
since by selling $\frac{1}{2}$ of the lemons and $\frac{1}{3}$ of the oranges for 40 cents, he cleared 8 cents,

therefore, $\frac{3x}{2}+\frac{5y}{3}=40-8=32$, (2);

from which $x=8$, and $y=12$.

(23) Let $x=$ A's money, and $y=$B's.
Then, $x+\frac{1}{5}y=500$, (1), and $y+\frac{1}{4}x=600$, (2);
from which $x=400$, and $y=500$.

(24) Let $x=$ the father's, and $y=$ the son's age.
Then, $x-6=3\frac{1}{3}(y-6)$, (1)
and $x+3=2\frac{1}{6}(y+3)$, (2);
from which $x=36$, and $y=15$.

(25) Let $x=$ number of bu. of oats, and $y=$ bu. of rye.
Then, by the 1st condition, $x+6 : y+6 :: 7 : 6$;
whence, $6(x+6)=7(y+6)$, (1).
By the 2d condition, $x-6 : y-6 :: 6 : 5$;
whence, $5(x-6)=6(y-6)$, (2);
from which $x=78$, and $y=66$.

(26) Let $x=$ the length, and $y=$ the breadth.
Then, by the 1st condition, $x+4 : y+4 :: 5 : 4$;
whence, $4(x+4)=5(y+4)$, (1).
By the 2d condition, $x-4 : y-4 :: 4 : 3$;
whence, $3(x-4)=4(y-4)$, (2);
from which $x=36$, and $y=28$.

(27) Let $x=$ number of acres of tillable, and y of pasture.
Then, $200x+140y=24500$, (1).
Also, $x : x-y :: 14 : 9$;
whence, $9x=14x-14y$, (2);
from which $x=98$, and $y=35$.

(28) Let $x=$ number of gal. in first, and y in second.
By the 1st condition, $x-15=\frac{2}{3}(y-15)$, (1);
also, $x-15-25=x-40$, and $y-15-25=y-40$
therefore, by the 2d condition, $x-40=\frac{1}{2}(y-40)$, (2);
from which $x=65$, and $y=90$.

(29) Let $x=$ the numerator, and $y=$ the denominator.
Then, $\frac{x+1}{x+y}=\frac{1}{4}$, (1), and $\frac{x+y}{y+1}=\frac{8}{7}$, (2);
from which $x=3$, and $y=13$.

(30) Represent the first two numbers by $5x$ and $7x$, and the other two by $3y$ and $5y$.
By the 1st condition, we have $5x+3y : 7x+5y :: 9 : 13$;
whence, $13(5x+3y)=9(7x+5y)$, (1);
the difference of their sums $=(7x+5y)-(5x+3y)=2x+2y$;
therefore, $2x+2y=16$, (2);
from which $x=6$, and $y=2$;
hence, $5x=30$, $7x=42$; $3y=6$, and $5y=10$.

(31) Let $x=$ number of bu. of rye, and y of wheat.
Then, $28+x+y=100$, (1).
And $28\times28+36x+48y=100\times40=4000$, (2);
from which $x=20$, and $y=52$.

(32) Let $x=$ value of the first horse, and y of 2d.
Then, $x+50=y+2+8$, (1);
$x+2=$ value of first horse with worst saddle.
$y+50=$ " " second " " best "
Therefore, $y+50 : x+2 :: 15 : 4$;
whence, $4(y+50)=15(x+2)$, (2);
from which $x=30$, and $y=70$.

(33) Since $4x$ and $5x$ have the same ratio as 4 and 5, let them represent the weights of the loaded wagons. Also, let $6y$ and $7y$, which have the same ratio as 6 and 7, represent the parts of the loads taken out.

Then, $4x-6y : 5x-7y :: 2 : 3$;

whence, $3(4x-6y)=2(5x-7y)$, (1),

and $4x-6y+5x-7y=10$, (2);

from which $x=4$, and $y=2$;

hence, $4x=16$, and $5x=20$.

(34) Let x=number of gal. in 1st, and y in 2d.

First.	Second.
x	y
y	y
$x-y$	$2y=$ gal. in each after 1st pouring.
$x-y$	$x-y$
$2x-2y$	$3y-x=$ gal. in each after 2d pouring.
$3y-x$	$3y-x$
$3x-5y$	$6y-2x=$ gal. in each after 3d pouring.

Therefore, $3x-5y=6y-2x$, (1), and $3x-5y=16$, (2);

from which $x=22$, and $y=10$.

QUESTIONS PRODUCING EQUATIONS CONTAINING THREE OR MORE UNKNOWN QUANTITIES.

Article 163.

(2) Let x, y, and z represent the numbers.

Then, $x+y=27$, (1),

$x+z=32$, (2),

and $y+z=35$, (3);

from which $x=12$, $y=15$, and $z=20$.

(3) Let x, y, and z represent the numbers. Then,

$$x+y+z=59,\ (1),\quad \frac{x-y}{2}=5,\ (2),\quad \frac{x-z}{2}=9,\ (3);$$

from which $x=29$, $y=19$, and $z=11$.

(4) Let x, y, and z represent the prices respectively of the three watches. Then,

$$x+\frac{y+z}{2}=25,\ (1),\quad y+\frac{x+z}{3}=26,\ (2),\quad z+\frac{x+z}{2}=29,\ (3);$$

from which $x=8$, $y=18$, and $z=16$.

(5) Let x, y, and z represent the three numbers. **Then,**

$$x+\frac{y+z}{3}=25,\ (1),\quad y+\frac{x+z}{4}=25,\quad (2),\quad z+\frac{x+y}{5}=25,\ (3)$$

from which $x=13$, $y=17$, and $z=19$.

(6) Let $v=$ cost of an apple, x of a pear, y of a peach, and z of an orange.

Then, $2v+5x=12$, (1),

$3x+4y=18$, (2),

$4x+5z=28$, (3),

and $5y+6z=39$, (4);

from which $v=1$, $x=2$, $y=3$, and $z=4$.

(7) Let $x=$ A's money, $y=$ B's, and $z=$ C's. Then,

$x+y=\frac{2}{3}z$, (1), $y+z=6x$, (2), $x+z=y+680$, (3)

from which $x=200$, $y=360$, and $z=840$.

(8) Let $x=$ A's money, $y=$B's, and $z=$ C's.

Then, $x+700=2(y-700)$, (1),

$y+1400=3(z-1400)$, (2),

and $z+420=5(x-420)$, (3);

from which $x=980$, $y=1540$, and $z=2380$.

(9) Let x, y, and z, represent the digits in hundred's, ten's, and unit's places respectively.

Then, $100x+10y+z$ represents the number.

Therefore, $x+y+z=11$, (1),

$z=2x$, (2),

and $100x+10y+z+297=100z+10y+x$, (3):

from which $x=3$, $y=2$, and $z=6$.

(10) Let x, y, and z represent the numbers.

Then, $x+y+z=83$, (1),

$x-7 : y-7 :: 5 : 3$;

whence, $3(x-7)=5(y-7)$, (2),

$y-3 : z-3 :: 11 : 9$;

whence, $9(y-3)=11(z-3)$, (3);

from which $x=37$, $y=25$, and $z=21$.

(11) Let $x=$ A's share, $y=$ B's, and $z=$C's,

Then, $x+y+z=180$, (1),

$2x+80=3y+40$, (2),

and $2x+80=4z+20$, (3);

from which $x=70$, $y=60$, and $z=50$.

(12) Let x, y, and z, represent the days respectively, in which A, B, and C each alone can perform the work.

Then, A can do $\frac{1}{x}$ part, B, $\frac{1}{y}$ part, and C $\frac{1}{z}$ part of it in 1 day. Also, A and B can perform $\frac{1}{12}$ of it, A and C $\frac{1}{15}$, and B and C $\frac{1}{20}$ in 1 day. Therefore,

$$\frac{1}{x}+\frac{1}{y}=\frac{1}{12}, (1), \quad \frac{1}{x}+\frac{1}{z}=\frac{1}{15}, (2), \text{ and } \frac{1}{y}+\frac{1}{z}=\frac{1}{20}, (3).$$

By subtracting Eq. (2) from (1), we have

$$\frac{1}{y}-\frac{1}{z}=\frac{1}{12}-\frac{1}{15}=\frac{1}{60}, \qquad (4).$$

By adding equations (4) and (3) together,

$$\frac{2}{y}=\frac{1}{20}+\frac{1}{60}=\frac{1}{15}, \qquad (5);$$

or $y=30$, by clearing of fractions.

By subtracting equation (4) from (3),

$$\frac{2}{z}=\frac{1}{20}-\frac{1}{60}=\frac{1}{30}, \qquad (6);$$

or $z=60$, by clearing of fractions.

The value of x may be found by substituting the value of y in Eq. (1), or by subtracting Eq. (3) from (2), and adding the resulting equation and Eq. (1) together.

(13) Let $x=$ digit in hundred's place, $y=$ digit in ten's place, and $z=$ digit in unit's place.

Then, $100x+10y+z=$ the number;

$$\text{also, } \frac{100x+10y+z}{x+y+z+9}=19, \qquad (1),$$

$$y=\frac{x+z}{2}, \quad (2),$$

$$\text{and } \quad 100x+10y+z+198=100z+10y+x, \qquad (3);$$

from which $x=4$, $y=5$, and $z=6$.

14) Let $x=$ bu. of barley, y of rye, and z of wheat.

$$\text{Then, } \quad x+y+z=100, \quad (1),$$

$$28x+36y+48z=4000, \ (2),$$

$$28x+36\times 2y+48(z+10)=40(100+y+10);$$

by reducing, $28x+32y+48z=3920$, (3);

from which $x=28, y=20$, and $z=52$.

15) Let x, y, and z represent the birds respectively which A B, and C killed.

$$\begin{array}{lll} x & y & z \\ \underline{y+z} & \underline{y} & \underline{z} \\ x-y-z & 2y & 2z, \text{ after 1st division} \\ \underline{x-y-z} & \underline{x-y-z+2z} & \underline{2z} \\ 2x-2y-2z & 3y-x-z & 4z, \text{ after 2d division;} \\ \underline{2x-2y-2z} & \underline{3y-x-z} & \underline{x+y-3z} \\ 4x-4y-4z & 6y-2x-2z, & 7z-x-y, \text{ after 3d division.} \end{array}$$

Therefore, $x+y+z=96$, (1),

$4x-4y-4z=32$, (2),

$6y-2x-2z=32$, (3);

from which $x=52$, $y=28$, and $z=16$.

GENERALIZATION.

Article 170.

(1) Let $x=$ one of the parts; then, $a-x$ will be the other

Therefore, $x=n(a-x)=na-nx$.

Transposing, $nx+x=na$.

Factoring, $(n+1)x=na$.

Dividing, $x=\frac{na}{n+1}$.

$$a-x=a-\frac{na}{n+1}=\frac{na+a-na}{n+1}=\frac{a}{n+1}.$$

(2) Let $x=$ one of the parts; then, $a-x$ will be the other

Therefore, $mx=n(a-x)=na-nx$.

Transposing, $mx+nx=na$.

Factoring, $(m+n)x=na$.

Dividing, $x=\frac{na}{m+n}$

$$a-x=\frac{ma+na}{m+n}-\frac{na}{m+n}=\frac{ma}{m+n}.$$

(3) Let $x=$ the number.

Then, $\frac{x}{m}+\frac{x}{n}=a$,

$nx+mx=mna$, by clearing of fractions.

whence, $x=\frac{mna}{m+n}$.

(4) Let $x=$ the number.

Then, $a+x : b+x :: m : n$;

whence, $n(a+x)=m(b+x)$.

Transposing, $nx-mx=mb-na$,

$$x=\frac{mb-na}{n-m}.$$

(5) Let $x=$ the number.

Then, $a-x : b-x :: m : n$;

whence, $n(a-x)=m(b-x)$.

Transposing, $mx-nx=mb-na$,

$$x=\frac{mb-na}{m-n}, \text{ or } \frac{na-mb}{n-m},$$ See Art. 182

(6) Let $x=$ the number of dollars he had at first.

Then, $x-\frac{1}{m}x-\frac{1}{n}x=a$,

$mnx-nx-mx=mna$, by clearing of fractions;

$(mn-m-n)x=mna$,

$$x=\frac{mna}{mn-m-n}.$$

(7) Let $x=$ the number of persons.

Then, $ax=$ the number of cents paid;

also, $(x-b)c=$ the number of cents paid;

therefore, $(x-b)c=ax$;

$cx-ax=bc$,

$$x=\frac{bc}{c-a}.$$

(8) Let $x=$ the number of bu. of oats; then, $n-x=$ the number of bu. of rye.

Then, $ax=$ cost of x bu. at a cents per bu.

$(n-x)b=$cost of $n-x$ bu. at b cents per bu.;

therefore, $ax+(n-x)b=nc$,

$(a-b)x=nc-nb=n(c-b)$,

$$x=\frac{n(c-b)}{a-b};$$

$$n-x=\frac{n(a-b)}{a-b}-\frac{n(c-b)}{a-b}=\frac{n(a-c)}{a-b}.$$

(9) Let $x=$ the money he had in his purse; $x+x=2x$; then, $2x-a=$ money he had after 1st spending.

$2x-a+(2x-a)-a=4x-3a=$ money after 2d spend'g;

$4x-3a+(4x-3a)-a=8x-7a$=money after 3d spend g;
$8x-7a+(8x-7a)-a=16x-15a$=money after 4th "

Therefore, $16x-15a=0$,

$16x=15a$, or $x=\frac{15}{16}a$.

(10) Let x=number of pieces of 1st kind; then, $c-x$=number of pieces of 2d kind.

Since a pieces of the first kind make $1, or 100 cts., therefore, $\frac{100}{a}$=value in cents of a piece of the first kind.

In like manner, $\frac{100}{b}$= value in cents of a piece of the 2d.

$\frac{100}{a}x$= value in cts. of x pieces of 1st kind.

$\frac{100}{b}(c-x)$= value in cts. of $(c-x)$ pieces of 2d kind.

Therefore, $\frac{100}{a}x+\frac{100}{b}(c-x)=100$;

$\frac{x}{a}+\frac{c-x}{b}=1$, by dividing both sides by 100;

$bx+ac-ax=ab$, by clearing of fractions.

$(b-a)x=a(b-c)$;

$$x=\frac{a(b-c)}{b-a},$$

$$c-x=\frac{c(b-a)}{b-a}-\frac{a(b-c)}{b-a}=\frac{b(c-a)}{b-a}.$$

To illustrate by numbers, take the following: How many 5 and 25-cent pieces must be taken, so that 8 shall make $1?

Ans. 5 five-cent, and 3 twenty-five-cent pieces.

Article 171.

(8) Let x= number of pages, and y= number of lines on a page; then, xy= number of lines in the book.

Therefore, $(x+5)(y+10)=xy+450$, (1),

and $(x-10)(y-5)=xy-450$, (2);

from which we find $x=20$, and $y=40$.

Article 172.

Enunciation of questions 2, 3, 4, and 5, so that the results will be true in an arithmetical sense.

2. What number must be *added* to 20, that the *sum* may be 25? *Ans.* 5.

3. What number must be *subtracted* from 11, that the *remainder* multiplied by 5, shall equal 40? *Ans.* 3.

4. What number is that, of which the $\frac{2}{3}$ is *less* than the $\frac{3}{4}$ by 3? *Ans.* 36.

5. A father, 45 years old, has a son aged 15: *how many years since*, was the son $\frac{1}{4}$ as old as his father? *Ans.* 5.

RADICALS OF THE SECOND DEGREE.

NOTE.—All the examples in the FORMATION OF POWERS, and EXTRACTION OF THE SQUARE ROOT, being performed by direct methods of operation, can present but few difficulties to the careful student. In the examples Art. 196, before commencing the operation, the pupil must be careful to arrange the terms of the polynomial with reference to a certain letter.

Article 199.

REDUCTION OF RADICALS OF THE SECOND DEGREE.

(1) $\sqrt{8a^2}=\sqrt{4a^2\times2}=\sqrt{4a^2}\times\sqrt{2}=2a\sqrt{2}.$

(2) $\sqrt{12a^3}=\sqrt{4a^2\times3a}=\sqrt{4a^2}\times\sqrt{3a}=2a\sqrt{3a}.$

(3) $\sqrt{20a^3b^3c^3}=\sqrt{4a^2b^2c^2\times5abc}=\sqrt{4a^2b^2c^2}\times\sqrt{5abc}$
$=2abc\sqrt{5abc}.$

(4) $4\sqrt{27a^3c^3}=4\sqrt{9a^2c^2\times3ac}=4\times3ac\sqrt{3ac}=12ac\sqrt{3ac}.$

(5) $7\sqrt{28a^5c^2}=7\sqrt{4a^4c^2\times7a}=7\times2a^2c\sqrt{7a}=14a^2c\sqrt{7a}.$

(6) $\sqrt{32a^6b^2c^4}=\sqrt{16a^6b^2c^4\times2}=$ - - - - $4a^3bc^2\sqrt{2}.$

(7) $\sqrt{44a^5b^3c}=\sqrt{4a^4b^2\times11abc}=$ - - - $2a^2b\sqrt{11abc}$

(8) $\sqrt{48a^8b^6c^4}=\sqrt{16a^8b^6c^4\times3}=$ - - - - $4a^4b^3c^2\sqrt{3}.$

(9) $\sqrt{75a^3b^3c^3}=\sqrt{25a^2b^2c^2\times3abc}=$ - - - $5abc\sqrt{3abc}.$

(10) $\sqrt{243a^3b^2c}=\sqrt{81a^2b^2\times 3ac}=$ - - $9ab\sqrt{3ac}$.

(12) $\sqrt{\frac{3}{5}}=\sqrt{\frac{3}{5}\times\frac{5}{5}}=\sqrt{\frac{1}{25}\times 15}=$ - - - $\frac{1}{5}\sqrt{15}$.

(13) $\sqrt{\frac{7}{8}}=\sqrt{\frac{7}{8}\times\frac{2}{2}}=\sqrt{\frac{1}{16}\times 14}=$ - - - $\frac{1}{4}\sqrt{14}$.

(14) $\sqrt{\frac{12}{25}}=\sqrt{\frac{4}{25}\times 3}=$ - - - - - $\frac{2}{5}\sqrt{3}$.

(15) $9\sqrt{\frac{16}{27}}=9\sqrt{\frac{16}{27}\times\frac{3}{3}}=9\sqrt{\frac{16}{81}\times 3}=9\times\frac{4}{9}\sqrt{3}=4\sqrt{3}$.

(16) $5\sqrt{\frac{9}{10}}=5\sqrt{\frac{9}{10}\times\frac{10}{10}}=5\sqrt{\frac{9}{100}\times 10}=5\times\frac{3}{10}\sqrt{10}=\frac{3}{2}\sqrt{10}$.

(17) $10\sqrt{\frac{3}{50}}=10\sqrt{\frac{3}{50}\times\frac{2}{2}}=10\sqrt{\frac{1}{100}\times 6}=10\times\frac{1}{10}\sqrt{6}=\sqrt{6}$.

(18) $5=\sqrt{5\times 5}=$ - - - - - - $\sqrt{25}$.

(19) $2a=\sqrt{2a\times 2a}=$ - - - - - - - $\sqrt{4a^2}$.

(20) $3\sqrt{5}=\sqrt{3\times 3}\times\sqrt{5}=\sqrt{3\times 3\times 5}=$ - - - - $\sqrt{45}$

(21) $3c\sqrt{2c}=\sqrt{3c\times 3c\times 2c}=$ - - - - - - $\sqrt{18c^3}$.

Article 200.

ADDITION OF RADICALS.

(4)
$$\begin{aligned}\sqrt{12}&=2\sqrt{3}\\ \sqrt{27}&=3\sqrt{3}\\ \text{Sum}&=5\sqrt{3}\end{aligned}$$

(5)
$$\begin{aligned}\sqrt{20}&=2\sqrt{5}\\ \sqrt{80}&=4\sqrt{5}\\ \text{Sum}&=6\sqrt{5}\end{aligned}$$

(6)
$$\begin{aligned}\sqrt{40}&=2\sqrt{10}\\ \sqrt{90}&=3\sqrt{10}\\ \sqrt{250}&=5\sqrt{10}\\ \text{Sum}&=10\sqrt{10}\end{aligned}$$

(7)
$$\begin{aligned}\sqrt{28a^2b^2}&=2ab\sqrt{7}\\ \sqrt{112a^2b^2}&=4ab\sqrt{7}\\ \text{Sum}&=6ab\sqrt{7}\end{aligned}$$

(8)
$$\begin{aligned}\sqrt{\tfrac{1}{3}}&=\tfrac{1}{3}\sqrt{3}\\ \sqrt{\tfrac{3}{25}}&=\tfrac{1}{5}\sqrt{3}\\ \text{Sum}&=\tfrac{8}{15}\sqrt{3}\end{aligned}$$

(9)
$$\begin{aligned}2\sqrt{\tfrac{3}{4}}&=\sqrt{3}\\ 3\sqrt{12}&=6\sqrt{3}\\ \text{Sum}&=7\sqrt{3}\end{aligned}$$

(10)
$$\begin{aligned}\tfrac{1}{2}\sqrt{\tfrac{1}{2}}&=\tfrac{1}{4}\sqrt{2}\\ \tfrac{3}{4}\sqrt{2}&=\tfrac{3}{4}\sqrt{2}\\ \text{Sum}&=\sqrt{2}\end{aligned}$$

(11)
$$\begin{aligned}\sqrt{48a^2c^2x}&=4ac\sqrt{3x}\\ \sqrt{12b^2x}&=2b\sqrt{3x}\\ \text{Sum}&=(4ac+2b)\sqrt{3x}\end{aligned}$$

(12)
$$\begin{aligned}\sqrt{(2a^3-4a^2c+2ac^2)}&=\sqrt{(a^2-2ac+c^2)\times 2a}=(a-c)\sqrt{2a}\\ \sqrt{(2a^3+4a^2c+2ac^2)}&=\sqrt{(a^2+2ac+c^2)\times 2a}=(a+c)\sqrt{2a}\\ &\text{Sum}=2a\sqrt{2a}\end{aligned}$$

(13)
$$\begin{aligned}\sqrt{a+x}&=\sqrt{a+x}\\ \sqrt{ax^2+x^3}&=x\sqrt{a+x}\\ \sqrt{(a+x)^3}&=(a+x)\sqrt{a+x}\\ \text{Sum}&=(1+a+2x)\sqrt{a+x}\end{aligned}$$

Article 201.

SUBTRACTION OF RADICALS.

(3) $\sqrt{45a^2}=3a\sqrt{5}$
$\sqrt{5a^2}=a\sqrt{5}$
Dif. $=2a\sqrt{5}$

(4) $\sqrt{54b}=3\sqrt{6b}$
$\sqrt{6b}=\sqrt{6b}$
Dif. $=2\sqrt{6b}$

(5) $\sqrt{27b^3c^3}=3bc\sqrt{3bc}$
$\sqrt{12b^3c^3}=2bc\sqrt{3bc}$
Dif. $=bc\sqrt{3bc}$

(6) $\sqrt{49ab^3c^2}=7bc\sqrt{ab}$
$\sqrt{25ab^3c^2}=5bc\sqrt{ab}$
Dif. $=2bc\sqrt{ab}$

(7) $5a\sqrt{27}=15a\sqrt{3}$
$3a\sqrt{48}=12a\sqrt{3}$
Dif. $=3a\sqrt{3}$

(8) $2\sqrt{\frac{3}{4}}=\sqrt{3}$
$3\sqrt{\frac{1}{3}}=\sqrt{3}$
Dif. $=0$

(9) $\sqrt{\frac{5}{6}}=\frac{1}{6}\sqrt{30}$
$\sqrt{\frac{10}{27}}=\frac{1}{9}\sqrt{30}$
Dif. $=\frac{1}{18}\sqrt{30}$

(10) $3\sqrt{\frac{1}{2}}=\frac{3}{2}\sqrt{2}$
$\sqrt{2}=\sqrt{2}$
Dif. $=\frac{1}{2}\sqrt{2}$

(11) $\sqrt{4a^2x}=2a\sqrt{x}$
$a\sqrt{x^3}=ax\sqrt{x}$
Dif. $=(2a-ax)\sqrt{x}$

(12) $\sqrt{3m^2x+6mnx+3n^2x}=(m+n)\sqrt{3x}$
$\sqrt{3m^2x-6mnx+3n^2x}=(m-n)\sqrt{3x}$
Dif. $=2n\sqrt{3x}$

Article 202.

MULTIPLICATION OF RADICALS.

(3) $\sqrt{8}\times\sqrt{2}=\sqrt{16}=4.$

(4) $2\sqrt{a}\times3\sqrt{a}=6\sqrt{a^2}=6a.$

(5) $\sqrt{27}\times\sqrt{3}=\sqrt{81}=9.$

(6) $3\sqrt{2}\times2\sqrt{3}=6\sqrt{6}.$

(7) $2\sqrt{15}\times3\sqrt{35}=6\sqrt{3\times5\times5\times7}=30\sqrt{21}$

(8) $\sqrt{a^3b^5c}\times\sqrt{abc}=\sqrt{a^4b^6c^2}=a^2b^3c.$

(9) $\sqrt{\frac{2}{5}}\times\sqrt{\frac{8}{9}}=\sqrt{\frac{16}{45}}=\sqrt{\frac{16}{225}\times5}=\frac{4}{15}\sqrt{5}.$

(10) $2\sqrt{\frac{a}{5}}\times3\sqrt{\frac{a}{10}}=6\sqrt{\frac{a^2}{50}}=6\sqrt{\frac{a^2}{100}\times2}=\frac{6a}{10}\sqrt{2}=\frac{3a}{5}\sqrt{2}$

(11)
$$\begin{array}{l} 2+\sqrt{2} \\ 2-\sqrt{2} \\ \hline 4+2\sqrt{2} \\ \quad -2\sqrt{2}-2 \\ \hline 4-2=2. \end{array}$$

(12) $\sqrt{x+2}\times\sqrt{x-2}=\sqrt{(x+2)(x-2)}=\sqrt{x^2-4}.$

(13) $\sqrt{a+x}\times\sqrt{a+x}=\sqrt{(a+x)(a+x)}=a+x.$

(14) $\sqrt{x+2}\times\sqrt{x+3}=\sqrt{(x+2)(x+3)}=\sqrt{x^2+5x+6}$.

(15)
$$\begin{array}{l} c\sqrt{a}+d\sqrt{b} \\ c\sqrt{a}-d\sqrt{b} \\ \hline c^2a+cd\sqrt{ab} \\ \quad -cd\sqrt{ab}-d^2b \\ \hline c^2a \qquad\qquad -d^2b \end{array}$$

(16)
$$\begin{array}{r} 7+2\sqrt{6} \\ 9-5\sqrt{6} \\ \hline 63+18\sqrt{6} \\ -35\sqrt{6}-10\times 6 \\ \hline 3-17\sqrt{6}. \end{array}$$

(17)
$$\begin{array}{l} \sqrt{a+x}+\sqrt{a-x} \\ \sqrt{a+x}-\sqrt{a-x} \\ \hline (a+x)+\sqrt{(a^2-x^2)} \\ \quad -\sqrt{(a^2-x^2)}-(a-x) \\ \hline (a+x)-(a-x)=2x. \end{array}$$

(18)
$$\begin{array}{r} x^2-x\sqrt{2}+1 \\ x^2+x\sqrt{2}+1 \\ \hline x^4-x^3\sqrt{2}+x^2 \\ +x^3\sqrt{2}-2x^2+x\sqrt{2} \\ +x^2-x\sqrt{2}+1 \\ \hline x^4+1 \end{array}$$

Article 203.

DIVISION OF RADICALS.

(2) $\frac{\sqrt{54}}{\sqrt{6}}=\sqrt{\frac{54}{6}}=\sqrt{9}=3$. (3) $\frac{6\sqrt{54}}{3\sqrt{27}}=\frac{6}{3}\sqrt{\frac{54}{27}}=2\sqrt{2}$

(4) $\frac{\sqrt{160}}{\sqrt{8}}=\sqrt{\frac{160}{8}}=\sqrt{20}=2\sqrt{5}$.

(5) $\frac{15\sqrt{378}}{5\sqrt{6}}=\frac{15}{5}\sqrt{\frac{378}{6}}=3\sqrt{63}=3\sqrt{9\times 7}=9\sqrt{7}$.

(6) $\frac{ab\sqrt{a^3b^3}}{b\sqrt{ab}}=\frac{ab}{b}\sqrt{\frac{a^3b^3}{ab}}=a\sqrt{a^2b^2}=a^2b$.

(7) $\sqrt{\frac{a}{b}}\div\sqrt{\frac{d}{c}}=\sqrt{\frac{a}{b}\times\frac{c}{d}}=\sqrt{\frac{ac}{bd}}=\sqrt{\frac{acbd}{b^2d^2}}=\frac{1}{bd}\sqrt{abcd}$.

(8) $\sqrt{\frac{1}{2}}\div\sqrt{\frac{1}{3}}=\sqrt{\frac{1}{2}\times\frac{3}{1}}=\sqrt{\frac{3}{2}}=\sqrt{\frac{6}{4}}=\sqrt{\frac{1}{4}\times 6}=\frac{1}{2}\sqrt{6}$

(9) $\frac{2}{3}\sqrt{18}\div\frac{1}{2}\sqrt{2}=\frac{2}{3}\times\frac{2}{1}\sqrt{\frac{18}{2}}=\frac{4}{3}\sqrt{9}=4$.

(10) $\frac{3}{5}\sqrt{\frac{1}{3}}\div\frac{1}{2}\sqrt{\frac{3}{5}}=\frac{3}{5}\times\frac{2}{1}\sqrt{\frac{1}{3}\times\frac{5}{3}}=\frac{6}{5}\sqrt{\frac{1}{9}\times 5}=\frac{6}{15}\sqrt{5}=\frac{2}{5}\sqrt{5}$

(11) $\frac{1}{2}\sqrt{\frac{1}{2}}=\frac{1}{2}\sqrt{\frac{1}{4}\times 2}=\frac{1}{2}\times\frac{1}{2}\sqrt{2}=\frac{1}{4}\sqrt{2}$;

$\sqrt{2}+3\sqrt{\frac{1}{2}}=\sqrt{2}+3\sqrt{\frac{1}{4}\times 2}=\sqrt{2}+\frac{3}{2}\sqrt{2}=\frac{5}{2}\sqrt{2}$;

$$\frac{1}{4}\sqrt{2}\div\frac{5}{2}\sqrt{2}=\frac{1}{4}\times\frac{2}{5}\sqrt{\frac{2}{2}}=\frac{2}{20}=\frac{1}{10}.$$

Article 204.

(1) $\frac{1}{\sqrt{2}}=\frac{1}{\sqrt{2}}\times\frac{\sqrt{2}}{\sqrt{2}}=\frac{\sqrt{2}}{2}=\frac{1}{2}\sqrt{2}.$

(2) $\frac{\sqrt{2}}{\sqrt{3}}=\frac{\sqrt{2}}{\sqrt{3}}\times\frac{\sqrt{3}}{\sqrt{3}}=\frac{\sqrt{6}}{3}=\frac{1}{3}\sqrt{6}.$

(3) $\frac{3}{6-\sqrt{3}}=\frac{3}{6-\sqrt{3}}\times\frac{6+\sqrt{3}}{6+\sqrt{3}}=\frac{3(6+\sqrt{3})}{36-3}=\frac{1}{11}(6+\sqrt{3})$

(4) $\frac{5}{\sqrt{7}+\sqrt{6}}=\frac{5}{\sqrt{7}+\sqrt{6}}\times\frac{\sqrt{7}-\sqrt{6}}{\sqrt{7}-\sqrt{6}}=\frac{5(\sqrt{7}-\sqrt{6})}{7-6}$
$=5(\sqrt{7}-\sqrt{6}).$

(5) $\frac{3}{\sqrt{5}}=\frac{3}{\sqrt{5}}\times\frac{\sqrt{5}}{\sqrt{5}}=\frac{3}{5}\sqrt{5}=\frac{3}{5}(2.2360679+)=1.3416407+.$

(6) $\frac{\sqrt{2}}{\sqrt{5}-\sqrt{3}}=\frac{\sqrt{2}}{\sqrt{5}-\sqrt{3}}\times\frac{\sqrt{5}+\sqrt{3}}{\sqrt{5}+\sqrt{3}}=\frac{\sqrt{10}+\sqrt{6}}{5-3}$

$=\frac{1}{2}(\sqrt{10}+\sqrt{6})=\frac{1}{2}(3.162277+2.449489+)=2.805833+.$

Article 205.

SIMPLE EQUATIONS CONTAINING RADICALS OF THE SECOND DEGREE.

(1) $\sqrt{(x+3)}+3=7.$

Transposing, $\sqrt{(x+3)}=4;$
squaring, $x+3=16;$ whence, $x=13.$

(2) $x+\sqrt{(x^2+11)}=11.$

Transposing, $\sqrt{(x^2+11)}=11-x;$
squaring, $x^2+11=121-22x+x^2;$ whence, $x=5$

(3) $\sqrt{(6+\sqrt{x-1})}=3.$

Squaring, $6+\sqrt{x-1}=9;$ transposing, $\sqrt{x-1}=3.$
squaring, $x-1=9;$ whence, $x=10.$

(4) $\sqrt{x(a+x)}=a-x.$

Squaring, $x(a+x)=a^2-2ax+x^2.$

Reducing, $3ax=a^2;$ whence, $x=\frac{a}{3}$

(5) $\sqrt{x}-2=\sqrt{(x-8)}$.

Squaring, $x-4\sqrt{x}+4=x-8$; reducing, $-4\sqrt{x}=-12$;
dividing, $\sqrt{x}=3$; squaring, $x=9$.

(6) $x+\sqrt{x^2-7}=7$.

Transposing, $\sqrt{x^2-7}=7-x$;
squaring, $x^2-7=49-14x+x^2$; whence, $x=4$.

(7) $\sqrt{x+7}=6-\sqrt{x-5}$.

Squaring, $x+7=36-12\sqrt{x-5}+x-5$
transposing and reducing, $\sqrt{x-5}=2$;
squaring, $x-5=4$; whence, $x=9$.

(8) $\sqrt{x-a}=\sqrt{x}-\frac{1}{2}\sqrt{a}$.

Squaring, $x-a=x-\sqrt{ax}+\frac{1}{4}a$;

transposing and reducing, $\sqrt{ax}=\frac{5a}{4}$;

squaring, $ax=\frac{25a^2}{16}$; whence, $x=\frac{25a}{16}$.

(9) $\sqrt{x+225}-\sqrt{x-424}-11=0$.

Transposing, $\sqrt{x+225}=11+\sqrt{x-424}$;
squaring, $x+225=121+22\sqrt{x-424}+x-424$;
reducing, $528=22\sqrt{x-424}$; dividing, $24=\sqrt{x-424}$;
squaring, $576=x-424$; whence, $x=1000$.

(10) $x+\sqrt{2ax+x^2}=a$.

Transposing, $\sqrt{2ax+x^2}=a-x$;
squaring, $2ax+x^2=a^2-2ax+x^2$;
reducing, $4ax=a^2$; whence, $x=\frac{1}{4}a$.

(11) $\sqrt{x+a}-\sqrt{x-a}=\sqrt{a}$.

Transposing, $\sqrt{x+a}=\sqrt{a}+\sqrt{x-a}$;
squaring, $x+a=a+2\sqrt{ax-a^2}+(x-a)$;
reducing, $a=2\sqrt{ax-a^2}$;
squaring $a^2=4(ax-a^2)$; whence, $x=\frac{5a}{4}$.

(12) $$\sqrt{x+12}=2+\sqrt{x}.$$
Squaring, $x+12=4+4\sqrt{x}+x$;
reducing, $2=\sqrt{x}$; squaring, $x=4$.

(13) $$\sqrt{8+x}=2\sqrt{1+x}-\sqrt{x}.$$
Squaring, $8+x=4(1+x)-4\sqrt{x+x^2}+x$;
transposing and reducing, $4\sqrt{x+x^2}=4(x-1)$;
dividing, $\sqrt{x+x^2}=x-1$; squaring, $x+x^2=x^2-2x+1$;
whence, $x=\frac{1}{3}$.

(14) $$\sqrt{5x}+\frac{12}{\sqrt{5x+6}}=\sqrt{5x+6}.$$
Multiply by $\sqrt{5x+6}$, $\sqrt{25x^2+30x}+12=5x+6$;
transposing, $\sqrt{25x^2+30x}=5x-6$;
squaring, $25x^2+30x=25x^2-60x+36$;
reducing, $90x=36$; whence, $x=\frac{2}{5}$.

(15) $$\sqrt{x}-4=\frac{237-10x}{4+\sqrt{x}}.$$
Multiplying by $4+\sqrt{x}$, $x-16=237-10x$;
transposing, $11x=253$; and $x=23$.

(16) $$\sqrt{x^2+\sqrt{4x^2+x+\sqrt{9x^2+12x}}}=1+x.$$
Squaring, $x^2+\sqrt{4x^2+x+\sqrt{9x^2+12x}}=1+2x+x^2$;
omitting x^2 on each side, and squaring again, we have
$$4x^2+x+\sqrt{9x^2+12x}=1+4x+4x^2;$$
reducing, $\sqrt{9x^2+12x}=1+3x$;
squaring, $9x^2+12x=1+6x+9x^2$;
reducing, $6x=1$, and $x=\frac{1}{6}$.

(17) $$\sqrt{a+\sqrt{ax}}=\sqrt{a}-\sqrt{a-\sqrt{ax}}.$$
Squaring, $a+\sqrt{ax}=a-2\sqrt{a^2-a\sqrt{ax}}+(a-\sqrt{ax})$;
transposing and reducing, $2\sqrt{a^2-a\sqrt{ax}}=a-2\sqrt{ax}$:
squaring, $4(a^2-a\sqrt{ax})=a^2-4a\sqrt{ax}+4ax$;
reducing, $3a^2=4ax$; whence, $x=\frac{3a}{4}$.

(18) $$b(\sqrt{x}+\sqrt{b})=a(\sqrt{x}-\sqrt{b}).$$
Transposing, $a\sqrt{x}-b\sqrt{x}=a\sqrt{b}+b\sqrt{b}$;
factoring, $(a-b)\sqrt{x}=(a+b)\sqrt{b}$;
squaring, $(a-b)^2x=(a+b)^2b$;
whence, $x=\frac{b(a+b)^2}{(a-b)^2}.$

(19) $$\sqrt{x}+\sqrt{ax}=a-1.$$
Factoring, $\sqrt{x}(1+\sqrt{a})=a-1=(\sqrt{a}+1)(\sqrt{a}-1)$;
dividing both sides by $1+\sqrt{a}$, and observing that $1+\sqrt{a}$ is the same as $\sqrt{a}+1$,
$$\sqrt{x}=(\sqrt{a}-1);\text{ squaring, } x=(\sqrt{a}-1)^2.$$

Article 211.

QUESTIONS PRODUCING PURE QUADRATIC EQUATIONS.

(2) Let $x=$ the number.
Then, $\frac{x}{3}\times\frac{x}{4}=108$; whence, $\frac{x^2}{12}=108$;
$x^2=1296$; and $x=36$.

(3) Let $x=$ the number.
Then, $x^2-16=\frac{x^2}{2}+16$; whence, $\frac{x^2}{2}=32$, and $x=8$.

(4) Let $x=$ the number.
Then, $\frac{x}{9}=\frac{16}{x}$; $x^2=9\times16$; and $x=3\times4=12$.

(6) Let $3x$ and $4x$ represent the numbers.
Then, $16x^2-9x^2=63$;
from which $7x^2=63$, and $x=3$.

(7) Let $5x=$ the breadth and $9x=$ the length.
Then, $5x\times9x=45x^2=$ the number of square feet;
therefore, $45x^2=1620$;
whence, $x^2=36$, and $x=6$.

(8) By placing $10x=$ their sum, we have the greater $=7x$, since their sum is to the greater as 10 to 7. And if $10x=$ their sum, and $7x=$ the greater, the less $=3x$.
Therefore, $10x\times3x=30x^2=270$;
whence. $x^2=9$, and $x=3$.

(9) Let $2x=$ their difference; then, $9x$ will be the greater, and $9x-2x=7x$, will be the less.

Therefore, $(9x)^2-(7x)^2=128$;

$$81x^2-49x^2=128;$$

whence, $x^2=4$, and $x=2$.

(10) Let $4x=$ the cost of 1 yard in cents, then $9x=$ the number of yards. Then, $9x\times 4x=36x^2=324$;

whence, $x^2=9$, and $x=3$.

(11) Let $\frac{1}{2}x$ and $\frac{2}{3}x$ represent the numbers.

Then, $\frac{1}{4}x^2+\frac{4}{9}x^2=225$.

$$9x^2+16x^2=225\times 4\times 9.$$

$$25x^2=225\times 4\times 9.$$

Dividing, $x^2=9\times 4\times 9$.

Extracting the sq. root, $x=3\times 2\times 3=18$.

Hence, $\frac{1}{2}x=9$, and $\frac{2}{3}x=12$.

We may avoid fractions by representing the numbers by $3x$ and $4x$, as recommended in the book.

(12) By reducing $\frac{1}{2}$, $\frac{2}{3}$, and $\frac{3}{4}$, to a common denominator, we find they are to each other as 6, 8, and 9; therefore, let the three numbers be represented by $6x$, $8x$, and $9x$.

Then, $36x^2+64x^2+81x^2=724$.

Adding, $181x^2=724$;

whence, $x^2=4$, and $x=2$.

Article 212.

AFFECTED QUADRATIC EQUATIONS.

(34)
$$2ax-x^2=-2ab-b^2.$$

Changing signs, $x^2-2ax=2ab+b^2$.

Completing square, $x^2-2ax+a^2=a^2+2ab+b^2$.

Extracting sq. root, $x-a=\pm(a+b)$.

Transposing, $x=a\pm(a+b)=2a+b$, or $-b$.

(35) $x^2+3bx-4b^2=0$.

$x^2+3bx=4b^2$, by transposing;

$x^2+3bx+\frac{9b^2}{4}=4b^2+\frac{9b^2}{4}=\frac{25b^2}{4}$, by completing the sq.;

$x+\frac{3b}{2}=\pm\frac{5b}{2}$, by extracting the square root;

$x=-\frac{3b}{2}\pm\frac{5b}{2}=+b$, or $-4b$.

(36) $x^2-ax-bx=-ab.$

$x^2-(a+b)x=-ab$, by factoring;

$$x^2-(a+b)x+\frac{(a+b)^2}{4}=\frac{(a+b)^2}{4}-ab=\frac{a^2-2ab+b^2}{4};$$

$$x-\frac{a+b}{2}=\pm\frac{a-b}{2}; \text{ and } x=\frac{a+b}{2}\pm\frac{a-b}{2}=+a, \text{or} +b$$

(37) $2bx^2+(a-2b)x=a.$

$$x^2+\frac{a-2b}{2b}x=\frac{a}{2b};$$

$$x^2+\frac{a-2b}{2b}x+\frac{(a-2b)^2}{16b^2}=\frac{(a-2b)^2}{16b^2}+\frac{a}{2b}=\frac{a^2+4ab+4b^2}{16b^2}$$

$$x+\frac{a-2b}{4b}=\pm\frac{a+2b}{4b};$$

$$x=-\frac{a-2b}{4b}\pm\frac{a+2b}{4b}=1, \text{ or } -\frac{a}{2b}.$$

(38) $x^2-(a-1)x-a=0.$

$x^2-(a-1)x=a;$

$$x^2-(a-1)x+\frac{(a-1)^2}{4}=\frac{(a-1)^2}{4}+\frac{4a}{4}=\frac{(a+1)^2}{4};$$

$$x-\frac{a-1}{2}=\pm\frac{a+1}{2}; x=\frac{a-1}{2}\pm\frac{a+1}{2}=a, \text{ or } -1.$$

(39) $x^2-(a+b-c)x=(a+b)c.$

$$x^2-(a+b-c)x+\frac{(a+b-c)^2}{4}=\frac{(a+b-c)^2}{4}+\frac{4(a+b)c}{4}$$

$$=\frac{a^2+2ab+b^2-2ac-2bc+c^2+4ac+4bc}{4}$$

$$=\frac{a^2+2ab+b^2+2ac+2bc+c^2}{4}=\frac{(a+b+c)^2}{4};$$

by extracting the square root of both sides, we find

$$x-\frac{a+b-c}{2}=\pm\frac{a+b+c}{2}:$$

$$x=\frac{a+b-c}{2}\pm\frac{a+b+c}{2}=a+b, \text{ or } -c.$$

Article 214.

PROBLEMS PRODUCING AFFECTED QUADRATIC EQUATIONS.

(6) Let $x=$ the number.

Then, $x^2-6x=7$;

from which $x=+7$, or -1.

The positive value satisfies the given question in an arithmetical sense, and the negative value satisfies the following question in an arithmetical sense.

Find a number, such that if its square be *increased* by 6 times the number itself, the *sum* shall be 7.

(7) Let $x=$ the number.

Then, $2x^2+3x=65$; whence, $x=+5$, or $-\frac{13}{2}$.

(8) Let $x=$ the number.

Then, $\frac{2}{3}(x^2-1)=\frac{5x}{2}$; whence, $x=+4$, or $-\frac{1}{4}$.

The negative value is the answer, in an arithmetical sense, to the following question.

Find a number such, that if 1 *be diminished by its square*, and $\frac{2}{3}$ of the remainder be taken, the result shall be equal to 5 times the number divided by 2.

(9) Let $x=$ the greater number; then, $x-8=$ the less.
Therefore, $x^2-8x=240$;
whence, $x=+20$, or -12; hence, $x-8=+12$, or -20.

(10) Let $x=$ the number of sheep.

Then, $\frac{80}{x}=$ cost of one; also, $\frac{80}{x+4}=$ cost of one, if he had bought 4 more for the same money

Therefore, $\frac{80}{x+4}+1=\frac{80}{x}$.

$80x+x^2+4x=80x+320$, by clearing of fractions

$x^2+4x=320$; from which $x=+16$, or -20.

The negative value is the answer, in an arithmetical sense to the following question.

A person bought a number of sheep for \$80; if he had bought 4 *less* for the same money, he would have paid \$1 *more* for each: how many did he buy?

(11) Let $x=$ the greater number; then, $x-10=$ the less.

Then, $\frac{600}{x-10}-\frac{600}{x}=10$.

$600x-600x+6000=10x^2-100x$.

Whence, $x^2-10x=600$; from which $x=+30$, or -20,

and $x-10=+20$, or -30.

(12) Let $x=$ the rate of travel. Then,

$\frac{45}{x}=$ number of hr. traveling at x miles per hr.

$\frac{45}{x+\frac{1}{2}}=$ number of hr. traveling at $(x+\frac{1}{2})$ miles per hr.

Therefore, $\frac{45}{x+\frac{1}{2}}+1\frac{1}{4}=\frac{45}{x}$; whence, $x=+4$, or $-4\frac{1}{2}$.

The negative value is the answer, in an arithmetical sense, to a question expressed in the same words, except that *increases* should be *diminishes*, and *sooner* should be *later*.

(13) Let $x=$ one of the numbers, then $14-x=$ the other.

Then, $x^2+(14-x)^2=100$;

$x^2+196-28x+x^2=100$;

reducing, $x^2-14x=-48$;

whence, $x=7\pm1=+8$, or $+6$; and $14-x=+6$, or $+8$.

(14) Let $x=$ the number of rows, then $x+5=$ number of trees in a row,

and $x(x+5)=$ the whole number of trees

Therefore, $x^2+5x=204$;

whence, $x=+12$, or -17;

and $x+5=+17$, or -12.

The negative value is the answer to a similar question, the word *more* being changed to *less*.

(15) Let $x=$ B's rate of travel; then, $x+3=$ A's rate.

Then, $\frac{150}{x}-\frac{150}{x+3}=8\frac{1}{3}$;

$150x+450-150x=8\frac{1}{3}x^2+25x$, by clearing of fractions:

reducing, $x^2+3x=54$;

whence, $x=+6$, or -9, and $x+3=+9$, or -6

(16) Let $x=$ the number in the company at first; then,

$\frac{175}{x}=$ what each ought to have paid, and

$\frac{175}{x-2}=$ what those paid who remained.

Therefore, $\frac{175}{x-2}-\frac{175}{x}=10$.

$175x-175x+350=10x^2-20x$, by clearing of fract'ns;

$x^2-2x=35$, by reducing; whence, $x=+7$, or -5.

(17) Let x= the larger number; then, $\frac{100}{x}$= the smaller.

Therefore, $(x-1)\left(\frac{100}{x}+1\right)=120;$

$$\frac{(x-1)(100+x)}{x}=120;$$

$$100x+x^2-100-x=120x;\ x^2-21x=100;$$

whence, $x=+25$, or -4; and $\frac{100}{x}=+4$, or -25.

(18) Let x^2= the father's age; then, $\frac{x^2-4}{3}$= the son's age.

Then, $\frac{1}{2}\left(\frac{x^2-4}{3}-1\right)=x.$

$x^2-4-3=6x$, by multiplying by 2 and then by 3;

$x^2-6x=7$, by transposing;

whence, $x=+7$, or -1; hence, $x^2=49$, and $\frac{x^2-4}{3}=15$.

(19) Let x^2= her age.

Then, $\frac{3x^2}{8}+x=10$; whence, $x=+4$, or $-\frac{20}{3}$.

Hence, $x^2=16$, or $44\frac{4}{9}$, the former of which satisfies the conditions of the question in its arithmetical sense.

(20) Let x= cost; then, $\frac{x}{100}$=per cent. of loss,

and $x\times\frac{x}{100}=\frac{x^2}{100}$=loss.

Therefore, $x-\frac{x^2}{100}=24;$

whence, $x=+60$, or $+40$.

Article 219.

QUADRATIC EQUATIONS CONTAINING TWO UNKNOWN QUANTITIES.

(6) $x^2+y^2=34,\qquad (1);$
$x^2-y^2=16,\qquad (2).$

By adding these equations together, and dividing by 2, we find $x^2=25$; from which $x=+5$, or -5.

The value of y may be found either by substituting 25 instead of x^2 or by subtracting Eq. (2) from (1).

(7) $x+y=16$, (1);
$xy=63$, (2).

The values of x and y are readily obtained by finding the value of either in terms of the other from Eq. (2), and substituting it in Eq. (1); or thus:

$$x^2+2xy+y^2=256, \text{ by squaring } (1);$$
$$4xy=252 \text{ by multiplying (2) by 4};$$
$$x^2-2xy+y^2=4, \text{ by subtracting};$$
$$x-y=2, \text{ by extracting the square root};$$
$$x+y=16.$$

From these equations, by adding and subtracting, the values of x and y are readily found.

(8) $x-y=5$, (1);
$xy=36$, (2).

From Eq. (1) $y=x-5$; this being substituted instead of y in Eq. (2) gives $x^2-5x=36$, from which x is readily found, then y.

Or, by squaring Eq. (1), then adding it to 4 times Eq. (2), and extracting the square root, we find $x+y=13$; from which, and Eq. (1), by adding and subtracting, the values of x and y are readily found.

(9) $x+y=9$, (1);
$x^2+y^2=53$, (2).

From Eq. (1), $y=9-x$; this being substituted instead of y in Eq. (2), gives, after reducing, $x^2-9x=-14$; from which we find $x=7$, or 2; consequently, $y=2$, or 7.

Or, by subtracting (2) from the square of (1) we obtain xy, then finish as in Ex. 7.

(10) $x-y=5$, (1);
$x^2+y^2=73$, (2).

From Eq. (1) $y=x-5$; this being substituted instead of y in Eq. (2), gives, after reducing, $x^2-5x=24$; from which x is found $=8$, or -3; hence, $y=3$, or -8.

Or, subtract the square of (1) from (2) and find xy; then finish as in Ex. 8.

(11) $x^3+y^3=152$, (1);
$x+y=8$, (2).

Dividing Eq. (1) by Eq. (2), we find $x^2-xy+y^2=19$, (3).

From Eq. (2) $y=8-x$; substituting this value of y in Eq (3) and reducing, we have $x^2-8x=-15$; from which we find $x=5$. or 3; hence, $y=3$, or 5.

Or, subtract (3) from the square of (2) and finish as in Ex. 7.

(12) $x^3-y^3=208$, (1);
$x-y=4$, (2).

Dividing Eq. (1) by Eq. (2), we find $x^2+xy+y^2=52$, (3)

From Eq. (2), $y=x-4$; substituting this value of y in Eq. (3) and reducing, we find $x^2-4x=12$; from which $x=6$, or -2; hence, $y=2$, or -6.

Or, subtract the square of (2) from (3) and find xy.

(13) $x^3+y^3=19(x+y)$, (1);
$x-y=3$, (2).

By dividing both sides of Eq. (1) by $x+y$,
$x^2-xy+y^2=19$, (3).

From Eq. (2) $y=x-3$; substituting this value of y in Eq. (3) and reducing, we find $x^2-3x=10$; from which $x=5$, or -2; hence, $y=2$, or -5.

Or, subtract the square of (2) from (3) and find xy.

(14) $x+y=11$, (1);
$x^2-y^2=11$, (2).

From Eq. (1) $y=11-x$; this being substituted in Eq. (2) instead of y, and the equation reduced, gives $22x=132$, from which $x=6$; hence, $y=5$.

Or, divide (2) by (1).

(15) $(x-3)(y+2)=12$, (1);
$xy=12$, (2).

Performing the operations indicated in Eq. (1) and then subtracting Eq. (2) from it, we find $2x-3y=6$, (3). From Eq. (3) we find $x=\frac{6+3y}{2}$, and this being substituted in Eq. (2), gives, after reducing, $y^2+2y=8$; from which $y=2$, or -4; hence, $x=6$, or -3.

(16) $y-x=2$, (1);
$3xy=10x+y$, (2).

From Eq. (1), $y=x+2$; this value of y being substituted in Eq. (2), gives, after reducing, $3x^2-5x=2$; from which $x=2$, or $-\frac{1}{3}$; hence, $y=4$, or $1\frac{2}{3}$.

(17) $3x^2+2xy=24$, (1);

$5x-3y=1$, (2).

From Eq. (2), $y=\frac{5x-1}{3}$; this being substituted in Eq. (1), gives, after reducing, $19x^2-2x=72$; from which $x=2$, or $-\frac{36}{19}$; hence, $y=3$, or $-\frac{199}{57}$.

(18) $\frac{1}{x}+\frac{1}{y}=\frac{5}{6}$, (1);

$\frac{1}{x^2}+\frac{1}{y^2}=\frac{13}{36}$, (2).

Let $\frac{1}{x}=v$, and $\frac{1}{y}=z$; then, $v+z=\frac{5}{6}$, (3);

and $v^2+z^2=\frac{13}{36}$, (4).

From Eq. (3), $z=\frac{5}{6}-v=\frac{5-6v}{6}$; substituting this value instead of z in Eq. (4) and reducing, we find $6v^2-5v=-1$; from which $v=\frac{1}{2}$, or $\frac{1}{3}$; and substituting in the equation, $z=\frac{5}{6}-v$ we find $z=\frac{1}{3}$, or $\frac{1}{2}$.

Hence, $v=\frac{1}{x}=\frac{1}{2}$, or $\frac{1}{3}$; from which $x=2$, or 3.

$z=\frac{1}{y}=\frac{1}{3}$, or $\frac{1}{2}$; from which $y=3$, or 2.

Or, subtracting (2) from the square of (1) we obtain the value of $\frac{2}{xy}$. Subtracting this from (2) and extracting the square root. we obtain $\frac{1}{x}-\frac{1}{y}$. Then add and subtract this and Eq. (1).

(19) $x-y=2$, (1);

$x^2y^2=21-4xy$, (2).

In Eq. (2), let $xy=z$; the equation then becomes

$z^2=21-4z$; from which z or $xy=3$, or -7

We then have $x-y=2$, and $xy=3$, to find x and y.

These equations are similar to those in example 8, and we readily find $x=3$, or -1; hence, $y=1$, or -3.

From the equations $x-y=2$ and $xy=-7$, we may also find two other values of x and y, but they are imaginary.

Article 219.

PROBLEMS PRODUCING QUADRATIC EQUATIONS, CONTAINING TWO UNKNOWN QUANTITIES.

(1) Let x and y represent the numbers.

Then, $x+y=10$, (1);

$x^2+y^2=52$, (2).

Solved like question 9, preceding.

(2) Let x and y represent the numbers.

Then, $x-y=3$, (1);

$x^2-y^2=39$, (2).

Divide Eq. (2) by Eq. (1) and we get $x+y=13$, (3); then from this and Eq. (1), we readily find $x=8$, and $y=5$.

(3) Let x^2 and y^2 represent the parts.

Then, $x^2+y^2=25$, (1);

$x+y=7$, (2).

The values of x and y may now be found in the same manner as in question 9, preceding.

(4) Let $x=$ the digit in ten's place, and $y=$ the digit in unit's place.

Then, $10x+y=$ the number;

$(10x+y)(x+y)=160$, (1);

$$\frac{10x+y}{4y}=4, \qquad (2).$$

Dividing Eq. (1) by Eq. (2), we get

$$4y(x+y)=40; \text{ from which } x=\frac{10-y^2}{y}$$

Substituting this instead of x, in Eq. (2), we get

$$10\left(\frac{10-y^2}{y}\right)+y=16y;$$

clearing of fractions, $100-10y^2+y^2=16y^2$;

from which $y=2$; hence, $x=3$.

(5) Let $x=$ the greater number, and $y=$ their difference: then, $x-y=$ the less.

Then, $xy=16$, (1);

and $xy-y^2=12$, (2).

Subtracting the 2d Eq. from the 1st, we get

$$y^2=4; \text{ hence, } y=2;$$

$$x=\frac{16}{y}=8, \text{ and } x-y=6.$$

(6) Let x and y represent the numbers.

Then, $x+y=10$, (1);

$xy-(x-y)=22$, (2).

Find the value of either x or y from Eq. (1), and substitute it instead of the same unknown quantity, in Eq. (2).

This may also be easily solved by means of one unknown quantity; thus, let $x=$ one of the parts, then $10-x=$ the other, and $10-2x=$ their difference.

Then, $x(10-x)-(10-2x)=22$;

from which $x=8$, or 4;

hence, $10-x=2$, or 6.

The numbers 4 and 6 satisfy the conditions of the question in an arithmetical sense. The numbers 8 and 2 satisfy the following problem. Divide 10 into two such parts, that their product *plus* their difference, may be 22.

(7) Let x and y represent the numbers.

Then, $x+y=10$, (1);

$x^3+y^3=370$, (2).

For the method of solution, see question 11, preceding.

(8) Let x and y represent the numbers.

Then, $x-y=2$, (1);

$x^3-y^3=98$, (2).

For the method of solution, see question 12, preceding.

(9) Let $x=$ the digit in ten's place, and $y=$ the digit in unit's place.

Then, $10x+y=$ the number.

$\frac{10x+y}{xy}=2$, (1);

$10x+y+27=10y+x$, (2).

From the 2d Eq., $y=x+3$; this being substituted in the 1st Eq., we get, after reducing,

$2x^2-5x=3$, from which we find

$x=3$; hence, $y=6$, and the number is 36.

(10) Let x, y, and z represent the numbers.

Then, $\frac{xy}{z}=a$, (1); $\frac{xz}{y}=b$, (2); $\frac{yz}{x}=c$, (3)

Multiply the three equations together, and we have

$xyz=abc$, (4).

Divide this successively by each of the equations (1), (2) and (3), and we obtain

$z^2=bc$, $y^2=ac$, and $x^2=ab$.

Hence, $x=\pm\sqrt{ab}$, $y=\pm\sqrt{ac}$, and $z=\pm\sqrt{bc}$.

(11) Let $x+y$, and $x-y$ represent the numbers.
Then, the sum of their squares $=2x^2+2y^2$;
the difference of their squares $=4xy$;
and their product $=x^2-y^2$.
Therefore, $2x^2+2y^2-2(x^2-y^2)=4$, (1),
$4xy-\frac{1}{2}(x^2-y^2)=4$, (2).

Reducing Eq. (1), we readily find $y=1$; this value being substituted in Eq. (2), we have, after reduction,

$x^2-8x=-7$, from which $x=7$.

Hence, $x+y=8$; and $x-y=6$.

(12) Let $x=$ the circumference of the less wheel, and $y=$ the circumference of greater.

Then, $\frac{120}{x}=\frac{120}{y}+6$, (1);

$\frac{120}{x+1}=\frac{120}{y+1}+4$, (2).

$120y=120x+6xy$, by clearing Eq. (1) of fractions;
$120y+120=120x+120+4xy+4x+4y+4$, by clearing Eq. (2) of fractions.

$116y=124x+4xy+4$, by reducing.

From Eq. (1) after clearing, we find $y=\frac{20x}{20-x}$; this being substituted in the last equation, gives, after clearing of fractions and reducing,

$11x^2-89x=20$; from which $x=4$; hence, $y=5$.

(13) Let x and y represent the rates of travel of A and B; then,

$2x=$ distance A travels in 2 hr. at x mi. per hr.

$2x+1=$ distance A travels in 2 hr. at $x+\frac{1}{2}$ mi. per hr.

$30-2x=$ distance A travels after B starts, in 1st case;

$42-(2x+1)=41-2x=$ distance A travels after B starts, in 2d case.

Therefore, $\frac{30-2x}{x}=\frac{30}{y}$, (1); $\frac{41-2x}{x+\frac{1}{2}}=\frac{42}{y+\frac{1}{2}}$, (2)

Clearing Eq. (1) of fractions, and reducing, we find

$$y=\frac{15x}{15-x}.$$

Clearing Eq. (2) of fractions, and reducing, we get

$$41y-2xy=43x+\tfrac{1}{2}.$$

Substituting the value of y before found, in this equation, clearing of fractions, and reducing, we get

$28x^2-59x=15$; whence, $x=2\frac{1}{2}$, and $y=3$.

(14) Let $x=$ the number of miles B traveled; then,

$x+30=$ the number of miles A traveled.

Then, since the distance traveled, divided by the number of days spent in traveling, gives the number of miles traveled per day,

$$\frac{x}{4}=\text{A's rate of travel; and } \frac{x+30}{9}=\text{B's}.$$

Then dividing the distance traveled, by each man's rate of travel,

$$(x+30)\div\frac{x}{4}=\frac{4(x+30)}{x}=\text{days A traveled.}$$

$$x\div\frac{x+30}{9}=\frac{9x}{x+30}=\text{days B traveled.}$$

But they both traveled the same number of days; therefore,

$$\frac{4(x+30)}{x}=\frac{9x}{x+30};$$

$4(x+30)^2=9x^2$, by clearing of fractions;

$2(x+30)=3x$, by extracting the square root;

from which $x=60$; hence, $x+30=90$,

and $60+90=150$ miles, the distance from A to B.

Article 222.

(9) Here $n=20$, $a=16\frac{1}{12}$, $d=48\frac{1}{4}-16\frac{1}{12}=32\frac{1}{6}$.

$l=a+(n-1)d=16\frac{1}{12}+(20-1)32\frac{1}{6}=16\frac{1}{12}+611\frac{1}{6}=627\frac{1}{4}$

Article 223.

(5) Here $l=a+(n-1)d=10-3\times9=-17$.

$$s=(l+a)\frac{n}{2}=(-17+10)\frac{10}{2}=-35.$$

Article 225.

(1) $s=(l+a)\frac{n}{2}=(1+1000)\frac{1000}{2}=500500.$

(2) $l=a+(n-1)d=1+(101-1)2=201.$

$$s=(l+a)\frac{n}{2}=(201+1)\frac{101}{2}=10201.$$

(3) First find how many times a clock strikes in 12 hours.
Here, $a=1$, $l=12$, $n=12$.

$$s=(12+1)\frac{12}{2}=78.$$

$78\times2=156=$ strokes per day;
$156\times7=1092$ strokes in a week.

(4) Since the 2d term is 2, the 3d term 3, and so on, the nth term is evidently n.
Or thus, $l=a+(n-1)d=1+(n-1)1=1+n-1=n$

$$s=(l+a)\frac{n}{2}=(n+1)\frac{n}{2}=\frac{1}{2}n(n+1).$$

(5) Substituting the values of l, a, and d, in the formula
$l=a+(n-1)d$, we have
$29=2+(n-1)3$; from which $n=10$.

$$s=(l+a)\frac{n}{2}=(29+2)\frac{10}{2}=155.$$

(6) Substituting the values of l, a, and n, in the formula,

$$l=a+(n-1)d, \text{ we have}$$

$$10=6+(9-1)d; \text{ from which } d=\tfrac{1}{2}.$$

$$s=(l+a)\frac{n}{2}=(10+6)\frac{9}{2}=72.$$

(7) Substituting the values of s, a, and n, in the formula,

$s=(l+a)\frac{n}{2}$, we have $85=(l+10)\frac{10}{2}$; from which $l=7$.

Substituting the values of l, a, and n, in the formula,

$l=a-(n-1)d$, we have

$7=10-(10-1)d$; from which $d=\frac{1}{3}$.

(8) Substituting the values of a, b, and m, in the formula,

$d=\frac{b-a}{m+1}$, we have $d=\frac{16-1}{4+1}=3$.

Hence, the series is 1, 4, 7, 10, 13, 16, &c.; or, put $a=1$, $l=16$, and $n=6$, and find d, from which write the series.

(9) Substituting the values of a, and d, in the formula, $l=a+(n-1)d$, we have $l=24-4(n-1)=28-4n$; substituting this value of l, and those of s and a in the formula,

$s=(l+a)\frac{n}{2}$, we have $72=(28-4n+24)\frac{n}{2}$; from which, by reducing, $n^2-13n=-36$; whence, $n=+9$, or $+4$.

(10) Let $n=$ No. of acres; then the nth acre cost n \$.

Substituting n for l in the formula, $s=(l+a)\frac{n}{2}$, and for s

and a their values, we get $12880=(n+1)\frac{n}{2}$;

by reducing, $n^2+n=25760$; whence, $n=160$.

Having the number of acres, the average price per acre is easily found.

(12) Let $n=$ the number of hours.

Then, $l=a+(n-1)d=5+(n-1)1=4+n$;

$$s=(l+a)\frac{n}{2}=(4+n+5)\frac{n}{2}=\frac{n}{2}(9+n).$$

Therefore, $\frac{n}{2}(9+n)=6(3\frac{1}{3}+n)$.

By reducing, $n^2-3n=40$; from which $n=8$.

(13) Let $x=$ the number of hours; then, the formula,

$$l=a-(n-1)d \text{ becomes } l=4-\frac{1}{2}(x-1)=4\tfrac{1}{2}-\tfrac{1}{2}x:$$

$$s=(l+a)\frac{n}{2}, \text{ becomes } s=(4\tfrac{1}{2}-\tfrac{1}{2}x+4)\frac{x}{2}=(8\tfrac{1}{2}-\tfrac{1}{2}x)\frac{x}{2};$$

but in x days, A travels $3x$ miles;

therefore, $3x=(8\tfrac{1}{2}-\tfrac{1}{2}x)\frac{x}{2}$; dividing both sides by x and reducing, we find $x=5$.

GEOMETRICAL PROGRESSION.

Article 229.

(4) Here, the ratio is $-\frac{1}{3}$; $s=\frac{a}{1-r}=\frac{1}{1-(-\frac{1}{3})}=\frac{1}{\frac{4}{3}}=\frac{3}{4}$.

(5) Here, the ratio is $\frac{1}{x^2}$; $s=\frac{a}{1-r}=\frac{1}{1-\frac{1}{x^2}}=\frac{x^2}{x^2-1}$.

(6) In this example, the ratio is $-\frac{b}{a}$.

$$s=\frac{a}{1-r}=\frac{a}{1-\left(-\frac{b}{a}\right)}=\frac{a}{1+\frac{b}{a}}=\frac{a^2}{a+b}.$$

(7) Here, the ratio is $\frac{1}{2}$; $s=\frac{a}{1-r}=\frac{10}{1-\frac{1}{2}}=\frac{10}{\frac{1}{2}}=20$.

KEY

TO

NEW HIGHER ALGEBRA.

GREATEST COMMON DIVISOR.

Article 108.

Note.—This article contains the first examples in the Algebra which the attentive student will find any real difficulty in solving

(4)

$$\begin{array}{ll}
a^4-x^4 & |\,a^3+a^2x-ax^2-x^3 \\
a^4+a^3x-a^2x^2-ax^3 & |\,a+1 \\
\quad -a^3x+a^2x^2+ax^3-x^4 & \\
=-x(a^3-a^2x-ax^2+x^3) & \\
\qquad a^3-a^2x-ax^2+x^3 & \\
\qquad a^3+a^2x-ax^2-x^3 & \\
\qquad -2a^2x \qquad +2x^3 & \\
\qquad -2x(a^2-x^2) &
\end{array}$$

After dividing, we find the first remainder contains a factor, $-x$, not found in the divisor; hence, it should be canceled. See Note 8.

By dividing $a^3+a^2x-ax^2-x^3$ by a^2-x^2, we find there is no remainder; hence, the latter is the G. C. D. required.

(5)

$$\begin{array}{ll}
x^3-5x^2+13x-9 & |\,x^3-2x^2+4x-3 \\
x^3-2x^2+4x-3 & |\,1 \\
\quad -3x^2+9x-6=-3(x^2-3x+2) & \\
 & \\
x^3-2x^2+4x-3 & |\,x^2-3x+2 \\
x^3-3x^2+2x & |\,x+1 \\
\qquad x^2+2x-3 & \\
\qquad x^2-3x+2 & \\
\qquad\qquad x-1 &
\end{array}$$

$x-1$ will be found to divide x^2-3x+2 without a remainder it is, therefore, the G. C. D.

NOTE.—In the solution of the remaining questions in this article, we shall merely exhibit so much of the operation as is necessary to show how the G. C. D. is obtained. The reasons for the different steps of the operation will be found in the rule, or in the notes following it.

(6) Multiplying the 1st polynomial by 2 to render it divisible by the 2d, and dividing by x (Note 3), we have

$$\begin{array}{r|l} 42x^2-52x+16 & 6x^2-x-2 \\ 42x^2-7x-14 & \overline{7} \\ \hline -45x+30 & \\ -15(3x-2) & \end{array}$$

Ans. $3x-2$.

(7) Multiplying the 1st polynomial by 7 to render it divisible by the 2d, we have

$$\begin{array}{r|l} 7x^4+14x^2+63 & 7x^3-11x^2+15x+9 \\ 7x^4-11x^3+15x^2+9x & \overline{x+11} \\ \hline 11x^3-x^2-9x+63 & \text{. . . . Multiply by 7.} \\ 77x^3-7x^2-63x+441 & \\ 77x^3-121x^2+165x+99 & \\ \hline 114x^2-228x+342 & \\ 114(x^2-2x+3) & \end{array}$$

Ans. x^2-2x+3

(8) This example presents no difficulty whatever.

(9) In this example, $2b$ is a factor of the 1st polynomial, and $3a$ of the 2d. Canceling these factors, arranging the terms in both, and multiplying the 2d by 4, to render it divisible by the 1st, we have

$$\begin{array}{r|l} 12a^3-12a^2b+4ab^2-4b^3 & 4a^2-5ab+b^2 \\ 12a^3-15a^2b+3ab^2 & \overline{3a+3b} \\ \hline 3a^2b+ab^2-4b^3 & \\ 4 & \\ \hline 12a^2b+4ab^2-16b^3 & \\ 12a^2b-15ab^2+3b^3 & \\ \hline 19ab^2-19b^3 & \\ 19b^2(a-b) & \end{array}$$

Ans. $a-b$.

(10)
$$\begin{array}{r|l} x^4+a^2x^2+a^4 & x^4+ax^3-a^3x-a^4 \\ x^4+ax^3-a^3x-a^4 & \overline{1} \\ \hline -ax^3+a^2x^2+a^3x+2a^4 & \\ -a(x^3-ax^2-a^2x-2a^3) & \end{array}$$

(*Concluded on page* 52.)

$$
\begin{array}{ll}
x^4+ax^3-a^3x-a^4 & |\underline{x^3-ax^2-a^2x-2a^3} \\
\underline{x^4-ax^3-a^2x^2-2a^3x} & |x+2 \\
a)\ +2ax^3+a^2x^2+a^3x-a^4 & \\
\quad +\ 2x^3+a\,x^2+a^2x-a^3 & \\
\quad \underline{+\ 2x^3-2ax^2-2a^2x-4a^3} & \\
+3a)\ \underline{+\ 3ax^2+3a^2x+3a^3} & \\
\qquad x^2+ax+a^2, \quad \textit{Ans.} &
\end{array}
$$

$$
\begin{array}{ll}
(11)\quad x^4-px^3+(q-1)x^2+px-q & |\underline{x^4-qx^3+(p-1)x^2+qx-p} \\
\underline{x^4-qx^3+(p-1)x^2+qx-p} & |1 \\
(q-p)x^3+(q-p)x^2-(q-p)x-(q-p), & \\
\text{or} \qquad x^3+x^2-x-1, \text{ by dividing by } q-p. &
\end{array}
$$

$$
\begin{array}{ll}
x^4-qx^3+(p-1)x^2+qx-p & |\underline{x^3+x^2-x-1} \\
\underline{x^4+\ x^3-x^2-x} & |x-(q+1) \\
-(q+1)x^3+px^2+(q+1)x-p & \\
\underline{-(q+1)x^3-(q+1)x^2+(q+1)x+(q+1)} & \\
\qquad (p+q+1)x^2-(p+q+1) & \\
\qquad =(p+q+1)(x^2-1). \qquad \textit{Ans. } x^2-1. &
\end{array}
$$

LEAST COMMON MULTIPLE.

Article 113.

(4) From Arts. 85 and 86, it is obvious that $a+x$ is the only divisor of both the quantities; hence, (Art. 113) $(a^3+x^3)(a^2-x^2)\div(a+x)=(a^3+x^3)(a-x)=a^4-a^3x+ax^3-x^4$, *Ans.*

(5) By examining these quantities, we see that the *second* quantity is divisible by the *first*, and the *fourth* by the *third*, and that these are the only cases of divisibility among the four quantities; hence, their L. C. M. will be the product of the 2d and 4th quantities.

(6) By factoring the several quantities, we find the 1st $=(x+1)(x-1)$, the 2d $=x^2+1$; 3d $=(x-1)(x-1)$; 4th $=(x+1)(x+1)$; 5th $=(x-1)(x^2+x+1)$; 6th $=(x+1)(x^2-x+1)$. It will now be seen that if we omit the 3d and 4th quantities, the remaining quantities will contain the factors of these, and no other factor not necessary to be found in the L. C. M.; hence, the L. C. M. will be $(x^2-1)(x^2+1)(x^3-1)(x^3+1)=(x^4-1)(x^6-1)=x^{10}-x^6-x^4+1$

(7) We first find the G. C. D. of the 1st and 2d polynomials, to be $x-3$; then, of the 1st and 3d to be $3x-2$. Hence,

$$\left.\begin{aligned}3x^2-11x+6&=(x-3)(3x-2)\\2x^2-\ 7x+3&=(x-3)(2x-1)\\6x^2-\ 7x+2&=(2x-1)(3x-2)\end{aligned}\right\}$$

It is evident the L. C. M is $(x-3)(3x-2)(2x-1)=6x^3-25x^2+23x-6$.

FRACTIONS TO LOWEST TERMS.

Article 119.

The only difficulty in solving any of the examples in this article, consists in finding the G. C. D. of the two terms. In general, it may be easily found by the rule (Art. 108), and in most cases by mere inspection. Thus:

(11) From Art. 86, we know that $x+1$ is a divisor of the denominator; and, by trial, it will be found to divide the numerator.

(12) Canceling x in the denominator, and multiplying by 5, we have

$$\begin{array}{r|l}135x^3+315x^2-60x-140 & 15x^3+35x^2+3x+7\\ \underline{135x^3+315x^2+27x+63} & 9\\ -87x-203 & \\ -29(3x+7). & \text{G. C. D.}=3x+7.\end{array}$$

(14) $ac+by+ay+bc=(a+b)c+(a+b)y=(a+b)(c+y)$;
$af+2bx+2ax+bf=(a+b)f+(a+b)2x=(a+b)(f+2x)$.
Hence, $a+b=$ G. C. D. of both terms.

(15) $x^8+x^6y^2+x^2y+y^3=(x^2+y^2)x^6+(x^2+y^2)y$
$=(x^2+y^2)(x^6+y)$; $x^4-y^4=(x^2+y^2)(x^2-y^2)$.
Hence, $x^2+y^2=$ G. C. D. of both terms.

(16) $a^3+(a+b)ax+bx^2=(a^2+bx)a+(a^2+bx)x=(a^2+bx)$
$(a+x)$; $a^4-b^2x^2=(a^2+bx)(a^2-bx)$.
Hence, $a^2+bx=$ G. C. D.

(17) $ax^m-bx^{m+1}=(ax-bx^2)x^{m-1}=x(a-bx)x^{m-1}$; $a^2bx-b^3x^2=bx(a^2-b^2x^2)=bx(a+bx)(a-bx)$.
Hence, $x(a-bx)=$ G. C. D. of both terms.

ADDITION AND SUBTRACTION.

Article 130.

(10) The L. C. M. of the denominators is readily found to be $4a^3(a+x)(a-x)(a^2+x^2)=4a^3(a^4-x^4)$. We then find for the numerators of the respective fractions, the following quantities:

$$\begin{array}{lll}
1^{st} & (a-x)(a^2+x^2)\ldots & =a^3+ax^2-a^2x-x^3 \\
2^{d} & (a+x)(a^2+x^2)\ldots & =a^3+ax^2+a^2x+x^3 \\
3^{d} & 2a(a+x)(a-x)\ldots & =2a^3-2ax^2 \\
\hline
 & \text{Sum} & =\dfrac{4a^3}{4a^3(a^4-x^4)}=\dfrac{1}{a^4-x^4},\ \textit{Ans.}
\end{array}$$

(11) It is most convenient to make the common denominator of the fractions, $abc(a-b)(a-c)(b-c)$. In doing this, we must change the signs of the factor $b-a$, in the denominator of the 2d fraction, which may be done if, at the same time, we change the sign of the numerator (Art. 124). The value of the 3d fraction will not be altered if we change the signs of *both* the factors $c-a$ and $c-b$, so as to have $a-c$ and $b-c$. Hence,

$$\frac{1}{a(a-b)(a-c)}=\frac{bc(b-c)}{abc(a-b)(a-c)(b-c)};$$

$$\frac{1}{b(b-a)(b-c)}=\frac{-ac(a-c)}{abc(a-b)(a-c)(b-c)};$$

$$\frac{1}{c(c-a)(c-b)}=\frac{ab(a-b)}{abc(a-b)(a-c)(b-c)}.$$

The sum of the numerators is $bc(b-c)-ac(a-c)+ab(a-b)$, which, by performing the multiplications indicated, and reducing, gives the same result as $(a-b)(a-c)(b-c)$. Hence, this product may be canceled in both terms, and the sum of the three fractions is found $=\frac{1}{abc}$.

(12) Reducing the 3d fraction to its lowest terms, it becomes $\frac{x^2}{y(x+y)}$. The 2d fraction subtracted from the 1st leaves $\frac{x^2+xy+y^2}{y(x+y)}$.

Subtracting the preceding from this leaves $\frac{xy+y^2}{y(x+y)}=1$, *Ans.*

(13) $\frac{1}{x-1}-\frac{1}{2(x+1)}=\frac{2(x+1)-(x-1)}{2(x^2-1)}=\frac{x+3}{2(x^2-1)}$;

$\frac{x+3}{2(x^2-1)}-\frac{x+3}{2(x^2+1)}=\frac{(x+3)(x^2+1)-(x+3)(x^2-1)}{2(x^4-1)}=\frac{x+3}{x^4-1}$, *Ans.*

MULTIPLICATION AND DIVISION.

Article 131.

REMARK.—In the solution of all questions in multiplication or division of fractions, it is important to separate the quantities into factors, before performing any actual multiplications, as this might so involve the factors that they could not be readily discovered. By attention to factoring, nearly all the examples are easily solved.

(9)
$$\begin{array}{l} \frac{4a}{3x}+\frac{3x}{2b} \\ \frac{2b}{3x}+\frac{3x}{4a} \\ \hline \frac{8ab}{9x^2}+1 \\ \qquad +1+\frac{9x^2}{8ab} \\ \hline \frac{8ab}{9x^2}+2+\frac{9x^2}{8ab}, \end{array}$$ *Ans.*

(10) $pr+(pq+qr)x+q^2x^2=(p+qx)r+(p+qx)qx=(p+qx)(r+qx)$;

$ps+(pt-qs)x+qtx^2=(p-qx)s+(p-qx)tx=(p-qx)(s+tx)$.

The factors in the denominator of the product will cancel the factors $p-qx$ and $p+qx$ in the numerator, leaving for the result $(r+qx)(s+tx)=rs+(rt+qs)x+qtx^2$.

Article 132.

(10) $x^4-\frac{1}{x^4}=\frac{x^8-1}{x^4}=\frac{(x^4-1)(x^4+1)}{x^4}=\frac{(x^2+1)(x^2-1)(x^4+1)}{x^4}$

$x-\frac{1}{x}=\frac{x^2-1}{x}$. (*Concluded on page* 56.)

$$\frac{(x^2+1)(x^2-1)(x^4+1)}{x^4}\times\frac{x}{x^2-1}=\frac{(x^2+1)(x^4+1)}{x^3}=\frac{x^6+x^4+x^2+1}{x^3}$$

$$=x^3+x+\frac{1}{x}+\frac{1}{x^3}, \text{ or } x^3+\frac{1}{x^3}+x+\frac{1}{x}.$$

This example may also be readily solved by ordinary division.

MISCELLANEOUS EXERCISES IN FRACTIONS.

Article 139.

(2) To reduce these fractions to a common denominator, it wil. be most convenient to change the signs of the factors, as in the solution to Ex. 11, Addition of Fractions, so that the common denominator may be $(a-b)(a-c)(b-c)$.

$$\frac{a^2+a+1}{(a-b)(a-c)}=\frac{a^2+a+1}{(a-b)(a-c)}\times\frac{b-c}{b-c}=\frac{a^2b-a^2c+ab-ac+b-c}{(a-b)(a-c)(b-c)};$$

$$\frac{-b^2-b-1}{(a-b)(b-c)}=\frac{-b^2-b-1}{(a-b)(b-c)}\times\frac{a-c}{a-c}=\frac{-ab^2+b^2c-ab+bc-a+c}{(a-b)(a-c)(b-c)};$$

$$\frac{c^2+c+1}{(a-c)(b-c)}=\frac{c^2+c+1}{(a-c)(b-c)}\times\frac{a-b}{a-b}=\frac{ac^2-bc^2+ac-bc+a-b}{(a-b)(a-c)(b-c)}.$$

$$\text{Sum}=\frac{a^2b-ab^2-a^2c+b^2c+ac^2-bc^2}{a^2b-ab^2-a^2c+b^2c+ac^2-bc^2}=1, \quad \textit{Ans.}$$

(3) Perform the operations indicated before substituting the value of x

(4) $x+2a=\frac{4ab}{a+b}+2a=\frac{6ab+2a^2}{a+b};$

$$x-2a=\frac{4ab}{a+b}-2a=\frac{2ab-2a^2}{a+b};$$

$$\text{first fraction}=\frac{6ab+2a^2}{2ab-2a^2}=\frac{3b+a}{b-a}=\frac{-a-3b}{a-b};$$

$$x+2b=\frac{4ab}{a+b}+2b=\frac{6ab+2b^2}{a+b};$$

$$x-2b=\frac{4ab}{a+b}-2b=\frac{2ab-2b^2}{a+b};$$

$$\text{second fraction} = \frac{6ab+2b^2}{2ab-2b^2} = \frac{3a+b}{a-b};$$

$$\frac{-a-3b}{a-b} + \frac{3a+b}{a-b} = \frac{2a-2b}{a-b} = 2, \quad \textit{Ans.}$$

(5) $\frac{x+y}{xy} = \frac{\frac{x}{xy}+\frac{y}{xy}}{1} = \frac{1}{y}+\frac{1}{x}$

Similarly, $\frac{x-y}{xy} = \frac{\frac{x}{xy}-\frac{y}{xy}}{1} = \frac{1}{y}-\frac{1}{x}$

By dividing both terms of each fraction by xy, and reducing.

(6) *First.*—Let $(a-b)(a-c)(b-c)$ be the common denominator of the three fractions; then, we must change the signs of the numerator of the 2d fraction, and the signs of the 1st factor of the denominator. We must also change the signs of both factors of the denominator of the third fraction. The numerators of the respective fractions when reduced to a common denominator will be

$$(a^2+h^2)(b-c) = a^2b-a^2c+bh^2-ch^2;$$
$$(-b^2-h^2)(a-c) = -ab^2+b^2c-ah^2+ch^2;$$
$$(c^2+h^2)(a-b) = ac^2-bc^2+ah^2-bh^2.$$

Sum of the numerators $=a^2(b-c)-b^2(a-c)+c^2(a-b)$;
$(a-b)(a-c)(b-c)=a^2(b-c)-b^2(a-c)+c^2(a-b)$;
hence, the value of the fraction is 1.

Second. $(a^2+h^2)(b-c)(b+c) = a^2b^2-a^2c^2+b^2h^2-c^2h^2;$
$-(b^2+h^2)(a-c)(a+c) = -a^2b^2+b^2c^2-a^2h^2+c^2h^2;$
$(c^2+h^2)(a-b)(a+b) = a^2c^2-b^2c^2+a^2h^2-b^2h^2.$

The sum of the numerators is 0; hence, the sum of the fractions is 0.

Third. $(a^2+h^2)(b-c)bc = a^2b^2c-a^2bc^2+b^2ch^2-bc^2h^2;$
$-(b^2+h^2)(a-c)ac = -a^2b^2c+ab^2c^2-a^2ch^2+ac^2h^2;$
$(c^2+h^2)(a-b)ab = a^2bc^2-ab^2c^2+a^2bh^2-ab^2h^2.$

The sum of the numerators is $h^2\{a^2(b-c)-b^2(a-c)+c^2(a-b)\}$, and since the denominator is the quantity within the brackets, the value of the fraction is h^2.

SIMPLE EQUATIONS.

REMARKS.—The attentive student will find no difficulty with the examples in Arts. 151 and 153, provided he attends carefully to the rules. (See Remark, page 10, Key to First Book.)

The ease and facility with which several of the examples may be solved, will depend on the particular method of solution. The shortest methods, however, are not always the best for learners. It is important that the pupil understand every step of the operation. Let the aim be first to perform the operations correctly and understandingly, and after this with facility.

In some cases, it is better to perform the operations indicated before clearing the equation of fractions. To illustrate this, we will take example 21, Art. 153.

Multiplying the terms in the parentheses in the 2d member by $\frac{1}{39}$, and removing it, we have

$$\tfrac{1}{2}\left(x-\frac{51}{26}\right)-\frac{2}{13}(1-3x)=x-\frac{5x}{39}+\frac{1-3x}{156}.$$

Now, 156 is evidently the L. C. M. of the denominators. Multiplying both members by this, we have

$$78x-153-24+72x=156x-20x+10-8x;$$

reducing, $17x=187$; whence, $x=11$.

QUESTIONS PRODUCING SIMPLE EQUATIONS.

Article 154.

(11) Let $x=$ the 1st; then, $2x=$ the 2d, and $4x=$ the 3d; and $x+2x+4x=133$. Whence, $x=19$, $2x=38$, and $4x=76$.

(12) Let $x=$ the 1st; then, $3x=$ the 2d, and $4\frac{1}{2}x=$ the 3d; and $x+3x+4\frac{1}{2}x=187$.
Whence, $x=22$, $3x=66$, and $4\frac{1}{2}x=99$.

(13) Let $x=$ the 2d; then, $3\frac{1}{2}x=$ the 1st, and $3\frac{1}{2}x-x=100$.
Whence, $x=40$, and $3\frac{1}{2}x=140$.

(14) Let $3x$ and $7x=$ the numbers. Then, $3x+16 : 7x-16 :: 7 : 3$. Hence, $49x-112=9x+48$.

(15) Let $2x$ and $3x=$ the numbers. Then, $2x+6 : 3x+6 :: 4$ 5. Hence, $12x+24=10x+30$.

(16) Let $x=$ wife's and $3x=$husband's age. Then, $3x+15=2(x+15)$.

(17) Let $x=$ No. of half-dollars and $100-x=$ No. of dimes. Then, $\frac{x}{2}=$ dollars paid in pieces of 1st kind, and $\frac{100-x}{10}$ — do. of 2d kind. Hence, $\frac{x}{2}+\frac{100-x}{10}=34$.

(18) Let $x=$ the 1st; then, $3\frac{1}{2}x=$ the 2d,
and $100-(3\frac{1}{2}x-x)=100-2\frac{1}{2}x=$ the 3d.
Then, $x+3\frac{1}{2}x+100-2\frac{1}{2}x=156$.
Whence, $x=28$, $3\frac{1}{2}x=98$, and $100-2\frac{1}{2}x=30$

(19) Let $x=$ the number; then, $\frac{x}{2}+\frac{x}{3}+\frac{x}{4}=52$

Whence, $\frac{13x}{12}=52$, and $x=48$.

(20) Let $x=$ the number; then, $x+\frac{6x}{7}-20=45$.

Whence, $x=35$.

(21) Let $x=$ the number; then, $x+\frac{x}{3}+\frac{x}{4}-\frac{x}{6}=51$.

Whence, $x=36$.

(22) Let $x=$ the number; then $4x-40=40-x$.
Whence, $x=16$.

(23) Let $x=$ the number; then, $4(x+16)=10(x+1)$.
Whence, $x=9$.

(24) Let $x=$ the number; then, $4x+20=32$. Whence, $x=3$

(25) Let $x=$ the number; then, $\frac{3x}{4}-5=\frac{x}{3}$. Whence, $x=12$.

(26) Let $x=$ rent last year; then, $x+\frac{8x}{100}=1890$. Whence. $x=1750$.

(27) Let x= estate; then, the shares are $\frac{x}{4}$, $\frac{20x}{100}$, and $\frac{15x}{100}$, and we have $x=\frac{x}{4}+\frac{x}{5}+\frac{3x}{20}+2168$. Whence $x=5420$, and the shares are 1355, 1084, and 813.

(28) Let x= the less number; then, $30-x$= the greater. and $\frac{1}{4}(30-x-x)=3$. Whence, $x=9$, and $30-x=21$.

(29) Let x= the number of days he worked; then, $28-x$= idle days; then, $75x-25(28-x)=1200$, or $\frac{3}{4}x-\frac{1}{4}(28-x)=12$.
Whence, $\frac{3}{4}x-7+\frac{1}{4}x=12$, or $x=19$.

(31) Let x= number of minute spaces the minute hand has passed from XII. Then, $x-60$= do. the hour hand has passed, and $12(x-60)=x$. Whence, $x=65\frac{5}{11}$ min. or 1 hr. $5\frac{5}{11}$ min.

(32) Let x= dist. in min. spaces the fast hand has passed from XII. Then, $x-10$= dist. the slow hand has gone, and $12(x-10)=x$. Whence, $x=10\frac{10}{11}$ min., or the time will be 8 hr. $10\frac{10}{11}$ min.

(33) Let x= B's money; then, $3x$= A's, and $3x+50=4(x-50)$. Whence, $x=250$, and $3x=750$.

(34) Let x= sum; then, $x-\frac{1}{2}x-20=\frac{x}{2}-20$;

$$\frac{x}{2}-20-\frac{1}{3}\left(\frac{x}{2}-20\right)-30=\frac{x}{2}-\frac{x}{6}-50+\frac{20}{3}=\frac{x}{3}-\frac{130}{3};$$

$$\frac{x}{3}-\frac{130}{3}-\frac{1}{4}\left(\frac{x}{3}-\frac{130}{3}\right)-40=0.$$ Whence, $x=290$.

(35) Observe that 20 % is $\frac{1}{5}$ and 25 % $\frac{1}{4}$.

Let x=capital; then, $x+\frac{15x}{100}=\frac{115x}{100}$ = cap. close 1st yr.

$$\frac{115x}{100}+\frac{1}{5}\text{ of }\frac{115x}{100}=\frac{115x}{100}+\frac{23x}{100}=\frac{138x}{100}=\text{cap. 2d yr.}$$

$$\frac{138x}{100}+\frac{1}{4}\text{ of }\frac{138x}{100}=\frac{138x}{100}+\frac{69x}{200}=\frac{345x}{200}=\text{cap. 3d yr.}$$

Therefore, $\frac{345x}{200}-x=1000.50$. Whence, $x=1380$.

(36) Let $x =$ B's age; then, $2x =$ A's, and $3(x-22)=2x-22$. Whence, $x=44$, and $2x=88$.

(37) To avoid fractions, we may take some multiple of x that is divisible twice by 2. Thus,

Let $4x =$ cost of 1st house; then, $4x+2x=6x=$ cost of 2d, and $6x+3x=9x=$ cost of 3d; also, $4x+9x=13x=$ cost of 4th. Hence, $4x+6x+9x+13x=8000$.
Whence, $4x=1000$, $6x=1500$, $9x=2250$, and $13x=3250$.

(38) Let $x=$ gal. the 3d conveys in 1 min.;
then, $3x=$ " " " " 3 "
and $3x+8=$ gal. 1st " " 3 "
also, $3x-7=$ " 2d " " 3 "
$\therefore$ $9x+1=$ " all convey " 3 "
$72x+8=$ " " " " 24 "
$\therefore$ $72x+8=1050$.
Whence, $x=14\frac{17}{36}$; $\frac{1}{3}(3x+8)=17\frac{5}{36}$; $\frac{1}{3}(3x-7)=12\frac{5}{36}$.

(40) Let $x=$ the number of days in which B can do it;

then, $\frac{1}{x}=$ part B does in one day; but A does $\frac{1}{10}$, and A and B together do $\frac{1}{7}$ in one day; $\therefore$ $\frac{1}{7}-\frac{1}{10}=\frac{1}{x}$.

Whence, $x=23\frac{1}{3}$.

(41) Let $x=$ the number of days in which A can do it;

then, $\frac{1}{x}=$ part A does in one day; but A does $\frac{1}{4}$ of $\frac{2}{7}=\frac{1}{14}$ in one day; $\therefore$ $\frac{1}{x}=\frac{1}{14}$, whence, $x=14$.

If A and B finish $\frac{5}{7}$ of the work in 6 days, they do $\frac{1}{6}$ of $\frac{5}{7}=\frac{5}{42}$ in one day; and since A does $\frac{1}{14}$ in one day, B does $\frac{5}{42}-\frac{1}{14}=\frac{1}{21}$ in one day, or the whole in 21 days.

The solution of this question mainly depends on arithmetical analysis, and the employment of algebraic symbols can scarcely be said to be of any advantage.

(42) Let $x=$ number of each; then, $3x=$ cost of sheep, $12x=$ cost of cows, and $18x=$ cost of oxen.
Therefore, $3x+12x+18x=330$; whence, $x=10$.

(43) Let $x=$ sum A rec'd; then $x-10=$ what B rec'd; $x-10+16=x+6=$ what C rec'd; $x+6-5=x+1=$ what D rec'd; $x+1+15=x+16=$ what E rec'd.

$\therefore\ x+1+x+16=x+x-10+x+6$. Whence, $x=21$, what A rec'd, from which, what the others rec'd, is readily found.

(44) Let $x=$ the number of eggs; then, $\frac{x}{12}=$number of dozen and $\frac{x}{12}\times 18=\frac{3x}{2}=$cost.

$\frac{x+5}{12}=$ number of dozen if he had bought 5 more; and since the whole cost divided by the number of dozen, must give the cost of one dozen, therefore,

$\frac{3x}{2}\div\frac{x+5}{12}=$ cost of one dozen under 2d supposition.

$$\frac{3x}{2}\div\frac{x+5}{12}=\frac{3x}{2}\times\frac{12}{x+5}=\frac{18x}{x+5};$$

$\therefore\ \frac{18x}{x+5}=18-2\frac{1}{2}=15\frac{1}{2}$; whence, $x=31$.

(45) Let $x=$ the number bought; then, $\frac{94}{x}=$ cost of each; and $\frac{1}{4}(x-7)=\frac{1}{4}$ the remainder.

$20\div\frac{1}{4}(x-7)=20\times\frac{4}{x-7}=\frac{80}{x-7}=$ what each sold for.

$\therefore\ \frac{94}{x}=\frac{80}{x-7}$; whence, $x=47$.

(46) Let $x=$ the number of hours each traveled; then, $\frac{x}{2}\times 3=\frac{3x}{2}=$ miles A traveled, and $\frac{x}{4}\times 5=\frac{5x}{4}=$mi. B traveled;

$\therefore\ \frac{3x}{2}+\frac{5x}{4}=154$; whence, $x=56$, $\frac{3x}{2}=84$, and $\frac{5x}{4}=70$.

(47) Let $x=$ price of harness. Then, $2x=$ price of horse, and $6x=$ price of chaise. Whence, $x+2x+6x=9x=450$, or $x=50$, $2x=100$, and $6x=300$.

(48) Let $x=$ weight of body. Then, $9+\frac{x}{2}=$ weight of head, and $x=9+\frac{x}{2}+9$, or $x=36$, weight of body. Weight of head $9+18=27$. Then, $9+27+36=72$, his whole weight

(49) Let $x=$ the number; then, $\frac{5x-24}{6}+13=x$; whence, $x=54$.

(50) Let $x=$ number of \$; then, $3x=$ number of eagles.
$\therefore$ $5(x-8)=3x-8$; whence, $x=16$, and $3x=48$.

(51) Let $x=$ number of apples; then, $100-x=$number of pears
$\frac{x}{10}\times 1=\frac{x}{10}=$ cost of apples;
and $\frac{100-x}{25}\times 2=\frac{200-2x}{25}=$ cost of pears;
$\therefore$ $\frac{x}{10}+\frac{200-2x}{25}=9\frac{1}{2}$; whence, $x=75$, and $100-x=25$

(52) Let $x=$ number of sheep;
then, $\frac{x}{8}=$ acres plowed, and $\frac{x}{5}=$ acres of pasture.
$\therefore$ $\frac{x}{8}+\frac{x}{5}=325$; whence, $x=1000$.

(53) Let $x=$ miles he can ride;
then, $\frac{x}{12}=$ time of riding, and $\frac{x}{4}=$ time of walking;
$\therefore$ $\frac{x}{12}+\frac{x}{4}=2$; whence, $x=6$

(54) Let $x=$ number of lbs; then, $\frac{2}{65+x}=$lbs of salt in 1 lb,
and $25\left(\frac{2}{65+x}\right)=$ lbs of salt in 25 lbs.
$\therefore$ $25\left(\frac{2}{65+x}\right)=\frac{1}{4}$; whence, $x=135$.

(55) In every 10 lbs of the mass, there are 7 lbs of copper and 3 lbs of tin; hence, in 80 lbs, there are $\frac{80}{10}\times 7=56$ lbs of copper, and $\frac{80}{10}\times 3=24$ lbs of tin.

Let $x=$ lbs of copper to be added; then, $56+x=$ lbs of copper in the new mass, and $24=$ lbs of tin; and since there are 11 lbs of copper for every 4 lbs of tin, $\frac{1}{11}$ of the copper must be equal to $\frac{1}{4}$ of the tin.

Therefore, $\frac{56+x}{11}=\frac{24}{4}$. Whence, $x=10$

(56) Let $x=$ stock; then, $x-250+\frac{1}{3}(x-250)=\frac{4x}{3}-\frac{1000}{3}=$ stock at the close of the 1st year.

$\frac{4x}{3}-\frac{1000}{3}-250=\frac{4x}{3}-\frac{1750}{3}$; and $\frac{4x}{3}-\frac{1750}{3}+\frac{1}{3}\left(\frac{4x}{3}-\frac{1750}{3}\right)$

$=\frac{16x}{9}-\frac{7000}{9}=$ stock at close of 2d year.

$\frac{16x}{9}-\frac{7000}{9}-250=\frac{16x}{9}-\frac{9250}{9}$; and $\frac{16x}{9}-\frac{9250}{9}$

$+\frac{1}{3}\left(\frac{16x}{9}-\frac{9250}{9}\right)=\frac{64x}{27}-\frac{37000}{27}=$ stock at close of 3d yr

$\therefore \frac{64x}{27}-\frac{37000}{27}=2x$. Whence, $x=3700$.

SIMPLE EQUATIONS.

Article 158.

(10) By multiplying eq. (1) by m and (2) by n, and subtracting, we find the value of x. Again, by multiplying (1) by n and (2) by m, and subtracting, we find the value of y.

(11) Transposing b^2y in eq. (2), multiplying by 3, and factoring, we have

$$(a^2-b^2)3y+(a+b+c)3bx=(a+2b)3ab+\frac{3ab^2c}{a+b}. \quad (4)$$

Separating eq. (1) into its parts, we have

$$(a^2-b^2)5x+(a^2-b^2)3y=(4a-b)2ab; \quad (1)$$

Subtracting eq. (4) from (1), we have

$$(5a^2-5b^2-3ab-3b^2-3bc)x=8a^2b-2ab^2-3a^2b-6ab^2-\frac{3ab^2c}{a+b}$$

Reducing and factoring, $(5a^2-8b^2-3ab-3bc)x=\frac{ab}{a+b}(5a^2-8b^2-3ab-3bc)$; whence, $x=\frac{ab}{a+b}$.

Substituting the value of x in eq. (1), we have

$\frac{5ab}{a+b}(a^2-b^2)+3y(a^2-b^2)=8a^2b-2ab^2$; reducing,

$3y(a^2-b^2)=3a^2b+3ab^2=3ab(a+b)$, or, $y(a-b)=ab$.

Therefore, $y=\frac{ab}{a-b}$.

Article 159.

(4) Let $x=$ number of sheep, and $y=$ number of cows;
then, $5x+7y=111$,
$7x+5y=93$.
Whence, $x=4$, and $y=13$.

(5) Let $x=$ cost of 1 lb tea, and $y=$ cost of 1 lb coffee;
then, $7x+9y=520$,
$4x+11y=385$.
Whence, $x=55$, and $y=15$ cts.

(6) Let $x=$ A's money, and $y=$ B's;
then, $x+50=y-20$.
$3x+5y=2350$.
Whence, $x=250$, and $y=320$.

(7) Let $6x=$ A's money, and $5y=$ B's;
then, $6x+5y=9800$;
also, $6x-x=5y-y$, or $5x-4y=0$.
Whence, $x=800$, and $y=1000$.
$\therefore$ $6x=4800$, and $5y=5000$.

(8) Let $x=$ the numerator and y the denominator of the fraction;

then, $\frac{x+1}{y+1}=\frac{1}{2}$, and $\frac{x-1}{y-1}=\frac{1}{3}$; whence, $x=3$, and $y=7$

(9) Let $x=$ the first number, and $y=$ the second;

then, $\frac{x}{3}=\frac{y}{4}+3$, and $\frac{x}{4}+\frac{y}{5}=10$.
Whence, $x=24$, and $y=20$.

(10) Let $x=$ number of lbs, and $y=$ cost per lb; then, $xy=$ cost.
$\therefore$ $30x-xy=100$, (1)
$xy-22x=300$. (2)
Adding eq. (1) and (2) together, we have
$8x=400$. Whence, $x=50$.
By substitution, the value of y is found to be 28.

(11) Let $x=$ number of bushels of wheat, and $y=$ bu. of corn;
then, $55x=33y$; and $55x+33y=$ rent;
also, $65x+41y-140=$ rent.
$\therefore$ $65x+41y-140=55x+33y$, or $10x+8y=140$.
Whence, $x=6$, and $y=10$.

(12) Let x and $y=$ the cubic feet which each discharges, then, $x:y::5\times8:13\times7$;

$\therefore\ 40y=91x$; (1)

also, $y-x=561$. (2)

Whence, $x=440$, and $y=1001$.

From (1) it is evident that y is greater than x; therefore, in (2), we write $y-x$.

(13) Let $5x$ and $7x$ represent the first two numbers, and $3y$ and $5y$ the other two; then,

$5x+3y:7x+5y::9:13$;

$\therefore\ 65x+39y=63x+45y$, or $2x=6y$; (1)

also, $7x+5y-(5x+3y)=16$,

or $2x+2y=16$. (2)

Whence, $x=6$, and $y=2$, $\therefore\ 5x=30$, $7x=42$; and $3y=6$, and $5y=10$.

(14) Let $x=$ number of apples, and $y=$ number of pears;

then, $\frac{x}{4}+\frac{y}{5}=30$, and $\frac{1}{2}$ of $\frac{x}{4}+\frac{1}{3}$ of $\frac{y}{5}$, or $\frac{x}{8}+\frac{y}{15}=13$.

Whence, $x=72$, and $y=60$.

(15) Let $x=$ acres of tillable land, and $y=$ acres of pasture; then, $200x+140y=24500$; (1)

also, $x:\frac{x-y}{2}::28:9$;

$\therefore\ 9x=14x-14y$, or $5x=14y$. (2)

Whence, $x=98$, and $y=35$.

(16) Let $x=$ digit in ten's place, and $y=$ digit in unit's place; then, $10x+y=$ the number, and $10y+x=$ the number when the digits are inverted.

Then, $10x+y+10y+x=121$, or $11x+11y=121$; (1)

and $10x+y-(10y+x)=9$, or $9x-9y=9$. (2)

Dividing (1) by 11, and (2) by 9, and adding and subtracting, we find $x=6$, and $y=5$.

REMARK.—It may be asked why, in obtaining eq. (2), we subtract $10y+x$ instead of $10x+y$, since we do not know which is the greater. The answer is, we can not tell which to subtract till we proceed to verify the result; but if we had subtracted the wrong quantity, the error would be made known in verifying the result, by some quantity being negative that ought to be positive. (See Art. 164.)

(17) Let $2x-6$, $3x-6$, and y be the numbers. This fulfills the first condition. The second condition gives

$2x-1 : y+5 :: 7 : 11$,

or $22x-11=7y+35$; (1)

also, $3x-42 : y-36 :: 6 : 7$,

or $21x-294=6y-216$. (2)

Whence, $x=18$, and $y=50$;

$\therefore$ the numbers are 30, 48, and 50.

(18) Let x and z represent the days respectively in which A and B can do it;

then, $\frac{1}{x}$ and $\frac{1}{z}=$ parts which each can do in a day.

Then, $\frac{1}{x}+\frac{1}{z}=\frac{1}{16}$. (1)

Also, in 4 days, A and B do $\frac{4}{x}+\frac{4}{z}$; and in 36 days, B does $\frac{36}{z}$ parts of the work;

$\therefore \frac{4}{x}+\frac{4}{z}+\frac{36}{z}=1$ (the whole work); or $\frac{4}{x}+\frac{40}{z}=1$. (2)

Multiplying eq. (1) by 4, and subtracting it from (2), we have $\frac{36}{z}=\frac{3}{4}$; whence, $z=48$, and by substitution x is readily found $=24$.

(19) First, 2 hrs., 48 min. $=2\frac{4}{5}$ hrs., and 4 hrs., 40 min. $=4\frac{2}{3}$ hrs

Let x and z represent the hours respectively in which A and B can drink it; then, $\frac{1}{x}$ and $\frac{1}{z}=$ parts which each can drink in an hour; and $\frac{2}{x}+\frac{2}{z}=$ parts drank by both in 2 hours;

$\frac{2\frac{4}{5}}{z}=\frac{14}{5z}=$ parts drank by B in $2\frac{4}{5}$ hours;

$\frac{4\frac{2}{3}}{x}=\frac{14}{3x}=$ parts drank by A in $4\frac{2}{3}$ hours;

$\therefore \frac{2}{x}+\frac{2}{z}+\frac{14}{5z}=1$ (the whole); (1)

$\frac{2}{x}+\frac{14}{3x}+\frac{2}{z}=1$ " (2)

By adding together the terms containing x, and those containing z,

$$\frac{2}{x}+\frac{24}{5z}=1; \quad (3) \qquad \frac{20}{3x}+\frac{2}{z}=1. \quad (4)$$

By multiplying (3) by $\frac{10}{3}$, and subtracting (4) from it, we have $\frac{14}{z}=\frac{7}{3}$ whence, $z=6$, and by substitution x is found $=10$.

(20) Let $x=$ numerator and $y=$ denominator of 1st fraction; then, $\frac{x}{y}=$ 1st fraction, and $\frac{8}{5}-\frac{x}{y}=\frac{8y-5x}{5y}=$ 2d fraction.

By adding the numerators together, also the denominators, we have $x+8y-5x=y+5y$, or $2y=4x$, or $2x=y$.

Whence, $\frac{x}{y}=\frac{1}{2}=$ the 1st fraction, and $\frac{8}{5}-\frac{1}{2}=\frac{11}{10}=$the 2d fraction.

(21) In solving questions of this kind, it is convenient to denote the capacity by 1; it may, however, be denoted by c, the object of the question being not to find either the size of a crown or guinea, or the size (capacity) of the purse, but the *ratio* of the size of a crown or guinea to the size of the purse.

Let $x=$ number of crowns, and $z=$ number of guineas; then, $\frac{1}{x}=$ part filled by 1 crown, and $\frac{1}{z}=$ part filled by 1 guinea.

Also, $\frac{19}{x}+\frac{6}{z}=1$ (1), and $\frac{4}{x}+\frac{5}{z}=\frac{17}{63}$ (2).

Multiplying eq. (1) by 5, and (2) by 6, and subtracting, we find $x=21$; then, by substitution, $z=63$.

(22) Let $x=$ number of bushels of wheat, and $y=$ bu. of rye. $\therefore$ $5x+3y=$ his money.

Observe that 7 bushels of rye will cost 21 shillings, and 6 bushels of wheat 30 shillings. Then, from the nature of the question, we have the following equations:

$$\frac{5x+3y-21}{5}+7=x+y-2, \qquad (1)$$

$$30+3(x+y-6)=5x+3y-6. \qquad (2)$$

Whence, $x=9$, and $y=12$.

SIMPLE EQUATIONS INVOLVING THREE OR MORE UNKNOWN QUANTITIES.

Article 160.

(10) (3) from (2) gives $\frac{1}{x}-\frac{1}{y}=b-c$; (4)

Sum of (1) and (4) gives $\frac{2}{x}=a+b-c$.

Whence, $x=\frac{2}{a+b-c}$; subtracting

(2) from (1) gives $\frac{1}{y}-\frac{1}{z}=a-b$; (5)

Sum of (3) and (5) gives $\frac{2}{y}=a-b+c$.

Whence, $y=\frac{2}{a-b+c}$; subtracting

(1) from (3) gives $\frac{1}{z}-\frac{1}{x}=c-a$, (6)

Sum of (2) and (6) gives $\frac{2}{z}=b+c-a$.

Whence, $z=\frac{2}{b+c-a}$.

(11) Adding the four equations together, and dividing by 2, we find the value of $x+y+z+v$. Then, subtracting from this each of the equations successively, and dividing by 2, we get the values of x, y, z, and v.

Article 161.

Let x, y, and z represent the respective shares; then,

$$x+y+z=760, \qquad (1)$$
$$x+y-z=240, \qquad (2)$$
$$y+z-x=360. \qquad (3)$$

Whence, $x=200$, $y=300$, and $z=260$.

(2) Let x, y, and z represent the numbers respectively; then,

$$x+y+z=20; \qquad (1)$$
$$x+y : y+z :: 4 : 5, \text{ or } 5x+5y=4y+4z; \qquad (2)$$
$$y-x : z-x :: 2 : 3, \text{ or } 3y-3x=2z-2x. \qquad (3)$$

Whence, $x=5$, $y=7$, and $z=8$.

(3) Let x, y, z, and v represent the numbers respectively, then

$$x+y+z=13, \quad (1) \qquad x+z+v=18, \quad (3)$$
$$x+y+v=15, \quad (2) \qquad y+z+v=20. \quad (4)$$

Adding the four equations together and dividing by 3, we have $x+y+z+v=22$; from which, by subtracting eqs. (4), (3), (2), and (1) respectively, we find $x=2$, $y=4$, $z=7$, and $v=9$.

(4) Let x=digit in hundred's place, y= digit in ten's place, and z= digit in unit's place; then, $100x+10y+z$= the number, and

$$x+y+z=16; \quad (1)$$

also, $x+y:y+z::3:3\frac{2}{3}$, or $3\frac{2}{3}x+3\frac{2}{3}y=3y+3z$; (2)

and $100x+10y+z+198=100z+10y+x$;

or
$$99x+198=99z. \quad (3)$$

From these equations we readily find $x=5$, $y=4$, and $z=7$.

(5) If x, y, and z represent the three numbers; then,

$$\tfrac{1}{2}x+\tfrac{1}{3}y+\tfrac{1}{4}z=46, \quad (1)$$
$$\tfrac{1}{2}x+\tfrac{1}{4}y+\tfrac{1}{5}z=35, \quad (2)$$
$$\tfrac{1}{4}x+\tfrac{1}{5}y+\tfrac{1}{6}z=28\tfrac{1}{3}. \quad (3)$$

By clearing these eqs. of fractions, the values of x, y, and z are readily found by elimination by addition and subtraction.

(6) Let x, y, and z represent the three numbers; then,

$$x+y=a, \quad (1)$$
$$x+z=b, \quad (2)$$
$$y+z=c. \quad (3)$$

Whence, x, y, and z are readily found.

(7) Let x, y, z, and v represent the capacity of the respective casks; then,

$$x-y=\frac{4x}{7}, \quad (1) \qquad y-z=\frac{y}{4}, \quad (2)$$

$$z=\frac{9v}{16}, \quad (3) \qquad x=z+v+15. \quad (4)$$

Whence, $x=140$, $y=60$, $z=45$, and $v=80$.

(8) Let x, y, and z, represent the number of guns, soldiers and sailors, respectively; then,

$$\frac{x}{3}\times22+10=z, \quad (1) \qquad y+z=5(x+y). \quad (2)$$

Since the number slain in the engagement was $\frac{1}{4}$ of the survivors; therefore, $\frac{1}{5}(y+z)$ represents the slain, and $\frac{4}{5}(y+z)$ the survivors.

$$\therefore \frac{4}{5}(y+z)+5=\frac{x}{2}\times 13. \qquad (3)$$

From these eqs., we readily find $x=90$, $y=55$, and $z=670$.

GENERALIZATION.

Article 163.

(13) Representing the parts by $x-m$, $x+m$, $\frac{x}{m}$, and mx, we have $x-m+x+m+\frac{x}{m}+mx=a$;

$$2x+\frac{x}{m}+mx=a;$$

$$2mx+x+m^2x=ma;$$

$$x(m^2+2m+1)=x(m+1)^2=ma.$$

Whence, $x=\frac{ma}{(m+1)^2}$, from which the parts are easily found.

(15) Let $x=$ distance he may ride; then,

$\frac{x}{b}=$ time employed in riding, and $\frac{x}{c}=$ in walking

$\therefore \frac{x}{b}+\frac{x}{c}=a$; whence, $x=\frac{abc}{b+c}$.

(17) Let $x=$ the less number; then, $bx=$ the greater, since the quotient of the greater divided by the less is b.

$\therefore bx+x=a$, or $(b+1)=a$.

Whence, $x=\frac{a}{b+1}=$ less, and $bx=\frac{ab}{b+1}=$ greater.

(19) Let $x=$ the number of beggars that received b cts. each; then, $n-x=$ the number that received c cts. each.

$\therefore bx+c(n-x)=a$.

Whence, $x=\frac{a-nc}{b-c}$, and $n-x=\frac{nb-a}{b-c}$.

(21) Let $x=$ the greater part, and $n-x=$ the less; then,

$\frac{x}{n-x}=q+\frac{r}{n-x}$. Whence, $x=\frac{nq+r}{1+q}$, and $n-x=\frac{n-r}{1+q}$

(23) Let x, y, and z represent the days respectively in which A, B, and C can perform the work.

Then, if A can do it in x days, he can, in one day, do $\frac{1}{x}$ part; so, B and C can do $\frac{1}{y}$ and $\frac{1}{z}$ parts in one day.

$\therefore\ \frac{1}{x}+\frac{1}{y}=\frac{1}{a}$; (1) $\frac{1}{x}+\frac{1}{z}=\frac{1}{b}$; (2) $\frac{1}{y}+\frac{1}{z}=\frac{1}{c}$. (3)

For the method of solution, see example 10, Art. 160.

(25) Let $x=$ A's share; then, $\frac{x}{a}=$ expense of one ox for m months, and $\frac{x}{a}\div m=\frac{x}{ma}=$ expense of one ox for 1 mo.

$\therefore\ \frac{x}{ma}\times nb=\frac{nbx}{ma}=$ B's share, and

$\frac{x}{ma}\times pc=\frac{pcx}{ma}=$ C's share;

$\therefore\ x+\frac{nbx}{ma}+\frac{pcx}{ma}=$P.

Whence, $x=\frac{ma\text{P}}{ma+nb+pc}$, from which the shares of B and C are easily found.

(27) Let $x=$ cost of 1 lb of the mixture; then, $(a+b+c)x=$ cost of the whole mixture.

But $ma=$ cost of a lbs at m shillings per lb,

$nb=$ " b " n " "

$pc=$ " c " c " "

$\therefore\ (a+b+c)x=ma+nb+pc.$

Whence, $x=\frac{ma+nb+pc}{a+b+c}$.

(29) Instead of representing either of the quantities to be found by a separate symbol, the simplest solution is obtained by taking x to represent the number of miles per hour the waterman goes when he rows *with* the current.

then, since he can row c miles with the current for d miles against it, we have

$$c : d :: x : \frac{dx}{c} = \text{rate of sailing up stream.}$$

And since the number of hours employed in sailing any given distance, is equal to the whole number of miles sailed, divided by the number of miles sailed in 1 hour, therefore,

$\frac{a}{x} =$ number of hours in sailing down stream, and

$a \div \frac{dx}{c} = \frac{ac}{dx} =$ number of hours in sailing up stream.

$$\therefore \frac{a}{x} + \frac{ac}{dx} = b, \text{ whence } x = \frac{ac+ad}{bd}, \text{and } \frac{dx}{c} = \frac{ac+ad}{bc}$$

$$a \div \frac{ac+ad}{bd} = \frac{bd}{c+d} = \text{time down;}$$

$$a \div \frac{ac+ad}{bc} = \frac{bc}{c+d} = \text{time up.}$$

It is evident that the rate of the current will be half the difference of the rates of sailing down and up; that is,

$$\frac{1}{2}\left\{\frac{ac+ad}{bd} - \frac{ac+ad}{bc}\right\} = \frac{a(c^2-d^2)}{2bcd}.$$

Lastly, the rate of rowing will be the difference between the rate of sailing and the rate of the current; that is,

$$\frac{ac+ad}{bd} - \frac{a(c^2-d^2)}{2bcd} = \frac{a(c+d)^2}{2bcd}$$

NEGATIVE SOLUTIONS.

Article 164.

Enunciations of questions 2, 3, 4, 5, and 6, so that the results shall be true in an arithmetical sense.

2. What number must be *subtracted* from the number 30, that the *remainder* shall be 19? *Ans.* 11.

3. The *difference* of two numbers is 9, and their *sum* 25; required the numbers. *Ans.* 17 and 8.

4. What number is that whose *third* subtracted from its *half* eaves a remainder 15? *Ans.* 90.

5 A father's age is 40 years; his son's age is 13 years; *how many years since* was the age of the father 4 times that of the son? *Ans.* 4

Article 169.

(1) Here, we find $x=\frac{mnq}{m-n}$.

1st. There will be a negative solution when $n > m$. 2d. The value of x will be infinite when $m=n$ (Art. 136). 3d. When q is 0, and $m=n$, there will be an indeterminate solution; that is, x may have any value whatever.

(2) 1st. The boats will meet half way between C and L., when $m=n$. 2d. They will meet at C when m is 0. 3d. They will meet at L when n is 0. 4th. They will meet above C when $m<n$, and the boat A runs in an opposite direction from C to L. 5th. They will meet below L when $m>n$, and the boat B runs in an opposite direction from L to C. 6th. They will never meet if m and n have different signs and are equal to each other. 7th. They will sail together when a is zero, and $-m=n$, or $m=-n$.

(3) We shall find the same values for x and y from any two of the equations, for example, from the 1st and 2d, 1st and 3d, 1st and 4th, 2d and 3d, 2d and 4th, or 3d and 4th. Hence, we may take either two of the equations and the other two will be redundant.

(4) From the 1st and 2d equations, we readily find $x=5$ and $y=3$. From the 1st and 3d, $x=6\frac{3}{7}$, and $y=2\frac{4}{7}$. From the 1st and 4th, $x=-5$ and $y=8$. Hence, the equations can not *all* be true at the same time.

Article 171.

(6) First divide both members by x^m.

(7) Let $x=$ the number; then,

$$4\left(\frac{x}{2}\times\frac{x}{2}\right)=\frac{x}{3}\times\frac{x}{3}\times\frac{x}{3}, \text{ or } x^2=\frac{x^3}{27}.$$

Multiplying both members by 27, and dividing by x^2, $x=27$

(8) Let $x=$ the length and $y=$ the breadth; then, $xy=$ the number of square feet.

From 1st supposition, $(x+4)(y+5)=xy+116$. (1)

From the 2d supposition, $(x+5)(y+4)=xy+113$. (2)

Performing the operations indicated, omitting xy on each side, and reducing,

We have $5x+4y=96$;

$4x+5y=93$.

Whence, $x=12$, and $y=9$.

INVOLUTION OR THE FORMATION OF POWERS.

Note.—The examples in the Formation of Powers, and the Extraction of Roots, being performed by direct methods of operation, which the attentive student will readily understand, it is not deemed necessary to give these solutions here. The last three only which present some peculiarity, will be given.

Article 172.

(1) $x+\frac{1}{x}=p$ (1).

Squaring, $x^2+2+\frac{1}{x^2}=p^2$, or $x^2+\frac{1}{x^2}=p^2-2$ (2).

Multiplying (1) by (2), $x^3+x+\frac{1}{x}+\frac{1}{x^3}=p^3-2p$ (3).

Substituting in (3) the value of $x+\frac{1}{x}$ from (1), and transposing, we have $x^3+\frac{1}{x^3}=p^3-3p$.

(2) Let x and y be the numbers; then,

$$x-y=1.$$

Multiplying both members by $x+y$, we have $x^2-y^2=x+y$.

(3) Let the numbers be represented by $x-1$, x, and $x+1$, the sum of which is $3x$. The cubes of these numbers will be x^3-3x^2+3x-1, x^3, and x^3+3x^2+3x+1, the sum of which is $3x^3+6x$. This is divisible by $3x$.

Or, take for the numbers x, $x+1$, and $x+2$, and proceed in a similar manner.

Article 183.

(12) The terms arranged with reference to x, give

$$49x^4-\frac{14x^3}{5}+\frac{1051x^2}{25}-\frac{6x}{5}+9.$$

(15)

$$\begin{array}{lll}
 & 1-x^2 & \Big|\, 1-\dfrac{x^2}{2}-\dfrac{x^4}{8}-\dfrac{x^6}{16}-\dfrac{5x^8}{128}-, \&c \\
 & 1 & \\
2-\dfrac{x^2}{2} & \Big|\, -x^2 & \\
 & -x^2+\dfrac{x^4}{4} & \\
2-x^2-\dfrac{x^4}{8} & \Big|\, -\dfrac{x^4}{4} & \\
 & -\dfrac{x^4}{4}+\dfrac{x^6}{8}+\dfrac{x^8}{64} & \\
2-x^2-\dfrac{x^4}{4}-\dfrac{x^6}{16} & \Big|\, -\dfrac{x^6}{8}-\dfrac{x^8}{64} & \\
 & -\dfrac{x^6}{8}+\dfrac{x^6}{16}+\dfrac{x^{10}}{64}+\dfrac{x^{12}}{256} & \\
 & -\dfrac{5x^8}{64}-\dfrac{x^{10}}{64}-\dfrac{x^{12}}{256}. &
\end{array}$$

A more elegant method of extracting the square root of $1-x^2$ is by means of Indeterminate coëfficients, Art. 317; or, by the Binomial theorem, Art. 321.

(16) The operations in this example are similar to those in the preceding.

Article 191.

(6) In solving this example, let $a+1$ be considered a single quantity. It may, for example, be represented by a single letter as b.

(7) $$\frac{1-x}{1}\;\Big|\;1-\frac{x}{3}-\frac{x^2}{9},\ \&c.$$

$$3-x+\frac{x^2}{9}\;\Big|\;-x$$

$$-x+\frac{x^2}{3}-\frac{x^3}{27}$$

$$3\;\Big|\;-\frac{x^2}{3}+\frac{x^3}{27}$$

Article 192.

$$\Big|\;x^4-2x^2+3-\frac{2}{x^2}+\frac{1}{x^4}=\text{sq. root.}$$

(7) $$x^8-4x^6+10x^4-16x^2+19-\frac{16}{x^2}+\frac{10}{x^4}-\frac{4}{x^6}+\frac{1}{x^8}$$

$$x^8$$

$$2x^4-2x^2\;\Big|\;-4x^6+10x^4$$

$$-4x^6+\ 4x^4$$

$$2x^4-4x^2\ +3\;\Big|\;6x^4-16x^2+19$$

$$6x^4-12x^2+\ 9$$

$$2x^4-4x^2+6-\frac{2}{x^2}\;\Big|\;-\ 4x^2+10-\frac{16}{x^2}+\frac{10}{x^4}$$

$$-\ 4x^2+\ 8-\frac{12}{x^2}+\frac{4}{x^4}$$

$$2x^4-4x^2+6-\frac{4}{x^2}+\frac{1}{x^4}\;\Big|\;+\ 2-\frac{4}{x^2}+\frac{6}{x^4}-\frac{4}{x^6}+\frac{1}{x^8}$$

$$+\ 2-\frac{4}{x^2}+\frac{6}{x^4}-\frac{4}{x^6}+\frac{1}{x^8}$$

The square root of $x^4-2x^2+3-\frac{2}{x^2}+\frac{1}{x^4}$ is now readily found to be $x^2-1+\frac{1}{x^2}$.

(8) The terms arranged with reference to the powers of a, give $a^6-6a^4+15a^2-20+\frac{15}{a^2}-\frac{6}{a^4}+\frac{1}{a^6}$. The square root of this, found as in the preceding example, is $a^3-3a+\frac{3}{a}-\frac{1}{a^3}$; and the cube root of this, found by the rule in Art. 191, is $a-\frac{1}{a}$.

It is proper to remark that both the preceding examples may be solved without using fractions in the operation, by multiplying all the terms of the polynomial in example 7, by x^8, and writing x^8 beneath it, and after extracting the fourth root of both terms dividing by x^2.

We thus find $x^8-2x^6+3x^4-2x^2+1$, the first square root of the numerator, and x^4-x^2+1 the second.

Similarly, in example 8, we must multiply all the terms by a^6. It is recommended to the pupil to solve these examples by both methods.

Article 194.

(5) By the 1st method, the first term of the root would be $2x$, the trial divisor $80x^4$, and the complete divisor $80x^4-80x^3+40x^2-10x+1$.

By the 2d method, the first term of the root would be $2x$, and the trial divisor $80x^4$. Dividing the 1st term of the 1st remainder by $80x^4$, we obtain for the 2d term of the root -1. Raising $2x-1$ to the 5th power, we obtain the original polynomial.

RADICALS.

Note.—As most of the examples in Radicals are performed by direct methods of operation, which the careful student can scarcely fail to apply properly, it is not deemed necessary to present all their solutions.

REDUCTION OF RADICALS.

In the reduction of fractional radicals of the second degree, there is a principle with which it is well pupils should be acquainted, as it both facilitates and simplifies the operations. This principle is, that

If a number contains a factor that is a perfect square, the number may be made a perfect square by multiplying it by the other factor.

Thus, if the denominator of a fraction is a^2b, it may be made a square by multiplying it by b. For example,

$$\sqrt{\frac{5}{72}}=\sqrt{\frac{5}{36\times2}}=\sqrt{\frac{5\times2}{36\times2^2}}=\sqrt{\frac{1}{36\times4}\times10}=\frac{1}{6\times2}\sqrt{10}=\frac{1}{12}\sqrt{10}.$$

If the denominator contains no factor that is a perfect square, it can only be rendered a perfect square by multiplying both terms by itself. Thus,

$$\sqrt{\tfrac{5}{11}}=\sqrt{\tfrac{5}{11}\times\tfrac{11}{11}}=\sqrt{\tfrac{1}{121}\times 55}=\tfrac{1}{11}\sqrt{55}.$$

Article 200.

In order to separate a quantity into two factors, one of which is a perfect power of any given degree, it is necessary to ascertain if the quantity contains a numerical factor that is a perfect power of that degree. To do this, we must see if the quantity is divisible by any of the perfect powers of that degree.

Thus, if the radical is of the third degree, the perfect powers to be tried as divisors are 8, 27, 64, 125, 216, 343, 512, 729, etc. If the radical is of the fourth degree, the divisors are 16, 81, 256, 625, etc. If the radical is of the fifth degree, the divisors are $32=2^5$, $243=3^5$, $1024=4^5$, and so on.

(3) $\sqrt[3]{\tfrac{1}{2}}=\sqrt[3]{\tfrac{1}{2}\times\tfrac{4}{4}}=\sqrt[3]{\tfrac{1}{8}\times 4}=\tfrac{1}{2}\sqrt[3]{4}$;

$\sqrt[3]{\tfrac{3}{4}}=\sqrt[3]{\tfrac{1}{8}\times 6}=\tfrac{1}{2}\sqrt[3]{6}$; $\sqrt[3]{\tfrac{1}{6}}=\sqrt[3]{\tfrac{1}{216}\times 36}=\tfrac{1}{6}\sqrt[3]{36}$;

$\sqrt[3]{\tfrac{5}{9}}=\sqrt[3]{\tfrac{1}{27}\times 15}=\tfrac{1}{3}\sqrt[3]{15}$;

$$\sqrt[4]{\frac{2}{3}}=\sqrt[4]{\frac{2}{3}\times\frac{3^3}{3^3}}=\sqrt[4]{\frac{1}{3^4}\times 2\times 3^3}=\tfrac{1}{3}\sqrt[4]{2\times 3^3}=\frac{1}{3}\sqrt[4]{54}.$$

$$\sqrt[5]{\frac{3}{4}}=\sqrt[5]{\frac{3}{2^2}}=\sqrt[5]{\frac{3}{2^2}\times\frac{2^3}{2^3}}=\sqrt[5]{\frac{1}{2^5}\times 3\times 2^3}=\frac{1}{2}\sqrt[5]{24}.$$

or thus $\sqrt[5]{\dfrac{3}{4}}=\sqrt[5]{\dfrac{3}{4}\times\dfrac{4^4}{4^4}}=\sqrt[5]{\dfrac{1}{4^5}\times 3\times 4^4}=\dfrac{1}{4}\sqrt[5]{768}=$

$\tfrac{1}{4}\sqrt[5]{32\times 24}=\tfrac{1}{2}\sqrt[5]{24}$;

$$\sqrt[6]{\frac{1}{2}}=\sqrt[6]{\frac{1}{2}\times\frac{2^5}{2^5}}=\sqrt[6]{\frac{1}{2^6}\times 2^5}=\frac{1}{2}\sqrt[6]{2^5}=\frac{1}{2}\sqrt[6]{32}.$$

Article 203.

(1) $3^{\frac{1}{2}}$ and $2^{\frac{1}{3}}=3^{\frac{3}{6}}$ and $2^{\frac{2}{6}}=\sqrt[6]{3^3}$ and $\sqrt[6]{2^2}=\sqrt[6]{27}$ and $\sqrt[6]{4}$, or $27^{\frac{1}{6}}$ and $4^{\frac{1}{6}}$

(2) $\sqrt[6]{5}$ and $\sqrt{4}=5^{\frac{1}{3}}$ and $4^{\frac{1}{2}}=5^{\frac{2}{6}}$ and $4^{\frac{3}{6}}=\sqrt[6]{5^2}$ and $\sqrt[6]{4^3}=\sqrt[6]{25}$ and $\sqrt[6]{64}$.

(3) a^2 and $b^{\frac{1}{2}}=a^{\frac{2}{1}}$ and $b^{\frac{1}{2}}=a^{\frac{4}{2}}$ and $b^{\frac{1}{2}}=\sqrt{a^4}$ and $\sqrt{b}$.

(4) $\sqrt[4]{a}=a^{\frac{1}{4}}=a^{\frac{6}{24}}=\sqrt[24]{a^6}=\sqrt[24]{a^6}$;

$\sqrt[6]{5b}=(5b)^{\frac{1}{6}}=(5b)^{\frac{4}{24}}=\sqrt[24]{(5b)^4}=\sqrt[24]{625b^4}$;

$\sqrt[8]{6c}=(6c)^{\frac{1}{8}}=(6c)^{\frac{3}{24}}=\sqrt[24]{(6c)^3}=\sqrt[24]{216c^3}$.

The remaining examples may be solved in a similar manner

ADDITION AND SUBTRACTION OF RADICALS

Article 204.

(9)
$$+\sqrt{128}=+\sqrt{64\times2}=+8\sqrt{2};$$
$$-2\sqrt{50}=-2\sqrt{25\times2}=-10\sqrt{2};$$
$$+\sqrt{72}=+\sqrt{36\times2}=+6\sqrt{2};$$
$$-\sqrt{18}=-\sqrt{9\times2}=-3\sqrt{2};$$
$$\therefore\ \text{Sum}=\sqrt{2},\quad \textit{Ans.}$$

(13)
$$2\sqrt[3]{\tfrac{1}{4}}=2\sqrt[3]{\tfrac{1}{8}\times2}=\sqrt[3]{2};$$
$$8\sqrt[3]{\tfrac{1}{32}}=8\sqrt[3]{\tfrac{1}{64}\times2}=2\sqrt[3]{2};$$
$$\therefore\ \text{Sum}=3\sqrt[3]{2},\quad \textit{Ans.}$$

(14)
$$6\sqrt[6]{4a^2}=6\sqrt[3]{\sqrt{4a^2}}=6\sqrt[3]{2a};$$
$$2\sqrt[3]{2a}=2\sqrt[3]{2a}=2\sqrt[3]{2a};$$
$$\sqrt[9]{8a^3}=\sqrt[3]{\sqrt[3]{8a^3}}=\sqrt[3]{2a};$$
$$\therefore\ \text{Sum}=9\sqrt[3]{2a},\quad \textit{Ans.}$$

(16) $\sqrt[4]{16}=2$, $\sqrt[3]{81}=\sqrt[3]{27\times3}=3\sqrt[3]{3}$, $-\sqrt[3]{-512}=-\sqrt{-8^3}$ $=8$, $\sqrt[3]{192}=\sqrt[3]{64\times3}=4\sqrt[3]{3}$, $-7\sqrt[6]{9}=-7\sqrt[3]{3}$;

$\therefore\ 2+3\sqrt[3]{5}+8+4\sqrt[3]{3}-7\sqrt[3]{3}=10.$

(17) $\sqrt{\dfrac{ab^3}{c^2}}=\sqrt{\dfrac{b^2}{c^2}\times ab}=\dfrac{b}{c}\sqrt{ab}$;

$\dfrac{1}{2c}\sqrt{(a^3b-4a^2b^2+4ab^3)}=\dfrac{1}{2c}\sqrt{ab(a^2-4ab+4b^2)}=$

$\dfrac{a-b}{2c}\sqrt{ab}$; $\dfrac{b}{c}\sqrt{ab}+\dfrac{a-b}{2c}\sqrt{ab}=\dfrac{a}{2c}\sqrt{ab}.$

Article 205.

(8) $8\sqrt[3]{b}=3b^{\frac{1}{3}}=3b^{\frac{4}{12}}=3\sqrt[12]{b^4}$;

$4\sqrt[4]{a}=4a^{\frac{1}{4}}=4a^{\frac{3}{12}}=4\sqrt[12]{a^3}$;

$\therefore$ Product $=12\sqrt[12]{a^3b^4}$, *Ans.*

(9) $\sqrt[2]{2}=\sqrt[12]{2^6}$, $\sqrt[3]{3}=\sqrt[12]{3^4}$, $\sqrt[4]{5}=\sqrt[12]{5^3}$;

$\sqrt[12]{2^6}\times\sqrt[12]{3^4}\times\sqrt[12]{5^3}=\sqrt[12]{2^6\times3^4\times5^3}=\sqrt[12]{64\times81\times125}$

$=\sqrt[12]{648000}$.

(10) $\sqrt[n]{x^2}=\sqrt[2n]{x^4}$, $\sqrt[3n]{x^3}=\sqrt[n]{x}=\sqrt[2n]{x^2}$;

$\sqrt[2n]{x}\times\sqrt[2n]{x^4}\times\sqrt[2n]{x^2}=\sqrt[2n]{x\times x^4\times x^2}=\sqrt[2n]{x^7}$.

(13) $\dfrac{70\sqrt[3]{9}}{7\sqrt[3]{18}}=10\sqrt[3]{\tfrac{1}{2}}=10\sqrt[3]{\tfrac{4}{8}}=\tfrac{10}{2}\sqrt[3]{4}=5\sqrt[3]{4}$, *Ans.*

(14) $\sqrt[6]{72}\div\sqrt{2}=\sqrt[6]{72}\div\sqrt[6]{8}=\sqrt[6]{9}=\sqrt[3]{\sqrt{9}}=\sqrt[3]{3}$.

(15) $4\sqrt[3]{9}\div2\sqrt{3}=4\sqrt[6]{9^2}\div2\sqrt[6]{3^3}=2\sqrt[6]{3}$.

(16) $\sqrt[6]{72}\div\sqrt[3]{3}=\sqrt[6]{72}\div\sqrt[6]{9}=\sqrt[6]{8}=\sqrt{\sqrt[3]{8}}=\sqrt{2}$.

(17) $\sqrt[4]{\dfrac{b}{a}}\div\sqrt[4]{\dfrac{a}{b}}=\sqrt[4]{\dfrac{b}{a}}\times\sqrt[4]{\dfrac{b}{a}}=\sqrt[4]{\dfrac{b^2}{a^2}}=\sqrt{\dfrac{b}{a}}$ *Ans.*

(19)

$\sqrt{2}+1$

$\sqrt{2}-1$

$2+\sqrt{2}$

$\quad-\sqrt{2}-1$

$2-1=1$.

(20)

$11\sqrt{2}-4\sqrt{15}$

$\sqrt{6}+\sqrt{5}$

$11\sqrt{12}-4\sqrt{90}$

$\quad+11\sqrt{10}-4\sqrt{75}$

$11\sqrt{12}-\sqrt{10}-4\sqrt{75}$

$=22\sqrt{3}-\sqrt{10}-20\sqrt{3}$

$=2\sqrt{3}-\sqrt{10}$

Observe that $-4\sqrt{90}=-12\sqrt{10}$.

(21)

$\sqrt{2}+\sqrt{3}$

$\sqrt{2}+\sqrt{3}$

$2+\sqrt{6}$

$\quad+\sqrt{6}+3$

$5+2\sqrt{6}$

$5+2\sqrt{6}$

$25+10\sqrt{6}$

$\quad+10\sqrt{6}+4\times6$

$49+20\sqrt{6}$.

(22) $\sqrt[3]{12+\sqrt{19}}\times\sqrt[3]{12-\sqrt{19}}=\sqrt[3]{\{(12+\sqrt{19})(12-\sqrt{19})\}}$
$=\sqrt[3]{\{144-19\}}=\sqrt[3]{144-19}=\sqrt[3]{125}=5.$

(23)
$$\begin{array}{l} x^2-x\sqrt{2}+1 \\ x^2+x\sqrt{2}+1 \\ \hline x^4-x^3\sqrt{2}+x^2 \\ \quad +^3\sqrt{2}-2x^2+x\sqrt{2} \\ \qquad +x^2-x\sqrt{2}+1 \\ \hline \end{array}$$
Adding, $x^4 \qquad +1$, *Ans.*

(24)
$$\begin{array}{l} x^2-x\sqrt{3}+1 \\ x^2+x\sqrt{3}+1 \\ \hline x^4-x^3\sqrt{3}+x^2 \\ \quad +x^3\sqrt{3}-3x^2+x\sqrt{3} \\ \qquad +x^2-x\sqrt{3}+1 \\ \hline \end{array}$$
x^4-x^2+1, by adding.
$$\begin{array}{l} x^2+1 \\ \hline x^6-x^4+x^2 \\ \quad +x^4-x^2+1 \\ \hline x^6 \qquad +1, \end{array}$$
Ans.

Article 206.

(5) $\dfrac{8-5\sqrt{2}}{3-2\sqrt{2}}=\dfrac{8-5\sqrt{2}}{3-2\sqrt{2}}\times\dfrac{3+2\sqrt{2}}{3+2\sqrt{2}}=\dfrac{4+\sqrt{2}}{9-8}=4+\sqrt{2}.$

(6) $\dfrac{\sqrt{3}+\sqrt{2}}{\sqrt{3}-\sqrt{2}}=\dfrac{\sqrt{3}+\sqrt{2}}{\sqrt{3}-\sqrt{2}}\times\dfrac{\sqrt{3}+\sqrt{2}}{\sqrt{3}+\sqrt{2}}=\dfrac{5+2\sqrt{6}}{3-2}=5+2\sqrt{6}.$

(7) $\dfrac{3\sqrt{5}-2\sqrt{2}}{2\sqrt{5}-\sqrt{18}}\times\dfrac{2\sqrt{5}+\sqrt{18}}{2\sqrt{5}+\sqrt{18}}=\dfrac{18+5\sqrt{10}}{20-18}=9+\frac{5}{2}\sqrt{10}.$

(8) $\dfrac{3+4\sqrt{3}}{\sqrt{6}+\sqrt{2}-\sqrt{5}}\times\dfrac{\sqrt{6}+\sqrt{2}+\sqrt{5}}{\sqrt{6}+\sqrt{2}+\sqrt{5}}$

$=\dfrac{(3+4\sqrt{3})(\sqrt{6}+\sqrt{2}+\sqrt{5})}{3+4\sqrt{3}}=\sqrt{6}+\sqrt{2}+\sqrt{5}$, *Ans.*

(9) $\dfrac{1}{x+\sqrt{x^2-1}}\times\dfrac{x-\sqrt{x^2-1}}{x-\sqrt{x^2-1}}=\dfrac{x-\sqrt{x^2-1}}{x^2-(x^2-1)}=x-\sqrt{x^2-1}$

$\dfrac{1}{x-\sqrt{x^2-1}}\times\dfrac{x+\sqrt{x^2-1}}{x+\sqrt{x^2-1}}=\dfrac{x+\sqrt{x^2-1}}{x^2-(x^2-1)}=x+\sqrt{x^2-1}.$

Sum $=2x$, *Ans.*

(10) $\dfrac{\sqrt{x^2+1}+\sqrt{x^2-1}}{\sqrt{x^2+1}-\sqrt{x^2-1}}\times\dfrac{\sqrt{x^2+1}+\sqrt{x^2-1}}{\sqrt{x^2+1}+\sqrt{x^2-1}}=x^2+\sqrt{x^4-1}$

$\dfrac{\sqrt{x^2+1}-\sqrt{x^2-1}}{\sqrt{x^2+1}+\sqrt{x^2-1}}\times\dfrac{\sqrt{x^2+1}-\sqrt{x^2-1}}{\sqrt{x^2+1}-\sqrt{x^2-1}}=x^2-\sqrt{x^4-1}$

Sum $=2x^2$, *Ans.*

(11) $\frac{2}{\sqrt{5}}\times\frac{\sqrt{5}}{\sqrt{5}}=\frac{2\sqrt{5}}{5}=\frac{2\times 2.236037+}{5}=.894427+$

$\frac{1}{\sqrt{2}}\times\frac{\sqrt{2}}{\sqrt{2}}=\frac{\sqrt{2}}{2}=\frac{1.414212+}{2}=.707106+.$

(12) $\frac{\sqrt{20}+\sqrt{12}}{\sqrt{5}-\sqrt{3}}\times\frac{\sqrt{5}+\sqrt{3}}{\sqrt{5}+\sqrt{3}}=\frac{16+2\sqrt{60}}{2}$

$=8+2\sqrt{15}=15.745966+.$

IMAGINARY, OR IMPOSSIBLE QUANTITIES.

Article 210.

(2) $(a\sqrt{-1})^3=(a\sqrt{-1})^2\times(a\sqrt{-1})=-a^2\times a\sqrt{-1}$

$=-a^3\sqrt{-1}.$

$(a\sqrt{-1})^4=(a\sqrt{-1})^2\times(a\sqrt{-1})^2=(-a^2)\times(-a^2)=a^4.$

(3) $(2\sqrt{-3})\times(3\sqrt{-2})=(2\sqrt{3}\sqrt{-1})\times(3\sqrt{2}\sqrt{-1})=-6\sqrt{6}$

(4) $6\sqrt{-3}=6\sqrt{3}\sqrt{-1}$; $2\sqrt{-4}=2\sqrt{4}\sqrt{-1}=4\sqrt{-1}$;

$6\sqrt{3}\sqrt{-1}\div 4\sqrt{-1}=\frac{6\sqrt{3}\sqrt{-1}}{4\sqrt{-1}}=\frac{3}{2}\sqrt{3}.$

(5) $\frac{1+\sqrt{-1}}{1-\sqrt{-1}}\times\frac{1+\sqrt{-1}}{1+\sqrt{-1}}=\frac{1+2\sqrt{-1}-1}{1-(-1)}=\frac{2\sqrt{-1}}{2}=\sqrt{-1}.$

(6) $(x+a\sqrt{-1})\times(x-a\sqrt{-1})=x^2-a^2(-1)=x^2+a^2$;

$(x+a)\times(x-a)=x^2-a^2$; $(x^2+a^2)(x^2-a^2)=x^4-a^4.$

(7) Multiply the quantities together.

MULTIPLICATION AND DIVISION OF QUANTITIES WITH FRACTIONAL EXPONENTS.

Article 213.

(4)
$$\begin{array}{l} a^{\frac{2}{3}}+a^{\frac{1}{3}}b^{\frac{1}{3}}+b^{\frac{2}{3}} \\ a^{\frac{1}{3}}-b^{\frac{1}{3}} \\ \hline a+a^{\frac{2}{3}}b^{\frac{1}{3}}+a^{\frac{1}{3}}b^{\frac{2}{3}} \\ \quad -a^{\frac{2}{3}}b^{\frac{1}{3}}-a^{\frac{1}{3}}b^{\frac{2}{3}}-b \\ \hline a-b,\ \textit{Ans.} \end{array}$$

(5)
$$\begin{array}{l} x^{\frac{1}{4}}y+y^{\frac{2}{3}} \\ x^{\frac{1}{4}}-y^{-\frac{1}{3}} \\ \hline x^{\frac{1}{2}}y+x^{\frac{1}{4}}y^{\frac{2}{3}} \\ \quad -x^{\frac{1}{4}}y^{\frac{2}{3}}-y^{\frac{1}{3}} \\ \hline x^{\frac{1}{2}}y-y^{\frac{1}{3}},\ \textit{Ans} \end{array}$$

(6) $(a+b)^{\frac{1}{m}}\times(a-b)^{\frac{1}{m}}=[(a+b)(a-b)]^{\frac{1}{m}}=(a^2-b^2)^{\frac{1}{m}}$

$(a+b)^{\frac{1}{n}}\times(a-b)^{\frac{1}{n}}=[(a+b)(a-b)]^{\frac{1}{n}}=(a^2-b^2)^{\frac{1}{n}};$

$(a^2-b^2)^{\frac{1}{m}}\times(a^2-b^2)^{\frac{1}{n}}=(a^2-b^2)^{\frac{1}{m}+\frac{1}{n}}=(a^2-b^2)^{\frac{m+n}{mn}}$

(7) Observe that $\frac{2}{3}-\frac{1}{4}=\frac{5}{12}$; $\frac{3}{m}-\frac{2}{n}=\frac{3n-2m}{mn}$.

(8) $a^{\frac{3}{4}}-b^{\frac{3}{4}}\ \big|\ a^{\frac{1}{4}}-b^{\frac{1}{4}}$

$a^{\frac{3}{4}}-a^{\frac{1}{2}}b^{\frac{1}{4}}\ \big|\ a^{\frac{1}{2}}+a^{\frac{1}{4}}b^{\frac{1}{4}}+b^{\frac{1}{2}}$, *Ans.*

$+a^{\frac{1}{2}}b^{\frac{1}{4}}$

$a^{\frac{1}{2}}b^{\frac{1}{4}}-a^{\frac{1}{4}}b^{\frac{1}{2}}$

$a^{\frac{1}{4}}b^{\frac{1}{2}}-b^{\frac{3}{4}}$

$a^{\frac{1}{4}}b^{\frac{1}{2}}-b^{\frac{3}{4}}$

(9) $a-b^2\ \big|\ a^{\frac{3}{4}}+a^{\frac{1}{2}}b^{\frac{1}{2}}+a^{\frac{1}{4}}b+b^{\frac{3}{2}}$

$a+a^{\frac{3}{4}}b^{\frac{1}{2}}+a^{\frac{1}{2}}b+a^{\frac{1}{4}}b^{\frac{3}{2}}\ \big|\ a^{\frac{1}{4}}-b^{\frac{1}{2}}$, *Ans.*

$-a^{\frac{3}{4}}b^{\frac{1}{2}}-a^{\frac{1}{2}}b-a^{\frac{1}{4}}b^{\frac{3}{2}}-b^2$

$-a^{\frac{3}{4}}b^{\frac{1}{2}}-a^{\frac{1}{2}}b-a^{\frac{1}{4}}b^{\frac{3}{2}}-b^2$

Article 215.

(3) $a-(ax-a^2)^{\frac{1}{2}}$

$a-(ax-a^2)^{\frac{1}{2}}$

$a^2-a(ax-a^2)^{\frac{1}{2}}$

$-a(ax-a^2)^{\frac{1}{2}}+ax-a^2$

$-2a(ax-a^2)^{\frac{1}{2}}+ax$, *Ans.*

(4) $a^{\frac{1}{3}}x^{-1}+a^{-\frac{1}{3}}x$ $\qquad a^0=1,\ x^0=1$, (Art. 82).

$a^{\frac{1}{3}}x^{-1}+a^{-\frac{1}{3}}x$

$a^{\frac{2}{3}}x^{-2}+a^0x^0$

$+a^0x^0+a^{-\frac{2}{3}}x^2$ (*Concluded on page* 85.)

$$\begin{array}{l} a^{\frac{2}{3}}x^{-2}+2\quad +a^{-\frac{2}{3}}x^2 \\ a^{\frac{1}{3}}x^{-1}+a^{-\frac{1}{3}}x \\ \hline ax^{-3}+2a^{\frac{1}{3}}x^{-1}+a^{-\frac{1}{3}}x \\ \qquad +\ a^{\frac{1}{3}}x^{-1}+2a^{-\frac{1}{3}}x+a^{-1}x^3 \\ \hline ax^{-3}+3a^{\frac{1}{3}}x^{-1}+3a^{-\frac{1}{3}}x+a^{-1}x^3,\ \textit{Ans.} \end{array}$$

(5) $\sqrt[3]{(27a^3x)^{\frac{1}{2}}}=(27a^3x)^{\frac{1}{6}}=27^{\frac{1}{6}}a^{\frac{3}{6}}x^{\frac{1}{6}}=3^{\frac{3}{6}}a^{\frac{3}{6}}x^{\frac{1}{6}}=3^{\frac{1}{2}}a^{\frac{1}{2}}x^{\frac{1}{6}}$ or $(3ax^{\frac{1}{3}})^{\frac{1}{2}}$, *Ans.*

$\sqrt[3]{(27a^3x)^{\frac{1}{3}}}=(27a^3x)^{\frac{1}{9}}=27^{\frac{1}{9}}a^{\frac{3}{9}}x^{\frac{1}{9}}=3^{\frac{3}{9}}a^{\frac{3}{9}}x^{\frac{1}{9}}=3^{\frac{1}{3}}a^{\frac{1}{3}}x^{\frac{1}{9}}$ or $(3ax^{\frac{1}{3}})^{\frac{1}{3}}$, *Ans.*

(6)
$$\begin{array}{r|l} & 5x^3-4x(5cx)^{\frac{1}{2}}+4c \quad \big|\ \underline{5^{\frac{1}{2}}x^{\frac{3}{2}}-2c^{\frac{1}{2}}},\ \textit{Ans.} \\ & \underline{5x^3} \\ \underline{2(5^{\frac{1}{2}}x^{\frac{3}{2}})-2c^{\frac{1}{2}}} & -4x(5cx)^{\frac{1}{2}}+4c \\ & \underline{-4x(5cx)^{\frac{1}{2}}+4c.} \end{array}$$

(7)
$$\begin{array}{r|l} & \frac{1}{8}a^3-\frac{3}{2}a^2b^{\frac{1}{2}}+6ab-8b^{\frac{3}{2}} \ \big|\ \underline{\tfrac{1}{2}a-2b^{\frac{1}{2}}}=\text{cube root.} \\ & \underline{\frac{1}{8}a^3} \\ \underline{\frac{3}{4}a^2-3ab^{\frac{1}{2}}+4b} & -\frac{3}{2}a^2b^{\frac{1}{2}}+6ab-8b^{\frac{3}{2}} \\ & \underline{-\frac{3}{2}a^2b^{\frac{1}{2}}+6ab-8b^{\frac{3}{2}}} \end{array}$$

EQUATIONS CONTAINING RADICALS.

Article 216.

(4) Transpose 3, and then square both sides.

(5) Square both sides, transpose 1, and square again.

(6) Square both sides, omit x on each side, divide both sides by $2a$, transpose $\sqrt{x}$, or $\frac{a}{2}$, and square. The answer is either $\frac{(a-1)^2}{4}$ or $\frac{(1-a)^2}{4}$, the two being equal.

(7) Square both sides, transpose $2x-3a+2x$, divide by 2, and square again.

(8) Square both sides, and transpose 13; square again, and transpose 7; square again, and transpose 3; whence, we have $\sqrt{x}=1$ and $x=1$.

(9) Multiply both sides by the first term, transpose $2+x$, and square both sides.

(10) Multiply both sides by $\sqrt{x}$, transpose $\sqrt{a}$, then square both sides, and omit x^2 on each side.

(11) Transpose the second term to the left member and square both sides, omit x on each side, transpose the known quantities to the left side, and square again.

(12) $a\sqrt{x}+b)\sqrt{x}-c\sqrt{x}=d$, or $(a+b-c)\sqrt{x}=d$;

whence, $\sqrt{x}=\dfrac{d}{(a+b-c)}$, and $x=\dfrac{d^2}{(a+b-c)^2}$.

(13) Multiply both sides by $\sqrt{x}$ to clear the equation of fractions, and we have $x-ax=1$, or $(1-a)x=1$.

(14) Square both sides, omit a^2 on each side, then divide by x, and square again.

(15) Since $x-4=(\sqrt{x}+2)(\sqrt{x}-2)$, the first member becomes $\sqrt{x}-2$; then, by transposing, we have $6=5\frac{1}{2}\sqrt{x}$, or $11\sqrt{x}=12$; whence, $x=\frac{144}{121}$.

(16) Since $x-a=(\sqrt{x}+\sqrt{a})(\sqrt{x}-\sqrt{a})$, the first member becomes $\sqrt{x}-\sqrt{a}$; then, by clearing of fractions and reducing, we find $\sqrt{x}=4\sqrt{a}$; whence, $x=16a$.

(17) Since $3x-1=(\sqrt{3x}+1)(\sqrt{3x}-1)$, the first member becomes $\sqrt{3x}-1$; then, by clearing of fractions, reducing and squaring, x is found $=3$.

(18) $\sqrt{4a+x}=2\sqrt{b+x}-\sqrt{x}$,

$4a+x=4b+4x-4\sqrt{bx+x^2}+x$, by squaring,

$\sqrt{bx+x^2}=(b-a)+x$, by transposing and reducing,

$bx+x^2=(b-a)^2+2(b-a)x+x^2$, by squaring,

$(2a-b)x=(b-a)^2$, by transposing,

$$x=\frac{(b-a)^2}{2a-b}$$

(19) $\sqrt{\frac{b}{a+x}}+\sqrt{\frac{c}{a-x}}=\sqrt[4]{\frac{4bc}{a^2-x^2}}$.

$\frac{b}{a+x}+2\sqrt{\frac{bc}{a^2-x^2}}+\frac{c}{a-x}=\sqrt{\frac{4bc}{a^2-x^2}}$ by squaring.

But $2\sqrt{\frac{bc}{a^2-x^2}}=\sqrt{\frac{4bc}{a^2-x^2}}$.

Therefore, $\frac{b}{a+x}+\frac{c}{a-x}=0$; whence, $x=\frac{a(b+c)}{b-c}$.

(20) Multiplying both terms of the first member by the numerator, and then clearing of fractions and transposing, we have

$2\sqrt{x^2+ax}=a\,(c-1)-2x$,

$4x^2+4ax=a^2(c-1)^2-4ax(c-1)+4x^2$ by squaring,

$4acx=a^2(c-1)^2$ by reducing and transposing;

Therefore, $x=\frac{a(c-1)^2}{4c}$.

(21) $\sqrt{\sqrt{x}+3}-\sqrt{\sqrt{x}-3}=\sqrt{2\sqrt{x}}$.

Squaring both sides, and observing that $\sqrt{\sqrt{x}+3}$ multiplied by $\sqrt{\sqrt{x}-3}$ produces $\sqrt{x-9}$, we have

$\sqrt{x}+3-2\sqrt{x-9}+\sqrt{x}-3=2\sqrt{x}$.

Reducing, and omitting $2\sqrt{x}$ on each side, we have

$-2\sqrt{x-9}=0$, and $4(x-9)=0$ by squaring;

whence, $x=9$.

(22) Square both members, omit $\frac{1}{a^2}$ on each side, square again, and omit $\frac{1}{x^4}$ on both sides; then, multiply both members by x^2, clear the equation of fractions, and the value of x is readily found.

(23) Square both members, omit equal quantities on each side, place all the terms not under the radical on the right side, and divide by 2, and we have

$\sqrt{\{(1-a^2)^2+2x(1+3a^2)+(1-a^2)x^2\}}=(a^2-1)-x$;

square both sides, and we have

$(1-a^2)^2+2x(1+3a^2)+(1-a^2)x^2=(a^2-1)^2-2x(a^2-1)+x^2$.

The square of $1-a^2$ is the same as the square of a^2-1: omitting these and x^2 on each side, and dividing by x and transposing,

we have $a^2x=8a^2$.

whence, $x=8$.

EXAMPLES IN INEQUALITIES.

The subject of inequalities, though interesting and highly important in itself, is not much used in the subsequent parts of Algebra. The last four examples, that is, from the 10th to the close, may be regarded as so many independent algebraic theorems, the study of which may be omitted by all except the higher class of students.

Article 223.

(7) Squaring both quantities, subtracting 19 from each, and dividing by 2, we have

$\sqrt{70}>$, or $<1+3\sqrt{6}$;

$70>$, or $<1+6\sqrt{6}+54$, by squaring;

$15>$, or $<6\sqrt{6}$, by subtracting 55 from each member;

$5>$, or $<2\sqrt{6}$, by dividing by 3;

$25>24$, by squaring;

hence, $\sqrt{5}+\sqrt{14}$ is greater than $\sqrt{3}+3\sqrt{2}$.

(8) Multiplying both members of the first comparison by 12, to clear it of fractions, and reducing, we get $x<6$.

Treating the second comparison in the same manner, we find $x>4$; hence, if x is a whole number and is greater than 4 and less than 6, it must be 5.

(9) $2x+7$ not >19, $\quad 3x-5$ not <13,

or $2x$ not >12, $\quad 3x$ not <18,

x not >6, $\quad x$ not <6.

Hence, if x is neither less nor greater than 6, it must be 6.

(10) Referring to example 6, we have

$a^2+b^2>2ab$,

$\frac{a^2}{ab}+\frac{b^2}{ab}>2$, by dividing by ab.

$\frac{a}{b}+\frac{b}{a}>2$, by reducing.

(11) From question 6, we have

$$a^2+b^2>2ab,$$

also, $a^2+c^2>2ac$,

and $b^2+c^2>2bc$,

from which, by adding together the corresponding members, and dividing each member by 2,

we have $a^2+b^2+c^2>ab+ac+bc$.

(12) If $x>y$, then $\sqrt{x}>\sqrt{y}$,

and $\sqrt{xy}>\sqrt{y}\times\sqrt{y}$, or y,

$$\sqrt{xy}>y,$$

$$2\sqrt{xy}>2y.$$

Therefore $-2y>-2\sqrt{xy}$.

Add $x+y$ to each member,

then $x-y>x-2\sqrt{xy}+y$,

or $x-y>(\sqrt{x}-\sqrt{y})^2$.

(13) $a^2>a^2-(b-c)^2$, since $(b-c)^2$ is necessarily positive,

$>(a+b-c)(a+c-b)$ by factoring;

$b^2>b^2-(a-c)^2$,

$>(a+b-c)(b+c-a)$;

$c^2>c^2-(a-b)^2$,

$>(a+c-b)(b+c-a)$.

Multiplying together the corresponding members of these inequalities, $a^2b^2c^2>(a+b-c)^2(a+c-b)^2(b+c-a)^2$; extracting the square root of both members,

we have $abc>(a+b-c)(a+c-b)(b+c-a)$.

QUADRATIC EQUATIONS.

PURE QUADRATIC EQUATIONS.

Article 228.

(8) Multiply both members by $\sqrt{a^2+x^2}$, transpose a^2+x^2 and square again.

(9) Multiply both members by the product of the denominators, and reduce.

(10) Clearing of fractions, transposing, and factoring, we have

$a(1-b) \quad =(b+1)\sqrt{a^2-x^2};$

$a^2(1-b)^2 \quad =(b+1)^2(a^2-x^2)$, by squaring,

$(b+1)^2x^2=4a^2b$, by transposing and reducing;

Therefore, $x^2=\frac{4a^2b}{(b+1)^2}$, and $x=\pm\frac{2a\sqrt{b}}{b+1}$.

Article 229.

(2) Let $x=$ the number; then, $x^2-17=130-2x^2$.
Whence, $x=7$.

(3) Let $x=$ the number; then, $(10-x)x=10(x-6\frac{2}{5})$.
Whence, $x=8$.

(4) Let $x=$ the number; then, $30-\frac{1}{3}x^2=\frac{1}{4}x^2+9$.
Whence, $x=6$.

(5) To avoid fractions, let $9x=$ the greater; then, $\frac{2}{9}$ of $9x=2x$, and $9x-2x=7x$, will represent the less.
Therefore, $(9x)^2-(7x)^2$, or $81x^2-49x^2=128$.
Whence, $x=2$, $\therefore$ $9x=18$, and $7x=14$.

(7) Let $x=$ the greater number; then, $14-x=$ the less;

then, $\frac{x}{14-x} : \frac{14-x}{x} :: 16 : 9$.

Whence, $\frac{9x}{14-x}=\frac{16(14-x)}{x}$; clearing of fractions,

$9x^2=16(14-x)^2$; extracting the square root

$3x=4(14-x)$.

Whence, $x=8$, and $14-x=6$.

(8) Let $x=$ the number; then, $(20+x)(20-x)=319$.
Whence, $x=9$.

(9) Let $x=$ the greater; then, $\frac{126}{x}=$ the less, and

$$x\div\frac{126}{x}=x\times\frac{x}{126}=\frac{x^2}{126}=3\frac{1}{2}.$$

Whence, $x^2=441$; $\therefore$ $x=21$ and $\frac{126}{x}=6$.

(10) Let $x=$ one of the numbers; then, $\frac{p}{x}=$ the other, and

$$x\div\frac{p}{x}=x\times\frac{x}{p}=\frac{x^2}{p}=q.$$

Whence, $x=\sqrt{pq}$; $\frac{p}{x}=\frac{p}{\sqrt{pq}}=\sqrt{\frac{p}{q}}$.

(11) Let $x=$ one of the numbers; then, its square is x^2, and the square of the other is $370-x^2$.
Therefore, $x^2-(370-x^2)=208$.
Whence, $x=17$, and $370-x^2=370-289=81$.
Therefore, the other $=\sqrt{81}=9$.

(12) Let $x=$ one of the numbers; then, its square $=x^2$, and the square of the other is $c-x^2$;
Therefore, $x^2-(c-x^2)=d$.

$$2x^2=c+d,$$
$$4x^2=2(c+d),$$
$$2x=\sqrt{2(c+d)},$$
$$x=\tfrac{1}{2}\sqrt{2(c+d)},$$
$$\sqrt{c-x^2}=\sqrt{c-\tfrac{1}{2}(c+d)}=\sqrt{\tfrac{1}{2}(c-d)}=\tfrac{1}{2}\sqrt{2(c-d)}.$$

(13) Let $x=$ the sum; then, $\frac{5x}{100}=$ interest for 1 year, and $\frac{1}{4}$ of $\frac{5x}{100}=\frac{5x}{400}=$ interest for 3 months, or $\frac{1}{4}$ of a year.

Therefore, $x\times\frac{5x}{400}=720$, or $\frac{5x^2}{400}=720$;

$$5x^2=720\times400,$$
$$x^2=144\times400,$$
$$x=12\times20=240.$$

(14) Let $x=$ the 1st; then, $\frac{a}{x}=$ the 2d, and $\frac{b}{x}=$ the 3d;

Therofore, $\frac{a^2}{x^2}+\frac{b^2}{x^2}=c$; whence, $x=\sqrt{\left(\frac{a^2+b^2}{c}\right)}$

$a\div\sqrt{\left(\frac{a^2+b^2}{c}\right)}=a\sqrt{\left(\frac{c}{a^2+b^2}\right)}$; and $b\div\sqrt{\left(\frac{a^2+b^2}{c}\right)}$
$=b\sqrt{\left(\frac{c}{a^2+b^2}\right)}$.

(17) Let $x=$ number of drawers; then, $x\times x=x^2$ the number of divisions, and $x^2\times4x=4x^3=5324$.
Whence, $x^3=1331$, and $x=11$.

(18) The solution of this question involves a knowledge of two elementary principles of Natural Philosophy, with which the student should be rendered familiar by simple illustrations.

1st. *In uniform motion, the space divided by the time is equal to the velocity or rate of moving.*

2d. *In uniform motion, the space divided by the velocity is equal to the time.*

Thus, if a man travels 80 miles in 4 days, his rate of traveling (velocity) is 20 miles per day; or, if a man travels 100 miles at the rate of 20 miles a day, the time of traveling is 5 days.

Let $x=$ the distance B traveled; then,
$x+18=$ " A "
Then, since the distance traveled, divided by the number of days, gives the number of miles traveled in one day, or the rate of traveling, we have

$\frac{x}{15\frac{3}{4}}$, or $\frac{4x}{63}=$ A's rate of traveling, and $\frac{x+18}{28}=$ B's.

But the distance traveled, divided by the rate of traveling, gives the time; therefore,

$$(x+18)\div\frac{4x}{63}=\frac{63(x+18)}{4x}=\text{time A traveled, and}$$

$$x\div\frac{x+18}{28}=\frac{28x}{x+18}=\text{" B "}$$

But since they both traveled the same time, we have

$$\frac{63(x+18)}{4x}=\frac{28x}{x+18}.$$

Divide each side by 7, to reduce to lower terms,

$$\frac{9(x+18)}{4x}=\frac{4x}{x+18}.$$

Multiplying by $4x$ and $x+18$, and indicating the operations, we have $9(x+18)^2=16x^2$;
Extracting the square root of both members, $3(x+18)=4x$.
Whence, $x=54$, and $x+18=72$; and $54+72=126$, the required distance.

(19) The solution of this question involves principles analagous to the preceding.

Let $x=$ the number of days; then, $x-4=$ days A worked, and $x-7=$days B worked.

Also, $\frac{75}{x-4}=$ A's daily wages, and $\frac{48}{x-7}=$ B's.

If B had played only 4 days, he would have worked $x-4$

days, and received $\left(\frac{48}{x-7}\right)(x-4)$ shillings.

If A had played 7 days, he would have worked $x-7$ days, and received $\left(\frac{75}{x-4}\right)(x-7)$ shillings. But by the question, each would have received the same sum; therefore, $\left(\frac{75}{x-4}\right)(x-7)=\left(\frac{48}{x-7}\right)(x-4)$.

Multiplying each side by $x-4$ and $x-7$, to clear the equation of fractions, and indicating the multiplication. we have $75(x-7)^2=48(x-4)^2$.

Dividing by 3 to reduce it to lower terms,

$25(x-7)^2=16(x-4)^2$.

Extracting the square root of both members,

$5(x-7)=4(x-4)$; whence, $x=19$.

(20) First Solution.—Let $\frac{1}{x}=$ the part of the wine drawn each time; then, $\frac{1}{x}$ of 1 (the whole, is $\frac{1}{x}=$ the part drawn at the 1st draught, and $1-\frac{1}{x}=\frac{x-1}{x}=$ the part remaining after the 1st draught.

$$\frac{x-1}{x}-\frac{1}{x}\text{ of }\frac{x-1}{x}=\frac{x(x-1)}{x^2}-\frac{(x-1)}{x^2}=\frac{(x-1)(x-1)}{x^2}$$

$$=\frac{(x-1)^2}{x^2}=\text{ part left after }2^d\text{ draught.}$$

$$\frac{(x-1)^2}{x^2}-\frac{1}{x}\text{ of }\frac{(x-1)^2}{x^2}=\frac{x(x-1)^2}{x^3}-\frac{(x-1)^2}{x^3}=$$

$$\frac{(x-1)(x-1)^2}{x^3}=\frac{(x-1)^3}{x^3}=\text{ part left after }3^d\text{ draught.}$$

$$\frac{(x-1)^3}{x^3}-\frac{1}{x}\text{ of }\frac{(x-1)^3}{x^3}=\frac{x(x-1)^3}{x^4}-\frac{(x-1)^3}{x^4}=$$

$$\frac{(x-1)(x-1)^3}{x^4}=\frac{(x-1)^4}{x^4}=\text{ part left after }4^{th}\text{ draught.}$$

But by the question there were 81 gal. of wine left after the 4th draught, or $\frac{81}{256}$ of the quantity at the beginning;

Therefore, $\frac{(x-1)^4}{x^4}=\frac{81}{256}$,

$\frac{x-1}{x}=\frac{3}{4}$, by extracting the 4th root.

Whence, $4x-4=3x$, or $x=4$, and $\frac{1}{x}=\frac{1}{4}$, the part of the wine drawn at each draught.

$\frac{1}{4}$ of $256=64$ gallons, drawn at 1st draught;
$256-64=192$, and $\frac{1}{4}$ of $192=48$ gallons, at 2d draught;
$192-48=144$, and $\frac{1}{4}$ of $144=36$ gallons, at 3d draught;
$144-36=108$, and $\frac{1}{4}$ of $108=27$ gallons, at 4th draught.

Second Solution.—Let $x=$ the number of gallons of wine drawn at 1st draught, and let $256=a$, for the sake of simplicity.

Then, $\frac{x}{a}=$the part of the whole wine drawn at 1st draught,

and $1-\frac{x}{a}=\frac{a-x}{a}=$ part left.

$\frac{x}{a}$ of $\frac{a-x}{a}=\frac{x(a-x)}{a^2}=$ part drawn at 2d draught,

and $\frac{a-x}{a}-\frac{x(a-x)}{a^2}=\frac{a(a-x)-x(a-x)}{a^2}=\frac{(a-x)(a-x)}{a^2}$

$=\frac{(a-x)^2}{a^2}=$ part left after 2d draught.

By proceeding as in the previous solution, we find

$\frac{(a-x)^4}{a^4}=$ part of the whole wine left after the 4th draught.

$\therefore\ \frac{(a-x)^4}{a^4}=\frac{81}{256}$;

$\frac{a-x}{a}=\frac{3}{4}$, whence, $x=\frac{1}{4}a=64$, from which the other draughts are easily found.

Article 231.

(23) Multiplying by x and transposing, we have

$x^2-\frac{4}{\sqrt{3}}x=-1$;

$x^2-\frac{4}{\sqrt{3}}x+\frac{4}{3}=-1+\frac{4}{3}=\frac{1}{3}$, by completing the square;

$x-\frac{2}{\sqrt{3}}=\pm\frac{1}{\sqrt{3}}$;

$x=\frac{2}{\sqrt{3}}\pm\frac{1}{\sqrt{3}}=\frac{3}{\sqrt{3}}=\sqrt{3}$, or $\frac{1}{\sqrt{3}}=\frac{1}{3}\sqrt{3}$.

(24) Multiplying both terms of the fractions in the left member by x, we have

$\frac{x^2+1}{x^2-1}+\frac{x+1}{x-1}=\frac{13}{4}$; multiplying both terms again by x^2-1, $x^2+1+x^2+2x+1=\frac{13}{4}x^2-\frac{13}{4}$; transposing and reducing, $x^2-\frac{8}{5}x=\frac{21}{5}$; whence, $x=3$, or $-\frac{7}{5}$.

(26) Transposing and dividing by c, we have

$$x^2-\frac{2a}{c}x=-\frac{a^2-b^2}{c^2}; \text{ completing the square,}$$

$$x^2-\frac{2a}{c}x+\frac{a^2}{c^2}=\frac{a^2}{c^2}-\frac{a^2-b^2}{c^2}=\frac{b^2}{c^2}; \text{ whence,}$$

$$x-\frac{a}{c}=\pm\frac{b}{c}; \text{ or } x=\frac{a\pm b}{c}.$$

(27) Transposing ab and completing the square, we have

$$x^2-(a+b)x+\frac{(a+b)^2}{4}=-ab+\frac{(a+b)^2}{4}=\frac{(a-b)^2}{4}.$$

Whence, $x=\frac{a+b}{2}\pm\frac{a-b}{2}=a$ or b.

(28) Dividing by $a-b$, transposing and completing the square, we have $x^2-\frac{a+b}{a-b}x+\frac{(a+b)^2}{4(a-b)^2}=\frac{a^2-6ab+9b^2}{4(a-b)^2}$

Whence, $x=\frac{(a+b)}{2(a-b)}\pm\frac{a-3b}{2(a-b)}=1$, or $\frac{2b}{a-b}$.

(29) Transposing np, dividing by mq and completing the square we have $x^2-\frac{mn-pq}{mq}x+\frac{(mn-pq)^2}{4m^2q^2}=\frac{(mn+pq)^2}{4m^2q^2}$.

Whence, $x=\frac{mn-pq}{2mq}\pm\frac{mn+pq}{2mq}=\frac{n}{q}$, or $-\frac{p}{m}$.

(30) First, $\frac{1}{(ab^2)^{-\frac{1}{2}}+(a^2b)^{-\frac{1}{2}}}=\frac{1}{\frac{1}{(ab^2)^{\frac{1}{2}}}+\frac{1}{(a^2b)^{\frac{1}{2}}}}=\frac{1}{\frac{1}{a^{\frac{1}{2}}b}+\frac{1}{ab^{\frac{1}{2}}}}$;

multiplying both terms of this fraction by ab it becomes $\frac{ab}{a^{\frac{1}{2}}+b^{\frac{1}{2}}}$; the equation then becomes

$$\frac{x^2}{a^{\frac{1}{2}}+b^{\frac{1}{2}}}-(a^{\frac{1}{2}}-b^{\frac{1}{2}})x=\frac{ab}{a^{\frac{1}{2}}+b^{\frac{1}{2}}}.$$

Multiplying both members of this equation by $a^{\frac{1}{2}}+b^{\frac{1}{2}}$, it becomes $x^2-(a-b)x=ab$; whence, $x=a$, or $-b$.

(31) Dividing both sides by $-ac$, transposing, and completing the square, we have

$$x^2-\frac{ad-bc}{ac}x+\frac{(ad-bc)^2}{4a^2c^2}=\frac{(ad+bc)^2}{4a^2c^2}.$$

Whence, $x=\dfrac{ad-bc}{2ac}\pm\dfrac{ad+bc}{2ac}=\dfrac{d}{c}$, or $-\dfrac{b}{a}$.

(32) Square both members, and then multiply both sides by $x+12$.

(33) Multiplying both members first by $4+\sqrt{x}$, and then by $\sqrt{x}$, we have

$\sqrt{4x^2}+2\sqrt{x}=16-x$; or, since $\sqrt{4x^2}=2x$,

$2\sqrt{x}=16-3x$,

$4x=256-96x+9x^2$; whence, $x=4$, or $\frac{64}{9}$.

The first value verifies the equation when $\sqrt{x}$ is taken *plus*, and the second when it is taken *minus*.

(34) Dividing each side by the square root of x, and observing that $\sqrt{x^2}=x$, we have $x-2=\sqrt{x}$, or

$x^2-4x+4=x$, by squaring.

Whence, $x^2-5x=-4$, and $x=4$ or 1.

The first value verifies the equation when $\sqrt{x}$ is taken positively, and the second when it it is taken negatively.

(35) Squaring both sides we have

$x+a+x+b-2\sqrt{[x^2+(a+b)x+ab]}=2x$;

omitting $2x$ on each side, transposing $a+b$ and squaring again, we have $4x^2+4(a+b)x+4ab=(a+b)^2$; from which by transposing and reducing, we find

$$x^2+(a+b)x=\frac{(a-b)^2}{4}.$$

Whence, $x^2+(a+b)x+\dfrac{(a+b)^2}{4}=\dfrac{(a+b)^2+(a-b)^2}{4}$

$=\dfrac{2a^2+2b^2}{4}$; $x=-\dfrac{a+b}{2}\pm\dfrac{1}{2}\sqrt{2a^2+2b^2}$.

(36) Multiplying both sides by $\sqrt{a+x}$, we have

$a+x+\sqrt{a^2-x^2}=\dfrac{12a}{5}$;

$$\sqrt{a^2-x^2}=\frac{7a}{5}-x, \text{ by transposing;}$$

$$a^2-x^2=\frac{49a^2}{25}-\frac{14a}{5}x+x^2, \text{ by squaring;}$$

$$x^2-\frac{7a}{5}x=-\frac{12a^2}{25}, \text{ by reducing; whence, } x=\frac{4a}{5}, \text{ or } \frac{3a}{5}$$

PROBLEMS PRODUCING AFFECTED QUADRATIC EQUATIONS.

Article 233.

(5) Let $x=$ one of the numbers; then, $20-x=$ the other and $x(20-x)=36$.
Whence, $x=2$ or 18; therefore, $20-x=18$ or 2.

Or, let $10+x=$ greater, and $10-x=$ less; then, $100-x^2=36$, from which $x=8$, and the numbers are 18 and 2.

In a similar manner, Probs. 6, 8, 9, 12, 20, etc., may be solved, especially when the sum of the numbers is even.

(6) Let $x=$ one part; then, $15-x=$ the other, and
$x(15-x) : x^2+(15-x)^2 :: 2 : 5$;
$\therefore\ 4x^2-60x+450=75x-5x^2$;
reducing $x^2-15x=-50$.
Whence, $x=10$ or 5, and $15-x=5$ or 10.

(7) Let $x=$ the number; then, $x(10-x)=21$.
Whence, $x=7$ or 3.

(8) Let $x=$ the less part; then, $24-x=$ the greater, and $x(24-x)=35(24-x-x)$; reducing, $x^2-94x=-840$.
Whence, $x=10$ or 84, the first of which is evidently only admissible; therefore, the parts are 10 and $24-10=14$.

(9) Denoting the square roots of the parts by x, and $26-x$, we have $x^2+(26-x)^2=346$;
reducing $x^2-26x=-165$.
Whence, $x=15$ or 11, and $26-x=11$ or 15.

(10) Let $x=$ the square root of the number; then, $x^2=$ the number, and $x^2+x=132$.
Whence, $x=11$ or -12, and $x^2=121$ or 144.

The last number is the answer to the question, "What number *diminished* by its square root gives 132?"

(11) Let $x =$ the square root of the number; then, $x^2 =$ the number, and $x^2 - x = 48\frac{3}{4}$.
Whence, $x = 7\frac{1}{2}$ or $-6\frac{1}{2}$, and $x^2 = 56\frac{1}{4}$ or $42\frac{1}{4}$.

The last number is the answer to the question, "What number *added* to its square root gives $48\frac{3}{4}$?"

(12) Let $x =$ one of the numbers; then, $41 - x =$ the other, and $x^2 + (41 - x)^2 = 901$.
Whence, $x = 15$ or 26, and $41 - x = 26$ or 15.

(13) Let $x =$ the less number; then, $x + 8 =$ the greater, and $x^2 + (x + 8)^2 = 544$.
Whence, $x = 12$ or -20, and $x + 8 = 20$ or -12;
hence, the two numbers are 12 and 20.
Or, let $x + 4 =$ greater and $x - 4 =$ less. Sum of their squares, $2x^2 + 32 = 544$ and $x = 16$. Whence, $x + 4 = 20$ and $x - 4 = 12$.

(14) Let $x =$ the first cost; then, $x =$ per cent. of gain, and

$$x \times \frac{x}{100} = \frac{x^2}{100} = \text{gain.} \quad \therefore\ x + \frac{x^2}{100} = 2400.$$

Whence, $x = 20$.

(15) Let $x =$ the number of miles B traveled per hour, and $x + \frac{1}{4} =$ the number of miles A traveled per hour; then, $\frac{39}{x + \frac{1}{4}}$ and $\frac{39}{x} =$ the hours respectively which A and B traveled.

$$\therefore\ \frac{39}{x + \frac{1}{4}} + 1 = \frac{39}{x}.$$

Whence, $x = 3$, and $x + \frac{1}{4} = 3\frac{1}{4}$.

(16) Let $x =$ number to whom B gave, and $x + 40 =$ number to whom A gave; then,

$\frac{1200}{x + 40} =$ what A gave to each, and

$\frac{1200}{x} =$ " B " " ;

$$\therefore\ \frac{1200}{x + 40} + 5 = \frac{1200}{x};$$

whence, $x = 80$, and $x + 40 = 120$

(17) Let $x =$ number of miles B traveled per day; then
$x + 8 =$ " " A " " , and
$\frac{1}{2}x =$ number of days each traveled;

$$\therefore\ x \times \tfrac{1}{2}x + (x + 8)\tfrac{1}{2}x = 320, \text{ or } x^2 + 4x = 320$$

Whence, $x = 16$, and $x + 8 = 24$.

(18) Let $x=$ the distance in miles from C to D; then,

$\frac{x}{19}=$ number of miles B traveled per day; also,

$\frac{x}{19}=$ number of days B traveled; then,

$32+7\times\frac{x}{19}=$ whole number of miles A traveled, and

$\frac{x}{19}\times\frac{x}{19}=\frac{x^2}{361}=$ number of miles B traveled.

$\therefore\ 32+\frac{7x}{19}+\frac{x^2}{361}=x.$

Clearing of fractions and transposing,

$x^2-228x=-11552$; whence, $x=76$, or 152.

(19) Let $x=$ the number bought; then,

$\frac{240}{x}=$ number of \$ each cost, and, since $240+59=299$,

$\frac{299}{x-3}=$ " " " sold for;

$\therefore\ \frac{299}{x-3}-\frac{240}{x}=8$; reducing, $8x^2-83x=720$.

Whence, $x=16$.

(20) Let $x=$one of the numbers; then, $100-x=$ the other; then, $x(100-x)=x^2-(100-x)^2$; reducing,

$100x-x^2=-10000+200x$, or

$x^2+100x=10000$.

Whence, $x=61.803+$, and $100-x=38.197$, nearly.

Or, by subtracting x^2 from the square of $100-x$, and reducing, we have the equation $x^2-300x=-10000$.

Whence, $x=38.197$ nearly.

(21) Since each received back \$450, they both received \$900, and the whole gain was \$900 — \$500=\$400.

Let $x=$ A's stock; then, $500-x=$ B's stock.

x \$ for 5 months is the same as $5x$ \$ for 1 month.

$(500-x)$ \$ for 2 months, is the same as $2(500-x)=(1000-2x)$ \$ for 1 month.

Hence, the gain, \$400, is to be divided into two parts having the same ratio to each other as $5x$ and $1000-2x$. But $5x+(1000-2x)=3x+1000$; therefore, the parts of the gain are $\frac{5x}{3x+1000}$ and

$\frac{1000-2x}{3x+1000}$, the sum of which is 1 the whole gain.

$$\therefore \text{ A's gain is } \frac{5x}{3x+1000} \text{ of } 400 = \frac{2000x}{3x+1000};$$

$$\text{B's gain is } \frac{1000-2x}{3x+1000} \text{ of } 400 = \frac{400000-800x}{3x+1000}.$$

But A's gain $=450-x$; $\therefore \frac{2000x}{3x+1000}=450-x$.

Whence, $x=200$, A's stock, and $500-x=300$, B's stock

(22) Let $x=$ first part of 11; then, $11-x=$ the second; also, $\frac{45}{x}=$ first part of 17, and $17-\frac{45}{x}=$ the second;

then, $(11-x)\left(17-\frac{45}{x}\right)=48$, or $(11-x)(17x-45)=48x$.

Whence, $x=5$, or $\frac{99}{17}$,

$11-x=6$, or $\frac{88}{17}$, and $\frac{45}{x}=9$, or $\frac{85}{11}$; $\therefore 17-\frac{45}{x}=8$, or $\frac{102}{11}$.

Hence, the numbers are 5, 6, and 9, 8, or, $\frac{99}{17}$, $\frac{88}{17}$, and $\frac{85}{11}$, $\frac{102}{11}$, either of which entirely satisfies the conditions.

(23) Let $3x=$ the first part of 21; then, $x=$ the first part of 30, and $(21-3x)^2+(30-x)^2=585$;
developing and reducing $x^2-\frac{93}{5}x=-\frac{378}{5}$.
Whence, $x=6$, or $12\frac{3}{5}$, and $3x=18$, or $37\frac{4}{5}$.

Since the second value of x gives for $3x$ a number greater than 21, it is inadmissible.

The first value of x gives for the parts of 21, 18 and $21-18=3$, and for the parts of 30, 6 and $30-6=24$.

(24) Let $x=$ the first part of 19; then, $19-x=$ the second part; and since the difference of the squares of the first parts of each is 72, therefore, $\sqrt{x^2+72}$ must represent the first part of 29, and $29-\sqrt{x^2+72}$ the second part.

$$\therefore (29-\sqrt{x^2+72})^2-(19-x)^2=180;$$

developing and reducing, $29\sqrt{x^2+72}=19x+186$;
squaring each side and reducing, $40x^2-589x=-2163$.
Whence, $x=7$ or $\frac{309}{40}$; this gives $\sqrt{x^2+72}=11$, or $\frac{459}{40}$.
$19-x=12$, or $\frac{451}{40}$, $29-\sqrt{x^2+72}=18$, or $\frac{701}{40}$.
Whence, the parts are 7, 12, and 11, 18,
or $\frac{309}{40}$, $\frac{451}{40}$, and $\frac{459}{40}$, $\frac{701}{40}$.

Article 239a.

(1) In order that the negative answer,—9, when taken positively, shall be correct, the question should read; Required a number such, that twice its square, *diminished* by 8 times the number itself, shall be 90.

(2) From this question, we see that the negative values satisfy the question equally well with the positive, the only difference being that in one case we subtract +3 from +7, and in the other, —7 from —3.

(3) Let $x=$ cost of watch; then, $x=$ per cent. of loss, and

$x\times\frac{x}{100}=\frac{x^2}{100}=$ actual loss.

$\therefore\ x-\frac{x^2}{100}=16$, or $x^2-100x=-1600$.

Whence, $x=50\pm30=20$, or 80, either of which fully satisfies the conditions. Thus,

$20-\frac{20}{100}$ of $20=20-\ 4=16$;

$80-\frac{80}{100}$ of $80=80-64=16$.

(4) These values of x show that no *positive* number can be found which will satisfy the question. But either of the numbers, 1 and 5, will satisfy the question, if changed so as to read thus:

Required a number such, that 6 times the number, diminished by the square of the number, and the result subtracted from 7, the remainder shall be 2.

(5) There is evidently but one solution, because if 4 is one of the numbers, 10—4=6 is the other; or, if 6 is one of the numbers, 10—6=4 is the other.

(6) These results show that the question is impossible in an arithmetical sense. This we also learn from Art. 236, since the greatest product that can be formed by dividing 10 into two parts is 25.

(7) Calling x the distance from the earth, $a=240000$, $b=80$, and $c=1$, we have by the solution to the problem of the lights, $x=\frac{a\sqrt{b}}{\sqrt{b}+\sqrt{c}}$, or $x=\frac{a\sqrt{b}}{\sqrt{b}-\sqrt{c}}$.

To prepare these formulæ for numerical calculation, multiply both terms of the first by $\sqrt{b}-\sqrt{c}$, and of the second by $\sqrt{b}+\sqrt{c}$; this gives

$$x=\frac{a(b-\sqrt{bc})}{b-c}=\frac{240000(80-\sqrt{80})}{79}=215865.5+$$

$$\text{or } x=\frac{a(b+\sqrt{bc})}{b-c}=\frac{240000(80+\sqrt{80})}{79}=270210.4+$$

$a-x=240000-215865.5=24134.5$,

and $x-a=270210.4-240000=30210.4$.

BINOMIAL SURDS.

Article 241.

(1)

$$x^2+y^2=15.$$

$$2xy=6\sqrt{6}.$$

$$x^2+2xy+y^2=15+6\sqrt{6}.$$

$$x^2-2xy+y^2=15-6\sqrt{6}.$$

$$x+y=\sqrt{15+6\sqrt{6}}.$$

$$x-y=\sqrt{15-6\sqrt{6}}.$$

$$x^2-y^2=\sqrt{225-216}=\sqrt{9}=\pm3.$$

$2x^2=18$, whence, $x^2=9$ and $x=3$.

$2y^2=12$, whence, $y^2=6$ and $y=\sqrt{6}$.

$$\therefore\ \sqrt{15+6\sqrt{6}}=3+\sqrt{6}.$$

(2) In this example, put $x^2+y^2=34$, and $2xy=24\sqrt{2}$, and proceed as in Ex. 1. The next may be easily solved in a similar manner.

Theorem II.

(3) $A=11$, $\sqrt{B}=6\sqrt{2}=\sqrt{72}$; $C=\sqrt{121-72}=\sqrt{49}=7$;

$$\therefore\ \sqrt{A+\sqrt{B}}=\sqrt{\frac{11+7}{2}}+\sqrt{\frac{11-7}{2}}=3+\sqrt{2}.$$

(4) $A=3$, $\sqrt{B}=2\sqrt{2}=\sqrt{8}$; $C=\sqrt{9-8}=1$;

$$\therefore \sqrt{A \pm \sqrt{B}} = \sqrt{\frac{3+1}{2}} \pm \sqrt{\frac{3-1}{2}} = \sqrt{2} \pm 1.$$

(5) $A=17$, $\sqrt{B}=2\sqrt{60}=\sqrt{240}$; $C=\sqrt{289-240}=7$;

$$\therefore \sqrt{A+\sqrt{B}} = \sqrt{\frac{17+7}{2}} + \sqrt{\frac{17-7}{2}} = 2\sqrt{3}+\sqrt{5}.$$

(6) $A=x$, $\sqrt{B}=2\sqrt{x-1}=\sqrt{4x-4}$; $C=\sqrt{x^2-4x+4}=x-2$;

$$\therefore \sqrt{A-\sqrt{B}} = \sqrt{\frac{x+x-2}{2}} - \sqrt{\frac{x-x+2}{2}} = \sqrt{x-1}-1.$$

(7) $A=0$, $\sqrt{B}=2a\sqrt{-1}=\sqrt{-4a^2}$; $C=\sqrt{4a^2}=2a$;

$$\therefore \sqrt{A+\sqrt{B}} = \sqrt{\frac{0+2a}{2}} + \sqrt{\frac{0-2a}{2}} = \sqrt{a}+\sqrt{-a} =$$

$\sqrt{a}(1+\sqrt{-1})$.

(8) $A=x+y+z$, $\sqrt{B}=2\sqrt{xz+yz}=\sqrt{4xz+4yz}$.

$$C=\sqrt{A^2-B}=\sqrt{(x^2+y^2+z^2+2xy+2xz+2yz-4xz-4yz)}$$

$$=\sqrt{(x^2+y^2+z^2+2xy-2xz-2yz)}=x+y-z.$$

$$\therefore \sqrt{A+\sqrt{B}} = \sqrt{\frac{x+y+z+x+y-z}{2}} + \sqrt{\frac{x+y+z-(x+y-z)}{2}}$$

$$=\sqrt{x+y}+\sqrt{z}.$$

(9) Proceeding as before, we find $\sqrt{28+10\sqrt{3}}=5+\sqrt{3}$, and $\sqrt{67-16\sqrt{3}}=8-\sqrt{3}$, and the sum of $5+\sqrt{3}$ and $8-\sqrt{3}$ is 13, *Ans.*

TRINOMIAL EQUATIONS.

Article 242.

(5) $x^4-25x^2=-144$,

$x^4-25x^2+\frac{625}{4}=+\frac{625}{4}-144=\frac{49}{4}$;

$x^2-\frac{25}{2}=\pm\frac{7}{2}$,

$x^2=\frac{25}{2}\pm\frac{7}{2}=16$ or 9.

$x=\pm 4$ or ± 3.

(6) $5x^4+7x^2=6732$; divide by 5 and complete the square

$x^4+\frac{7}{5}x^2+\frac{49}{100}=\frac{49}{100}+\frac{6732}{5}=\frac{134689}{100}$,

$x^2+\frac{7}{10}=\pm\frac{367}{10}$,

$x^2=-\frac{7}{10}\pm\frac{367}{10}=36$, or $-\frac{374}{10}=-\frac{187}{5}$;

$$x=\pm 6, \text{ or } \pm\sqrt{-\frac{187}{5}}=\pm\sqrt{\frac{-935}{25}}=\pm\frac{1}{5}\sqrt{-935}.$$

The last answer in the book is $\pm\frac{1}{10}\sqrt{-3740}$, which is the same as $\pm\frac{1}{5}\sqrt{-935}$, since $\sqrt{-3740}=\sqrt{-935\times 4}=2\sqrt{-935}$.

(7) $9x^6-11x^3=488$, divide by 9 and complete the square,

$x^6-\frac{11}{9}x^3+\frac{121}{324}=\frac{121}{324}+\frac{488}{9}=\frac{17689}{324}$; $x^3-\frac{11}{8}=\pm\frac{133}{18}$,

$x^3=\frac{11}{18}\pm\frac{133}{18}=8$ or $-\frac{183}{27}$, $x^3=8$ or $-\frac{183}{27}$,

$x=\pm 2$, or $\pm\sqrt[3]{-\frac{1}{27}\times 183}=\pm\frac{1}{3}\sqrt[3]{-183}$ or $\pm\frac{1}{3}\sqrt[3]{183}$.

(8) Completing the square by adding $\frac{1}{4}$ to each member, we have

$x^3-x^{\frac{3}{2}}+\frac{1}{4}=\frac{62001}{4}$; whence, $x^{\frac{3}{2}}-\frac{1}{2}=\pm\frac{249}{2}$;

$x^{\frac{3}{2}}=\frac{1}{2}\pm\frac{249}{2}=125$ or -124;

$x^3=(125)^2=(5\times 5\times 5)^2$ or $(-124)^2$;

$x=5^2=25$ or $(-124)^{\frac{2}{3}}$.

(9) Arranging the terms and completing the square, by adding $\frac{1}{4}$ to each member, we have

$x^{\frac{5}{3}}+x^{\frac{5}{6}}+\frac{1}{4}=\frac{4225}{4}$; whence, $x^{\frac{5}{6}}+\frac{1}{2}=\pm\frac{65}{2}$,

$x^{\frac{5}{6}}=-\frac{1}{2}\pm\frac{65}{2}=32$ or -33;

$x^{\frac{1}{6}}=2$ or $(-33)^{\frac{1}{5}}$,

$x=64$ or $(-33)^{\frac{6}{5}}$.

(10) Let $\sqrt{x+5}=y$; then, $x+5=y^2$, and the equation becomes by substitution and transposition, $y^2-y=6$.

Whence, $y=3$ or -2.

$\therefore\ \sqrt{x+5}=3$ or -2,

$x+5=9$ or 4,

$x=4$ or -1.

It will be advisable for the pupil to solve this and the five examples which follow, without the substitution of y; thus,

$x+5-\sqrt{x+5}=6.$

Completing square, $x+5-\sqrt{x+5}+\frac{1}{4}=6+\frac{1}{4}=\frac{25}{4}$,

$\sqrt{x+5}+\frac{1}{2}=\pm\frac{5}{2}$,

$\sqrt{x+5}=2$ or -3,

$x+5=4$ or 9,

$x=-1$ or 4.

(11) Add 3 to each side, let $\sqrt{x^2-3x+11}=y$; then, by substituting the value of y^2 and transposing, we have
$y^2-2y=3$.
Whence, $y=3$ or -1.
$\therefore\ \sqrt{x^2-3x+11}=9$ or 1.

From which, by squaring and solving the resulting equations, we readily find $x=2$ or 1, or $\frac{3}{2}\pm\frac{1}{2}\sqrt{-31}$.

(12) Add 18 to each member, let $\sqrt{x^2-7x+18}=y$;
then. $y^2+y=42$.
Whence, y, or $\sqrt{x^2-7x+18}=6$ or -7.
Squaring, $x^2-7x+18=36$ or 49.
Whence, $x=9$, -2, or $\frac{1}{2}(7\pm\sqrt{173})$.

(13) To render this equation of a quadratic form, the quantity in the parenthesis in the right member must be made the same as that in the parenthesis on the left. This may be done by adding -7 to the quantity in the vinculum, and its equal, $+7\times11=77$, without; the equation then becomes
$(x^2-9)^2=3+77+11(x^2-2-7)=80+11(x^2-9)$.
Putting y and y^2 to represent x^2-9, and $(x^2-9)^2$, we have
$y^2-11y=80$; whence, $y=16$, or -5.
$\therefore\ x^2-9=16$ or -5, and $x=\pm5$ or ±2.

(14) Transposing $\frac{8}{x}$ and putting $y=x+\frac{8}{x}$, we have
$y^2+y=42$; whence, $y=+6$ or -7.
$\therefore\ x+\frac{8}{x}=+6$ or -7,
and $x^2-6x=-8$, or $x^2+7x=-8$.
Whence, $x=4$ or 2, or $\frac{1}{2}(-7\pm\sqrt{17})$.

(15) This equation may be placed under the form

$$x^4\left(1+\frac{1}{3x}\right)^2-3x^2\left(1+\frac{1}{3x}\right)=70.$$

Putting $x^2\left(1+\frac{1}{3x}\right)=y$, we have $y^2-3y=70$;
whence, $y=10$ or -7.
$\therefore\ x^2\left(1+\frac{1}{3x}\right)=10$ or -7,
$x^2+\frac{1}{3}x=10$ or -7.
Whence, $x=3$ or $-3\frac{1}{3}$, or $\frac{1}{6}(-1\pm\sqrt{-251})$.

(16) Multiplying both sides by $\sqrt{x}$, we have

$x\sqrt{6-x^2}=1+x^2$.

Squaring $x^2(6-x^2)=1+2x^2+x^4$.

Transposing and reducing, $x^4-2x^2=-\frac{1}{2}$.

Whence, $x=\pm\sqrt{(1\pm\frac{1}{2}\sqrt{2})}$.

Article 243.

(2) We find the square root is x^2-x, with the remainder $-3x^2+3x$; hence, the equation may be written thus,

$(x^2-x)^2-3(x^2-x)=108$.

Putting $x^2-x=y$, we find $y=12$ or -9.

$\therefore\ x^2-x=12$ or -9.

Or, the same result may be attained by completing the square, etc., without the substitution of y.

Whence, $x=4$ or -3, or $\frac{1}{2}(1\pm\sqrt{-35})$.

(3) The square root of the left member is x^2-x, with the remainder $-x^2+x$; hence, the equation may be written thus, $(x^2-x)^2-(x^2-x)=30$.

Whence, $x=3$ or -2, or $\frac{1}{2}(1\pm\sqrt{-19})$.

(4) Multiplying both sides by x, we then find the square root of the left member is x^2-3x with the remainder $+2x^2-6x$; hence, the equation may be written thus,

$(x^2-3x)^2+2(x^2-3x)=0$.

Whence, $x=0$, or 3, or 2, or 1.

The value, $x=0$, does not satisfy the given equation, but is a root of the equation $x(x^3-6x^2+11x-6)=0$, and was introduced by multiplying the given equation by x.

(5) The square root of the left member is x^2-3x with the remainder $-4x^2+12x$; hence, the equation may be written thus, $(x^2-3x)^2-4(x^2-3x)=60$.

Whence, $x=5$, -2, or $\frac{1}{2}(3\pm\sqrt{-15})$.

(6) The square root of the left member is x^2-4x, with the remainder $-6x^2+24x$; hence, the equation may be written $(x^2-4x)^2-6(x^2-4x)=-5$.

Whence, $x=5$, or -1, or $2\pm\sqrt{5}$.

(7) Multiplying both members by 4, to clear the equation of fractions and render the first term a perfect square; then

transposing $16x^3$, we find the square root of the left member is $4x^2-2x$, with the remainder $-4x^2+2x$; hence, the equation may be written $(4x^2-2x)^2-(4x^2-2x)=132$. Whence, $x=2$, $-\frac{3}{2}$, or $\frac{1}{4}(1\pm\sqrt{-43})$.

(8) Observe that $\frac{12+\frac{1}{2}x}{3x}=\frac{4}{x}+\frac{1}{6}$; then, omitting $\frac{1}{6}$ on each side, and multiplying both sides of the equation by $14x^3$, clear it of fractions; after transposing, we have $x^4-14x^3+56x^2-49x=60$.

The square root of the left member is x^2-7x, with the remainder $7x^2-49x$; hence, the equation may be written

$(x^2-7x)^2+7(x^2-7x)=60$.

$\therefore\ x^2-7x=5$ or -12.

Whence, $x=4$, or 3, or $\frac{1}{2}(7\pm\sqrt{69})$.

PURE EQUATIONS CONTAINING TWO OR MORE UNKNOWN QUANTITIES.

Article 245.

NOTE.—Instead of indicating each step of the solution of the examples in this article, it has only been deemed necessary in most cases to point out the particular step on which the solution depends.

(5) Subtract the square of the first equation from the second, then add the remainder to the second, and extract the square root, which will give $x+y$.

(6) Add twice the second equation to the first, and extract the square root; also, subtract twice the second equation from the first, and extract the square root.

(7) Subtract the second equation from the square of the first; then subtract the remainder from the second equation, and extract the square root.

(8) Divide the first equation by the second, this will give $x+y$.

(9) From the cube of the first equation subtract the second, divide the remainder by 3, and we have $xy(x+y)=308$; divide by $x+y=11$, and we have $xy=28$. Having $x+y$ and xy, we readily find x and y, as in Form 1, Art. 245.

Or, thus, Divide the second equation by the first, subtract the quotient from the square of the first, and divide by 3, which will give xy.

(10) From the first equation, by transposing and extracting the cube root of both members, we have $x=2y$; then, by substitution in the second, we readily find the value of y, and then x.

(11) Subtract the second equation from the first; add the remainder to the first and extract the square root, which will give $x+y=\pm 12$; then, divide the second equation by this, and we have $x-y=\pm 2$.

Or, after factoring the first equation, divide it by the second, and find the value of x, to be substituted in either equation.

(12) Divide the first equation by the second, this gives $x+y=8$; from the square of this, subtract the second equation, and divide by 3, this gives $xy=15$; subtract this from the second equation, and extract the square root, which will give $x-y=\pm 2$. Or, divide both members of the first equation by $x+y$, and equate the values.

(13) Subtract the first equation from the square of the second, this gives $xy=48$; subtract three times this equation from the first and extract the square root, this gives $x-y=\pm 8$.

(14) Divide the first equation by the second, transpose $3\frac{1}{2}xy$, and subtract the resulting equation from the square of the second, this gives $\frac{1}{2}xy=4$, or $xy=8$; then, by the method explained in Form 1, Art. 245, we readily find $x+y=\pm 6$.

(15) Dividing the first equation by the second, we find $x^2-xy+y^2=7$; subtracting this from the second equation, we have $2xy=6$, or $xy=3$; then, adding this to the second equation and extracting the square root, we find $x+y=\pm 4$; also, subtracting $xy=3$ from the equation $x^2-xy+y^2=7$, and extracting the square root, we find $x-y=\pm 2$.

(16) Let $x^{\frac{1}{2}}=P$ and $y^{\frac{1}{2}}=Q$, the equations then become

$P^2-Q^2=P+Q.$ (1)

$P^3-Q^3=37$ (2)

Dividing each side of (1) by $P+Q$, we have $P-Q=1$; then, dividing each side of (2) by $P-Q=1$, we have

$P^2+PQ+Q^2=37$, (3)

$P^2-2PQ+Q^2=1$, by squaring $P-Q=1$.

Subtracting and divining by 3, we find $PQ=12$; then, by adding this to (3) and extracting the square root, we find $P+Q=\pm 7$, but $P-Q=1$.

Whence, $P=4$ or -3, and $Q=3$ or -4.

$\therefore x=16$ or 9. and $y=9$ or 16.

(17) Let $x^{\frac{1}{4}}=P$ and $y^{\frac{1}{3}}=Q$; then, by substitution the equations become $P+Q=5$,

$P^2+Q^2=13$.

The values of P and Q found as in example 1, page 221 are $P=2$ or 3, and $Q=3$ or 2.

$\therefore x^{\frac{1}{4}}=2$ or 3, and $x=16$ or 81;

$y^{\frac{1}{3}}=3$ or 2, and $y=27$ or 8.

(18) Let $x^{\frac{1}{3}}=P$ and $y^{\frac{1}{3}}=Q$; then, by substitution the equations become $P+Q=5$,

$P^3+Q^3=35$.

The values of P and Q, found as in example 3, page 222, are $P=2$ or 3, $Q=3$ or 2.

$\therefore x^{\frac{1}{3}}=2$ or 3, and $x=8$ or 27;

$y^{\frac{1}{3}}=3$ or 2, and $y=27$ or 8.

(19) Let $x^{\frac{1}{2}}=P$ and $y^{\frac{1}{2}}=Q$; then, by substitution the equations become $P+Q=4$,

$P^3+Q^3=28$.

The values of P and Q, found as in the preceding example, are $P=3$ or 1, $Q=1$ or 3.

$\therefore x^{\frac{1}{2}}=3$ or 1, and $x=9$ or 1.

$y^{\frac{1}{2}}=1$ or 3, and $y=1$ or 9.

(20) Square both members of the first equation, and from the result subtract four times the cube of the second, and we have $x^6-2x^3y^3+y^6=112225$.

Extracting the sq. root $x^3-y^3=\pm 335$; but $x^3+y^3=351$.

Whence, by adding and subtracting, dividing by 2 and extracting the oube root, we have $x=7$ or 2, and $y=2$ or 7.

Or, find the value of x in the second and substitute in first.

(21) Raising both sides of (1) to the fourth power we have

$$x^4+4x^3y+6x^2y^2+4xy^3+y^4=256,$$

but $x^4 \qquad\qquad +y^4=82;$

$$\therefore\ 2x^4+4x^3y+6x^2y^2+4xy^3+2y^4=338;$$

or $x^4+2x^3y+3x^2y^2+2xy^3+ y^4=169.$

Extracting the sq. root $x^2+xy+y^2=13.$ (3)

Squaring eq. (1) $x^2+2xy+y^2=16.$

Subtracting, $xy=3$; hence, $3xy=9$, and subtracting this from (3), and extracting the square root of the resulting equation, we get $x-y=\pm 2$; from this, and $x+y=4$, we get $x=3$ or 1, and $y=1$ or 3.

Or, find value of x in first and substitute in second.

(22) Adding the three equations together, and dividing by 2, we have $xy+xz+yz=\frac{a+b+c}{2}$. (4)

Subtracting from this successively the three given equations, we have $yz=\frac{b+c-a}{2}$, (5)

$$xz=\frac{a+c-b}{2}, \qquad (6)$$

$$xy=\frac{a+b-c}{2}. \qquad (7)$$

Multiplying the three equations together, and extracting the sq. root,

$$xyz=\sqrt{\left\{\frac{(a+b-c)(a+c-b)(b+c-a)}{8}\right\}} \qquad (8)$$

Dividing eq. (8) by eqs. (5), (6), (7), respectively, we obtain the values of x, y, and z. Thus, to find x

$$\frac{xyz}{yz}=x=\frac{\sqrt{\left\{\frac{(a+b-c)(a+c-b)(b+c-a)}{8}\right\}}}{\frac{b+c-a}{2}}$$

$$=\sqrt{\left\{\frac{(a+b-c)(a+c-b)(b+c-a)}{8}\times\frac{4}{(b+c-a)^2}\right\}}$$

$$=\pm\sqrt{\frac{(a+b-c)(a+c-b)}{2(b+c-a)}}.$$

Article 250.

(3) Adding the two equations together, and dividing by 2, we find $x^2+x=240$.

Subtracting the second equation from the first, and dividing by 2, we find $y^2+y=90$.

(4) Multiplying the first eq. by 4, and subtracting the result from the second, and transposing, we find $y^2-18y=45$. Whence, $y=3$ or 15, and $x=14-4y=2$ or -46.

Or, substitute the value of x from eq. first in eq. second.

(5) From the first eq. $y=\dfrac{3x+14}{2}=1\frac{1}{2}x+7$, this substituted in the second, gives $3x^2+2(1\frac{1}{2}x-4)^2=14$.
Developing and reducing, we have $x^2-\frac{16}{5}x=-\frac{12}{5}$.
Whence, $x=2$ or $1\frac{1}{5}$, and $y=10$ or $8\frac{4}{5}$.

Or, substitute the value of x from eq. first in eq. second.

(6) Clearing the 2d eq. of fractions by multiplying by xy, and substituting the value of $x=y+2$, found from the 1st eq., and reducing, we have $y^2-\frac{7}{4}y=\frac{15}{4}$, and $y=3$ or $-1\frac{1}{4}$.

(7) Let $y=tx$; then, substituting this instead of y, finding the value of x^2 from the resulting equations, placing these values equal to each other, and reducing, we find $t=\pm1\frac{1}{2}$. Then, substituting this in the value of x^2, we find x, and thence y.

(8) Let $y=tx$; then, substituting this instead of y, finding the value of x^2 from the resulting equations, placing these values equal to each other, and reducing, we find $t=+1\frac{1}{2}$ or $-\frac{4}{5}$. Having this, the values of x and y are readily found by substitution.

(9) According to the suggestion on page 227, we find $xy=+8$ or -12. Having the values of $x+y$ and xy, we readily find x and y by the method explained in Form 1, Art. 245.

(10) Completing the square as in the last example, we find $\dfrac{x}{y}=+\dfrac{5}{3}$ or $-\dfrac{17}{3}$. From this eq. and $x-y=2$, we readily find x and y.

(11) From the first equation, $xy=+10$ or -18.

From the equations $xy=+10$, and $x+3y=11$, we find $x=5$ or 6, and $y=2$ or $\frac{5}{3}$.

From the equations $xy=-18$, and $x+3y=11$, we find $x=\frac{11}{2}\mp\frac{1}{2}\sqrt{337}$, and $y=\frac{11}{6}\pm\frac{1}{6}\sqrt{337}$.

(12) Let $\sqrt{x+y}=v$; then, from the 1st eq., we have $v^2+v=12$, from which $v=3$ or -4; hence, v^2, or $x+y=9$ or 16. Having the values of $x+y$ and x^2+y^2, we can find the values of x and y by the method explained in example 1st, Art. 245. The eqs. $x+y=9$, and $x^2+y^2=41$, give $x=5$ or 4, and $y=4$ or 5.

The equations $x+y=16$, and $x^2+y^2=41$, give

$$x=8\pm\tfrac{1}{2}\sqrt{-174}, \text{ and } y=8\mp\tfrac{1}{2}\sqrt{-174}.$$

(13) Adding twice the second equation to the first, we have $x^2+2xy+y^2+x+y=30$, or $(x+y)^2+(x+y)=30$. Whence, $x+y=+5$ or -6.

From these equations and the value of $xy=6$, we readily find the values of x and y.

(14) Transposing $2xy$ in the first equation, and then adding both equations together, we have

$x^2+2xy+y^2+4x+4y=117$, or $(x+y)^2+4(x+y)=117$.

Whence, $x+y=+9$ or -13, and $x=9-y$ or $-13-y$.

Substituting these values of x in the second of the given equations, we have $y^2+2y=35$, or $y^2+2y=57$.

From the 1st equation, we find $y=5$ or -7; whence, $x=4$ or 16.

From the 2d equation, we find $y=-1\pm\sqrt{58}$; whence, $x=-12\pm\sqrt{58}$.

(15) From the first equation, $xy(1+y)=12$, and from the 2d, $x(1+y^3)=18$. Dividing the 2d by the 1st, we find $\frac{1-y+y^2}{y}=\frac{3}{2}$, and from this equation, we readily find $y=2$ or $\frac{1}{2}$; whence, $x=2$ or 16.

(16) Adding twice the second equation to the first, we have $x^2+2xy+y^2+x+y=156$, or $(x+y)^2+(x+y)=156$.

Whence, $x+y=+12$ or -13.

By substituting the value of $x+y$ in the second equation, we find $xy=27$ or 52.

From the equations, $x+y=12$, and $xy=27$, we find $x=9$ or 3. and $y=3$ or 9.

From the equations, $x+y=-13$, and $xy=52$, we find

$$x=\tfrac{1}{2}(-13\pm\sqrt{-39}), \text{ and } y=\tfrac{1}{2}(-13\mp\sqrt{-39}).$$

(17) Let $\left(\frac{3x}{x+y}\right)^{\frac{1}{2}}=v$; then, $\left(\frac{x+y}{3x}\right)^{\frac{1}{2}}=\frac{1}{v}$, and $v+\frac{1}{v}=2$, or $v^2-2v=-1$; whence, $v=+1$.

$\frac{3x}{x+y}=1$; whence, $2x=y$.

Substituting the $2x$ instead of y in 2d eq., we have $2x^2-3x=54$.

Whence, $x=6$ or $-4\frac{1}{2}$; hence, $y=12$ or -9.

Or, square the 1st eq., transpose, and extract the root, and we find $3x-(x+y)=0$. From this and eq. 2d, we readily find x and y.

(18) The 1st eq. is $\frac{y}{(x+y)^{\frac{3}{2}}}+\frac{\sqrt{x+y}}{y}=\frac{17}{4\sqrt{x+y}}$.

Multiplying both members by $\sqrt{x+y}$, we have

$$\frac{y}{x+y}+\frac{x+y}{y}=\frac{17}{4}.$$

Let $\frac{y}{x+y}=v$; then, $v+\frac{1}{v}=\frac{17}{4}$.

Whence, v or $\frac{y}{x+y}=4$ or $\frac{1}{4}$.

From eqs. $\frac{y}{x+y}=4$ or $\frac{1}{4}$, we find $x=-\frac{3}{4}y$ or $+3y$.

Substituting the first value of x in the eq. $x=y^2+2$, we find $y=-\frac{3}{8}\pm\frac{1}{8}\sqrt{-119}$; hence, $x=\frac{9}{32}\mp\frac{3}{32}\sqrt{-119}$.

Substituting the second value of x in the eq. $x=y^2+2$, we find $y=2$ or 1; hence, $x=6$ or 3.

QUESTIONS PRODUCING SIMULTANEOUS QUADRATIC EQUATIONS, CONTAINING TWO OR MORE UNKNOWN QUANTITIES.

Article 251.

NOTE.—As the first five examples may be solved without completing the square, their solutions will be given in this form.

(1) Let x represent the greater number and y the less;

then, $y(x+y)=4x$, (1)

and $x(x+y)=9y$. (2)

Multiplying the eqs. together, dividing both members by xy, and extracting the square root, we find $x+y=6$.

Substituting 6 for $x+y$ in (1), we have $6y=4x$, or $y=\frac{2}{3}x$. Then, from eq. $x+y=6$, we have $x+\frac{2x}{3}=x$; whence, $x=3.6$, and $y=2.4$.

(2) Let $x=$ the digit in ten's place, and $y=$ the digit in unit's place; then, $10x+y=$ the number, and

$$x(10x+y)=10x^2+xy=46, \quad (1)$$

also $x(x+y)= \quad x^2+xy=10. \quad (2)$

Subtracting (2) from (1), $9x^2=36$; whence, $x=2$ and y is readily found $=8$.

(3) Let $x=$ the greater number and y the less; then,

$(x-y)(x^2-y^2)=32.$

$(x+y)(x^2+y^2)=272.$

For the method of finding the values of x and y, see the Algebra, example 4, page 222.

(4) Let x and y represent the numbers; then,

$xy=10$, and $x^3+y^3=133$.

For the method of finding the values of x and y, see the solution to example 20, Art. 245.

(5) Let $x=$ the greater number, and $y=$ the less; then,

$x^2+xy=120$, (1), and $xy-y^2=16$. (2)

Let $y=vx$; then, by substitution the equations become

$x^2+x^2v=120$, and $vx^2-v^2x^2=16$.

Whence, $x^2=\dfrac{120}{1+v}$, and $x^2=\dfrac{16}{v-v^2}$.

$\therefore \dfrac{120}{1+v}=\dfrac{16}{v-v^2}$. From which, $v=\dfrac{2}{3}$, or $\dfrac{1}{5}$.

Then, $x^2=\dfrac{120}{1+v}=72$ or 100;

$x=6\sqrt{2}$ or 10, and $y=4\sqrt{2}$ or 2.

The answers 10 and 2 are the only ones given in the Algebra, but it may be easily shown that the others are strictly true in an arithmetical sense.

(6) Let x and y represent the numbers; then,

$x^2+y^2+x+y=42$, (1), and $xy=15$. (2)

If we add twice the second equation to the first, the resulting equation is

$(x+y)^2+(x+y)=72$. Whence, $x+y=8$, or -9.

Having $x+y$ and xy, the values of x and y are to be found as in example 13, Art. 250.

We thus find $x=5$ or 3, and $y=3$ or 5;

or $x=\frac{-9\pm\sqrt{21}}{2}$, and $y=\frac{-9\mp\sqrt{21}}{2}$.

(7) Let x and y represent the numbers; then,

$x+y+xy=47$, (1)

$x^2+y^2-(x+y)=62$. (2)

For the method of finding the values of x and y, see the solution to example 16, Art. 250.

(8) Let $x=$ the greater number, and $y=$ the less; then,

$xy=x+y$, (1), and $x^2-y^2=x+y$. (2)

Dividing each member of (2) by $x+y$, we have

$x-y=1$, or $x=y+1$.

Substituting this value of x in (1), and reducing, we find

$y^2-y=1$. Whence, $y=\frac{1}{2}\pm\frac{1}{2}\sqrt{5}$, and $x=\frac{3}{2}\pm\frac{1}{2}\sqrt{5}$.

In order that the numbers may be positive, we can only use the upper sign. This gives $x=2.668$, and $y=1.668$ nearly.

(9) Let $x=$ the less number, and $xy=$ the greater: then,

$x^2y=x^2y^2-x^2$, (1)

$x^2y^2+x^2=x^3y^3-x^3$. (2)

Dividing each member of (1) by x^2, we have $y=y^2-1$, or $y^2=y+1$, from which we find $y=\frac{1}{2}+\frac{1}{2}\sqrt{5}$.

Dividing each member of (2) by x^2, we have $y^2+1=x(y^3-1)$, but $y^2=y+1$, and multiplying both sides by y, we have $y^3=y^2+y=y+y+1=2y+1$.

Substituting these values of y^2 and y^3, the equation becomes

$y+2=x(2y)$;

hence, $x=\frac{y+2}{2y}=\frac{\frac{5}{2}+\frac{1}{2}\sqrt{5}}{1+\sqrt{5}}=\frac{(\frac{5}{2}+\frac{1}{2}\sqrt{5})}{1+\sqrt{5}}\times\frac{1-\sqrt{5}}{1-\sqrt{5}}$

$=\frac{\frac{5}{2}-2\sqrt{5}-\frac{5}{2}}{1-5}=\frac{-2\sqrt{5}}{-4}=\frac{1}{2}\sqrt{5}$. $\therefore x=\frac{1}{2}\sqrt{5}$, and

$xy=(\frac{1}{2}+\frac{1}{2}\sqrt{5})(\frac{1}{2}\sqrt{5})=\frac{1}{4}\sqrt{5}+\frac{5}{4}=\frac{1}{4}(5+\sqrt{5})$.

Or let $x=$ the greater, and $y=$ the less. Then,

$x^2-y^2=xy$, (1)

$x^2+y^2=x^3-y^3$. (2)

From eq. (1), $x^2-xy=y^2$. Whence, $x^2-xy+\frac{y^2}{4}=y^2+\frac{y^2}{4}=\frac{5y^2}{4}$,

and $x=\frac{y}{2}(1\pm\sqrt{5})$. Substituting this value of x in (2), and dividing by y^2, we may find the value of y.

This difficult problem may also be solved by putting $y=tx$, in the above equations.

(10) This question may be solved by using only one unknown quantity. Thus,

Let $3x=$ A's gain; then, $20x=$ B's stock, and $100-3x=$ B's gain, and $40x-200=$ A's stock.

Therefore, $40x-200 : 20x :: 3x : 100-3x$.

Since the product of the means is equal to the product of the extremes, $60x^2=(40x-200)(100-3x)$.

Reducing, $x^2-\frac{230}{9}x=-\frac{1000}{9}$.

Whence, $x=20$; hence, $3x=60=$ A's gain, &c.

(11) Let x and y represent the numbers; then, by the question,

$$xy+x+y=23, \quad (1)$$
$$x^2+y^2-5(x+y)=8. \quad (2)$$

Adding twice eq. (1) to eq. (2), we have

$$x^2+2xy+y^2-3(x+y)=54.$$
or $$(x+y)^2-3(x+y)=54.$$

This is a quadratic form, and we readily find $x+y=9$; then, by substituting the value of $x+y$ in eq. (1), we find $xy=14$. Having $x+y$ and xy, we can find x and y.

(12) Let x, y, and z represent the numbers; then,

$$x-y-(y-z)=x-2y+z=5, \quad (1)$$
$$x+y+z=44, \quad (2)$$
$$xyz=1950. \quad (3)$$

Subtracting eq. (1) from (2), and dividing by 3 we find $y=13$; then, substituting this value of y in (2) and (3), we have

$$x+z=31, \text{ and } xz=150.$$

Whence, we readily find $x=25$, and $z=6$.

FORMULÆ.

Article 252.

NOTE.—Examples 1 to 4 have either been solved before, or are so simple as to require no explanation. We shall, therefore, merely express the respective formula in the form of Rules.

(1) PROBLEM.—To find two numbers, having given the sum of their squares, and the difference of their squares.

Rule.—*Add the difference of the squares to the sum of the squares, multiply the sum by 2 and extract the square root; half the result will be the greater number.*

To find the less number, proceed in the same manner, except that the difference of the squares must be subtracted from their sum.

Ex. The sum of the squares of two numbers is $120\frac{1}{2}$, and the difference of their squares 60; required the numbers.

Ans. $9\frac{1}{2}$, and $5\frac{1}{2}$.

(2) Problem.—Having given the difference of two numbers, and their product, to find the numbers.

Rule.—*To the square of the difference, add four times the product, extract the square root of the sum; add the result to the difference, and also subtract the difference from it, then half the sum will be the greater number, and half the difference the less number.*

Ex. The difference of two numbers is 11, and their product 80; required the numbers. *Ans.* 5 and 16

(3) Problem.—To find a number, having given the sum of the number and its square root.

Rule.—*To the given sum add $\frac{1}{4}$, and extract the square root, subtract the result from the given sum increased by $\frac{1}{2}$, and the remainder will be the required number.*

Ex. The sum of a number and of its square root is $8\frac{3}{4}$; required the number.

Ans. $6\frac{1}{4}$.

(4) Problem.—To find a number, having given the difference of the number and its square root.

Rule.—*To the given difference add $\frac{1}{4}$, extract the square root of the sum, and to the result add the given difference increased by $\frac{1}{2}$; the sum will be the required number.*

Ex. The difference of a number and its square root is $8\frac{3}{4}$; required the number.

Ans. $12\frac{1}{4}$.

(5) $x+y=s$. (1)

Squaring, $x^2+2xy+y^2=s^2$;

but $xy=p$; therefore, by transposing $2xy$, or $2p$,

$x^2+y^2=s^2-2p$.

Cubing eq. (1) $x^3+3x^2y+3xy^2+y^3=s^3$,

or $x^3+3xy(x+y)+y^3=s^3$,

or $x^3+3ps+y^3=s^3$.

$\therefore\ x^3+y^3=s^3-3ps$.

Again, squaring $x^2+y^2=s^2-2p$,

$$x^4+2x^2y^2+y^4=s^4-4ps^2+4p^2,$$

$$x^4+2p^2+y^4=s^4-4ps^2+4p^2.$$

$$\therefore\ x^4+y^4=s^4-4ps^2+2p^2.$$

As an additional example, let the following problem be proposed:

PROBLEM.—To find two numbers, having given their product, and the difference of their cubes.

Let x and y represent the numbers; then,

$x^3-y^3=a$, (1), and $xy=b$. (2)

Squaring equation (1), adding to the result four times the cube of (2), and extracting the square root, we have

$x^3+y^3=a^2+4b^3$. (3)

Adding together equations (1) and (3), dividing by 2, and extracting the cube root, we find

$$x=\sqrt[3]{\{\tfrac{1}{2}(a+\sqrt{a^2+4b^3})\}}.$$

Similarly, by subtracting equations (1) from (3), we find

$$y=\sqrt[3]{\{\tfrac{1}{2}(\sqrt{a^2+4b^3}-a)\}}.$$

These formulæ give the following

Rule.—*To the square of the difference of the cubes, add four times the cube of their product, extract the square root of the sum; add the result to the difference of the cubes, also subtract the difference from it, then the cube root of one-half the sum will be the greater number, and the cube root of one-half the difference the less number.*

Ex. The difference of the cubes of two numbers is 604, and their product is 45; required the numbers. *Ans.* 5 and 9.

In a similar manner, special rules might be formed for the solution of nearly all the questions on pages 223, 224 of the Algebra.

SPECIAL SOLUTIONS AND EXAMPLES.

Article 253.

(2) By adding $2x$ to each member, the equation becomes

$x^3-x=2+2x$, or $x(x^2-1)=2(x+1)$.

Divide both members by $x+1$, $x(x-1)=2$.

Whence, $x=-1$ or 2.

(3) Transposing $\frac{1}{3}$ and $\frac{2}{3x}$, the equation becomes

$$x^2-\frac{4}{9}=1+\frac{2}{3x}, \text{ or } (x+\tfrac{2}{3})(x-\tfrac{2}{3})=\frac{1}{x}(x+\tfrac{2}{3});$$

$$\therefore\ x+\tfrac{2}{3}=0, \text{ or } x=-\tfrac{2}{3}; \text{ also, } x-\tfrac{2}{3}=\frac{1}{x}.$$

Whence, $x=\frac{1}{3}(1\pm\sqrt{10})$.

(4) Transpose 1 to the left member; then, the equation may be placed under the form
$2x^2(x-1)+x^2-1=0$, or $2x^2(x-1)+(x+1)(x-1)=0$;
$\therefore\ x-1=0$, or $x=1$; also, $2x^2+x+1=0$.
Whence, $x=\frac{1}{4}(-1\pm\sqrt{-7})$.

(5) The equation may be placed under the following form:
$x^3-2x^2-x^2+2x-x+2=0$,
or $x^2(x-2)-x(x-2)-(x-2)=0$.
$\therefore\ x-2=0$, or $x=2$; also, $x^2-x-1=0$.
Whence, $x=\frac{1}{2}(1\pm\sqrt{5})$.

(6) Multiplying both sides by x, we have $x^4=6x^2+9x$,
or, $x^4+3x^2=9x^2+9x$,
$x^4+3x^2+\frac{9}{4}=9x^2+9x+\frac{9}{4}=9(x^2+x+\frac{1}{4})$,
$x^2+\frac{3}{2}=\pm3(x+\frac{1}{2})$,
$x^2=3x$, or $x=3$,
or, $x^2+3x=-3$, and $x=\frac{1}{2}(-3\pm\sqrt{-3})$.
Or, thus, $x^3=6x+9$.
$\therefore\ x^3-27=6x-18=6(x-3)$.
Dividing by $x-3$, $x^2+3x+9=6$, from which the value of x is readily obtained.

(7) $x+7x^{\frac{1}{3}}-22=(x-8)+7(x^{\frac{1}{3}}-2)=0$.
Dividing by $x^{\frac{1}{3}}-2$, we have

$$x^{\frac{2}{3}}+2x^{\frac{1}{3}}+4+7=0,$$
$$x^{\frac{2}{3}}+2x^{\frac{1}{3}}=-11,$$
$$x^{\frac{2}{3}}+2x^{\frac{1}{3}}+1=-10,$$
$$x^{\frac{1}{3}}=-1\pm\sqrt{-10},$$
$$x=(-1\pm\sqrt{-10})^3=29\pm7\sqrt{-10}.$$

From $x^{\frac{1}{3}}-2=0$, we have $x^{\frac{1}{3}}=2$, and $x=8$.

(8) This equation may be written under the form
$x^4-81+\frac{13}{3}(x^2-9)x=0$,

or $(x^2+9)(x^2-9)+\frac{13}{3}(x^2-9)x=0$.

$\therefore\ x^2-9=0$, and $x=+3$, or -3.

Also, $x^2+9+\frac{13}{3}x=0$.

Whence, $x=\frac{1}{6}(-13\pm\sqrt{-155})$.

(10) Multiplying both members by x, and adding $x+1$ to each side, we have $x^2-2x+1=4+4\sqrt{x}+x$.

Extracting the square root, $x-1=\pm(2+\sqrt{x})$.

From the equation $x-1=2+\sqrt{x}$, by transposing $\sqrt{x}$ and -1, we have $x-\sqrt{x}=3$.

Whence, $\sqrt{x}=\frac{1}{2}\pm\frac{1}{2}\sqrt{13}$, and $x=\frac{1}{2}(7\pm\sqrt{13})$.

From the equation $x-1=-2-\sqrt{x}$, we find similarly $\sqrt{x}=-\frac{1}{2}\pm\frac{1}{2}\sqrt{-3}$, and $x=\frac{1}{2}(-1\mp\sqrt{-3})$.

(11) Adding $\frac{1}{x^2}$ to each member, we have

$$\frac{49x^2}{4}-49+\frac{49}{x^2}=9+\frac{6}{x}+\frac{1}{x^2}$$

Extracting the square root, $\frac{7x}{2}-\frac{7}{x}=\pm\left(3+\frac{1}{x}\right)$.

From the equation $\frac{7x}{2}-\frac{7}{x}=3+\frac{1}{x}$, by clearing of fractions, transposing and reducing, we find $x^2-\frac{6}{7}x=\frac{16}{7}$.

Whence, $x=2$, or $-\frac{8}{7}$.

From the equation $\frac{7x}{2}-\frac{7}{x}=-3-\frac{1}{x}$, we find similarly $x^2+\frac{6}{7}x=\frac{12}{7}$; whence, $x=\frac{1}{7}(-3\pm\sqrt{93})$.

(12) Transposing $-34x$, and adding $\left(\frac{17x}{4}\right)^2$ to each side, we have $x^4+\frac{17x^3}{2}+\left(\frac{17x}{4}\right)^2=16+34x+\left(\frac{17x}{4}\right)^2$.

Extracting the sq. root, $x^2+\frac{17x}{4}=\pm\left(4+\frac{17x}{4}\right)$.

From eq. $x^2+\frac{17x}{4}=4+\frac{17x}{4}$, we have $x^2=4$, and $x=\pm2$.

From eq. $x^2+\frac{17x}{4}=-4-\frac{17x}{4}$, we have $x^2+\frac{17x}{2}=-4$

Whence, $x=-8$, or $-\frac{1}{2}$.

(13) First, $-(3x^2+x)=-3x^2\left(1+\frac{1}{3x}\right)$.

Dividing both members of the equation by x^4, and adding to each side $\frac{9}{4x^4}$, we have

$$\left(1+\frac{1}{3x}\right)^2-\frac{3}{x^2}\left(1+\frac{1}{3x}\right)+\frac{9}{4x^4}=\frac{70}{x^4}+\frac{9}{4x^4}=\frac{289}{4x^4}.$$

Extracting the square root, $1+\frac{1}{3x}-\frac{3}{2x^2}=\pm\frac{17}{2x^2}$;

hence, $1+\frac{1}{3x}=+\frac{10}{x^2}$, or $-\frac{7}{x^2}$.

Clearing of fractions, $x^2+\frac{1}{3}x=+10$, or -7.

Whence, $x=3$ or $-3\frac{1}{3}$, or $\frac{1}{6}(-1\pm\sqrt{-251})$.

(14) Multiplying by 2, and adding $\frac{8x}{36}+\frac{81}{36}$ to each side, we have $\frac{36}{x^2}+\frac{18}{x}+\frac{81}{36}=\frac{x^2}{36}+\frac{8x}{36}+\frac{16}{36}$.

Extracting the sq. root, $\frac{6}{x}+\frac{9}{6}=\pm\left(\frac{x}{6}+\frac{4}{6}\right)$.

Taking the positive sign, we have the equation $x^2-5x=36$, from which $x=9$ or -4.

From the equation $\frac{6}{x}+\frac{9}{6}=-\left(\frac{x}{6}+\frac{4}{6}\right)$, we have the equation $x^2+13x=-36$, from which $x=-9$ or -4.

∴ The values of x are $+9$, -9, and -4.

(15) Multiplying both sides by 3, transposing $\frac{841}{x^2}$ and $\frac{1}{x^2}$ and adding 1 to each side, we have

$$81x^2+18+\frac{1}{x^2}=\frac{841}{x^2}+\frac{232}{x}+16.$$

Extracting the square root, $9x+\frac{1}{x}=\pm\left(\frac{29}{x}+4\right)$.

Taking the plus sign, we find $x=2$, or $-\frac{14}{9}$.

Taking the minus sign, we find $x=\frac{1}{9}(-2\pm\sqrt{-266})$.

(19) Let $x+y=s$, and $xy=p$;

then, $x^2+y^2=s^2-2p$, and $x^3+y^3=s^3-3sp$;

and by substitution the first equation becomes

$2s^3+1=(s^2-2p)(p+s^3-3sp)$;

but $s=x+y=3$; hence, by substitution the equation becomes $55=(9-2p)(p+27-9p)=243-126p+16p^2$,

or $16p^2-126p=-188$; whence, $p=\frac{47}{8}$ or 2.

Taking $x+y=3$, and $xy=2$, we readily find $x=2$, and $y=1$.

(20) Dividing both sides of the equation by $1+x$, we have

$1-x+x^2=a(1+x)^2=a+2ax+ax^2$.

Transposing and reducing, $(a-1)x^2+(2a+1)x=1-a$,

or $x^2+\frac{2a+1}{a-1}x=\frac{1-a}{a-1}=-\frac{a-1}{a-1}=-1$.

$$x^2+\frac{2a+1}{a-1}x+\frac{(2a+1)^2}{4(a-1)^2}=\frac{(2a+1)^2}{4(a-1)^2}-1=\frac{12a-3}{4(a-1)^2}.$$

$$x+\frac{2a+1}{2(a-1)}=\frac{\pm\sqrt{12a-3}}{2(a-1)}$$

$$x=\frac{-2a-1\pm\sqrt{12a-3}}{2(a-1)}=\frac{1+2a\pm\sqrt{12a-3}}{2(1-a)}.$$

Since both members of the equation are divisible by $1+x$, therefore, $1+x=0$, and $x=-1$.

(21) $\frac{a}{x^2}-\frac{1}{x}\sqrt{x-2a-\frac{a}{x}}=1$.

Transposing, multiplying by x, and arranging the terms under the radical, we have

$$\frac{a}{x}-x=\sqrt{-\left(\frac{a}{x}-x\right)-2a};$$

$\left(\frac{a}{x}-x\right)^2+\left(\frac{a}{x}-x\right)=-2a$, by squaring and transposing

Putting $\frac{a}{x}-x=$ a single unknown quantity, and finding its value, we have

$\frac{a}{x}-x=-\frac{1}{2}\pm\frac{1}{2}\sqrt{1-8a}=b$; whence, $a-x^2=bx$,

or $x^2+bx=a$,

$$x=-\frac{b}{2}\pm\frac{1}{2}\sqrt{b^2+4a}.$$

Substituting the value of b, we find

$b^2=\frac{1}{2}+\frac{1}{2}\sqrt{1-8a}-2a$,

$b^2+4a=\frac{1}{4}(2+2\sqrt{1-8a}+8a)$

$$\therefore\ x=\tfrac{1}{2}(+\tfrac{1}{2}\pm\tfrac{1}{2}\sqrt{1-8a})\pm\tfrac{1}{2}\sqrt{\tfrac{1}{4}(2+2\sqrt{1-8a}+8a)}$$

$$=\tfrac{1}{4}\left\{1\pm\sqrt{1-8a}\pm\sqrt{2\pm2\sqrt{1-8a}+8a}\right\}.$$

(22) Let $x+y=s$, and $xy=p$; then, the equations become

$$s+ps+p^2=85, \qquad (1)$$
$$p+s^2+ps=97. \qquad (2)$$

Adding, $s^2+2ps+p^2+p+s=182$,

or, $(s+p)^2+(p+s)=182$.

Whence, $s+p=+13$, or -14.

Taking $s+p=13$, $s=13-p$, and substituting this in (1), $13-p+p(13-p)+p^2=85$; whence, $p=6$.

$\therefore$ $x+y=7$, and $xy=6$, from which we find $x=6$ or 1, and $y=1$ or 6.

(23) $$\frac{2c^2}{d^2}+\frac{ac}{d}-(a-b)(2c+ad)\frac{x}{d}=(a+b)\frac{cx}{d}-(a^2-b^2)x^2.$$

$2c^2+acd-(a-b)(2c+ad)dx=(a+b)cdx-(a^2-b^2)d^2x^2$,

$(a^2-b^2)d^2x^2-2acdx-a^2d^2x+2bcdx+abd^2x-acdx-bcdx=-acd-2c^2$,

$(a^2-b^2)d^2x^2-3acdx+bcdx-a^2d^2x+abd^2x=-acd-2c^2$,

$$x^2-\frac{3acd-bcd+a^2d^2-abd^2}{(a^2-b^2)d^2}x=-\frac{acd+2c^2}{(a^2-b^2)d^2}$$

$$x^2-\frac{(3a-b)cd+(a-b)ad^2}{(a^2-b^2)d^2}x+\frac{(3a-b)^2c^2d^2+(a-b)^2a^2d^4+2acd^3(3a-b)(a-b)}{4(a^2-b^2)^2d^4}$$

$$=\frac{-4a^3cd^3-8a^2c^2d^2+4ab^2cd^3+8b^2c^2d^2}{4(a^2-b^2)^2d^4}+\frac{(3a-b)^2c^2d^2+(a-b)^2a^2d^4+2acd^3(3a-b)(a-b)}{4(a^2-b^2)^2d^4},$$

$$=\frac{(a-3b)^2c^2d^2+(a-b)^2a^2d^4+2acd^3(a-3b)(a-b)}{4(a^2-b^2)^2d^4},$$

$$x-\frac{(3a-b)cd+(a-b)ad^2}{2(a^2-b^2)d^2}=\pm\frac{(a-3b)cd+(a-b)ad^2}{2(a^2-b^2)d^2}$$

$$x=\frac{(3a-b)cd+(a-b)ad^2}{2(a^2-b^2)d^2}\pm\frac{(a-3b)cd+(a-b)ad^2}{2(a^2-b^2)d^2}$$

$$=\frac{4(a-b)cd+2(a-b)ad^2}{2(a^2-b^2)d^2}=\frac{2c+ad}{(a+b)d},$$

$$\text{or}=\frac{2(a+b)cd}{2(a^2-b^2)d^2}=\frac{c}{(a-b)d}.$$

(24) $(x^3+1)(x^2+1)(x+1)=30x^3$,

or, $\left(x^2+\frac{1}{x}\right)\left(x+\frac{1}{x}\right)\left(1+\frac{1}{x}\right)=30$,

$$\text{or, } \left(x^2+\frac{1}{x^2}+x+\frac{1}{x}\right)\left(x+\frac{1}{x}\right)=30.$$

$$\text{Let } x+\frac{1}{x}=s;\ x^2+\frac{1}{x^2}=\left(x+\frac{1}{x}\right)^2-2=s^2-2$$

$$(s^2-2+s)s=30, \text{ or } s^3-2s+s^2=30,$$

$$s^4+s^3-2s^2=30s,$$

$$s^4+s^3+\frac{s^2}{4}=\frac{9s^2}{4}+30s,$$

$$\left(s^2+\frac{s}{2}\right)^2=\frac{9s^2}{4}+30s,$$

$$\left(s^2+\frac{s}{2}\right)^2+10\left(s^2+\frac{s}{2}\right)=\frac{49s^2}{4}+35s,$$

$$\left(s^2+\frac{s}{2}\right)^2+10\left(s^2+\frac{s}{2}\right)+25=\frac{49s^2}{4}+35s+25.$$

$$s^2+\frac{s}{2}+5=\frac{7s}{2}+5,$$

$$s^2=3s, \text{ and } s=3=x+\frac{1}{x},$$

$$x+\frac{1}{x}=3; \text{ whence, } x=\tfrac{1}{2}(3\pm\sqrt{5}).$$

(25) $x^3+y^3=35$, and $x^2+y^2=13$.

Let $x+y=v$, and $xy=z$;

then, $v^3-3vz=35$, (3)

and $v^2-2z=13$. (4)

$2v^3-6vz=70$, (5) by multiplying (3) by 2.

$3v^3-6vz=39v$, (6) by multiplying (4) by $3v$.

$v^3=39v-70$, by subtracting (5) from (6)

$$v^3-39v=-70,$$

$$v^4-39v^2=-70v,$$

$$25v^2=25v^2,$$

$$v^4-14v^2=25v^2-70v,$$

$$v^4-14v^2+49=25v^2-70v+49,$$

$$v^2-7=\pm(5v-7),$$

$v^2=5v$, and $v=5$,

or $v^2+5v=14$, and $v=+2$ or -7;

but $v^2-2z=13$,

$25-2z=13$, and $z=6$,

or $4-2z=13$, and $z=-\frac{9}{2}$,

or $49-2z=13$, and $z=18$.

From $\left.\begin{aligned}x+y&=5,\\ xy&=6,\end{aligned}\right\}$ $\begin{aligned}x&=3 \text{ or } 2,\\ y&=2 \text{ or } 3.\end{aligned}$

From $\left.\begin{array}{l}x+y=2,\\ xy=-\frac{9}{4},\end{array}\right\}\begin{array}{l}x=1\pm\frac{1}{2}\sqrt{22},\\ y=1\mp\frac{1}{2}\sqrt{22}.\end{array}$

From $\left.\begin{array}{l}x+y=-7,\\ xy=18,\end{array}\right\}\begin{array}{l}x=-\frac{7}{2}\pm\frac{1}{2}\sqrt{-23},\\ y=-\frac{7}{2}\mp\frac{1}{2}\sqrt{-23}.\end{array}$

(26) Let $xyz=p$, and $x+y+z=s$; then, the equations become

$$\frac{p}{s-z}=a, \quad (1) \quad \frac{p}{s-y}=b, \quad (2) \quad \frac{p}{s-x}=c; \quad (3)$$

hence, $z=s-\frac{p}{a}$, (4) $y=s-\frac{p}{b}$, (5) $x=s-\frac{p}{c}$. (6)

Adding, $x+y+z$, or $s=3s-p\left(\frac{1}{a}+\frac{1}{b}+\frac{1}{c}\right)$.

Whence, $s=\frac{(ab+ac+bc)p}{2abc}$.

Substituting this value of s in equations (4), (5), and (6),

we get $z=\frac{(ab+ac-bc)p}{2abc}$, (7)

$$y=\frac{(ab+bc-ac)p}{2abc}, \quad (8)$$

$$x=\frac{(ac+bc-ab)p}{2abc}. \quad (9)$$

Multiplying equations (7), (8), and (9) together, we find

xyz, or $p=\frac{(ac+bc-ab)(ab+bc-ac)(ab+ac-bc)p^3}{8a^3b^3c^3}$;

whence, $p=2abc\sqrt{\left\{\frac{2abc}{(ac+bc-ab)(ab+bc-ac)(ab+ac-bc)}\right\}}$.

Substituting this value of p in equations (7), (8), and (9),

we get $x=\sqrt{\left\{\frac{2abc(ac+bc-ab)}{(ab+ac-bc)(ab+bc-ac)}\right\}}$,

$$y=\sqrt{\left\{\frac{2abc(ab+bc-ac)}{(ac+bc-ab)(ab+ac-bc)}\right\}},$$

$$z=\sqrt{\left\{\frac{2abc(ab+ac-bc)}{(ac+bc-ab)(ab+bc-ac)}\right\}}.$$

(27) Dividing both members of (1) by x^3, and both members of (2) by y^3, we have

$$\left(x^3+\frac{1}{x^3}\right)y=y^2+1,$$

$$\text{or } x^3+\frac{1}{x^3}=y+\frac{1}{y}, \quad (3)$$

$$\text{and } y^3+\frac{1}{y^3}=9\left(x+\frac{1}{x}\right),$$

$$\text{or } \tfrac{1}{3}\left(y^3+\frac{1}{y^3}\right)=3\left(x+\frac{1}{x}\right);$$

$$\therefore\ \tfrac{1}{3}\left(y^3+\frac{1}{y^3}\right)+y+\frac{1}{y}=x^3+3\left(x+\frac{1}{x}\right)+\frac{1}{x^3},$$

$$y^3+\frac{1}{y^3}+3\left(y+\frac{1}{y}\right)=3\left(x+\frac{1}{x}\right)^3;$$

$$\therefore\ y+\frac{1}{y}=\left(x+\frac{1}{x}\right)\sqrt[3]{3}, \text{ by extracting the cube root.}$$

$$\text{And } x^3+\frac{1}{x^3}=\left(x+\frac{1}{x}\right)\sqrt[3]{3} \text{ by (3);}$$

dividing both members by $x+\dfrac{1}{x}$, we have

$$x^2-1+\frac{1}{x^2}=\sqrt[3]{3},$$

$$x^2+2+\frac{1}{x^2}=\sqrt[3]{3}+3, \text{ by adding } +3;$$

$$x+\frac{1}{x}=\sqrt{\sqrt[3]{3}+3}, \text{ by extracting the square root}$$

$$\text{Similarly, } x-\frac{1}{x}=\sqrt{\sqrt[3]{3}-1}, \text{ by subtracting 1}$$

$$\therefore\ x=\tfrac{1}{2}\left\{\sqrt{\sqrt[3]{3}+3}+\sqrt{\sqrt[3]{3}-1}\right\}.$$

$$\text{But } y+\frac{1}{y}=\left(x+\frac{1}{x}\right)\sqrt[3]{3}=\sqrt[3]{3}\sqrt{\sqrt[3]{3}+3}.$$

$$\text{Whence, } y=\tfrac{1}{2}\left\{\sqrt[3]{3}.\sqrt{\sqrt[3]{3}+3}\pm\sqrt{3\sqrt[3]{9}-1}\right\}.$$

RATIO, PROPORTION, AND PROGRESSIONS.

Article 278.

Note.—The solutions of these exercises are given, not because they are difficult, but because many of them are of a character not heretofore presented to the notice of Teachers.

(1) 3 to 4 $=\frac{4}{3}$; 3^2 to 4^2 $=\frac{16}{9}$; $\frac{4}{3}=\frac{12}{9}$, and since $\frac{16}{9}$ is greater than $\frac{12}{9}$, the ratio of 3^2 to 4^2 is greater than the ratio of 3 to 4.

(2) Duplicate ratio of 2 to 3 is 2^2 to $3^2 = 4$ to 9;
triplicate ratio of 3 to 4 is 3^3 to $4^3 = 27$ to 64;
subduplicate ratio of 64 to 36 is $\sqrt{64}$ to $\sqrt{36} = 8$ to 6;
$4 \times 27 \times 8$ to $9 \times 64 \times 6 = 864$ to $3456 = 1$ to 4;
or, by canceling thus,

$$\frac{\not 9 \times \not 6\not 4 \times 6}{4 \times \not 2\not 7 \times \not 8} = \frac{\not 8 \times \not 6}{\not 4 \times \not 3} = \frac{2 \times 2}{1} = \frac{4}{1} = 1 \text{ to } 4.$$

(3) Let $x =$ the quantity; then, $\frac{n+x}{m+x} = \frac{q}{p}$;
whence, $np + px = mq + qx$, and $x = \frac{mq - np}{p - q}$.

(4) $\frac{b}{a} = 2\frac{2}{3} = \frac{8}{3}$; dividing both terms of each fraction by 2,
$\frac{b}{2a} = \frac{4}{3} = 1\frac{1}{3}$.

Multiplying both terms of the fractions $\frac{b}{a} = \frac{8}{3}$, by 4, we have $\frac{4b}{3a} = \frac{8}{3} \times \frac{4}{3} = \frac{32}{9} = 3\frac{5}{9}$.

(5) $\frac{b}{a} = 1\frac{2}{3} = \frac{5}{3}$; $\therefore \frac{b}{a+b} = \frac{5}{3+5}$, or $\frac{b}{a+b} = \frac{5}{3}$.
Since $\frac{b}{a} = \frac{5}{3}$; $\therefore \frac{a}{b} = \frac{3}{5}$, and $\frac{a}{b-a} = \frac{3}{5-3} = \frac{3}{2}$.

(6) $\frac{n}{m} = \frac{4}{7}$, and $\frac{m}{n} = \frac{7}{4}$; also, $4m = 7n$, and $m = \frac{7n}{4}$.
$m - n = \frac{7n}{4} - n = \frac{3n}{4}$.
Dividing $6m$ by each member of this equality
$\frac{6m}{m-n} = 6m \div \frac{3n}{4} = \frac{8m}{n} = 8 \times \frac{7}{4} = 14$.
Also, dividing $5n$ by each member, we have
$\frac{5n}{m-n} = 5n \times \frac{4}{3n} = \frac{20n}{3n} = 6\frac{2}{3}$.

(7) $\frac{7x - 5y}{5y - 8x} = 6$, or $7x - 5y = 30y - 48x$,
$55x = 35y$, or $11x = 7y$,
$\frac{11}{7} = \frac{y}{x}$, or $x : y :: 7 : 11$.

(9) $x^2+y^2=2ax$, or $y^2=2ax-x^2$,
or $y\times y=x(2a-x)$; whence, (Art. 268,) $x:y::y:2a-x$.

(10) Let $x=$ the number; then,
$a+x:b+x::c+x:d+x$;
$\therefore (a+x)(d+x)=(b+x)(c+x)$,
or $ad+ax+dx+x^2=bc+bx+cx+x^2$,
or $ax-bx-cx+dx=bc-ad$,
or $(a-b-c+d)x=bc-ad$,

$$x=\frac{bc-ad}{a-b-c+d}.$$

The pupil should verify this answer by using numbers.

(11) Let a, b, c, and d, be four quantities in proportion, and if possible, let x be a number that being added to each will make the resulting four quantities proportionals; then, $a+x:b+x::c+x:d+x$.
$\therefore (a+x)(d+x)=(b+x)(c+x)$,
or $ad+ax+dx+x^2=bc+bx+cx+x^2$;
whence, $x=\dfrac{bc-ad}{a-b-c+d}$.
But since a, b, c, d, are in proportion (Art. 287), $ad=bc$
$\therefore x=\dfrac{bc-bc}{a-b-c+d}=\dfrac{0}{a-b-c+d}=0$, (Art. 135);
hence, there is no number which being added to each will leave the resulting quantities proportional.

(12) Cubing each term of the second proportion, we have
$a^3:b^3::c+x:d+y$;
but $x:y::a^3:b^3$.
$\therefore x:y::c+x:d+y$, by Art. 272.
Placing the product of the means equal to that of the extremes, and omitting xy on each side, we find $x=\dfrac{cy}{d}$.

(13) Let ma and mb be equal multiples of two quantities, a and b; then, since $\dfrac{mb}{ma}=\dfrac{b}{a}$, we have (Art. 263), $ma:mb::a:b$.

(14) Let $\dfrac{a}{n}$ and $\dfrac{b}{n}$ be like parts of two quantities, a and b; then
$\dfrac{b}{n}\div\dfrac{a}{n}=\dfrac{b}{n}\times\dfrac{n}{a}=\dfrac{b}{a}$, and we have (Art. 263), $\dfrac{a}{n}:\dfrac{b}{n}::a:b$

(15) Since $a:b::c:d$, $\therefore\ \frac{b}{a}=\frac{d}{c}$ (Art. 263);

but $\frac{mb}{ma}=\frac{b}{a}$, and $\frac{nd}{nc}=\frac{d}{c}$; therefore, $ma:mb::nc:nd$.

Again, if we take the equation $\frac{b}{a}=\frac{d}{c}$, and multiply both sides by $\frac{n}{m}$, we have $\frac{nb}{ma}=\frac{nd}{mc}$, which gives the proportion $ma:nb::mc:nd$, (Art. 263)

(16) Let $a:b::c:d$, (1)
and $e:f::g:h$, (2)
from (2) by Art. 271, $f:e::h:g$. (3)
Multiplying together the corresponding terms of (1) and (3) (Art. 277), we have $af:be::ch:dg$;

whence, $\frac{be}{af}=\frac{dg}{ch}$,

but $\frac{be}{af}=\frac{b}{f}\times\frac{e}{a}=\frac{b}{f}\div\frac{a}{e}$, and $\frac{dg}{ch}=\frac{d}{h}\times\frac{g}{c}=\frac{d}{h}\div\frac{c}{g}$;

$\frac{b}{f}\div\frac{a}{e}=\frac{d}{h}\div\frac{c}{g}$; whence, (Art. 263), $\frac{a}{e}:\frac{b}{f}::\frac{c}{g}:\frac{d}{h}$.

Article 279.

(3) By Art. 275, the proportion gives
$2x:2y::4:2$, or $4x=8y$, or $x=2y$.
By substituting the value of x in the eq. $x^3-y^3=56$, we have $(2y)^3-y^3=56$.
Reducing, $7y^3=56$; whence, $y=2$, and $x=4$.

(4) By Division (Art. 274), the proportion gives
$x+y-x:x::7-5:5$, or $y:x::2:5$;

whence, $x=\frac{5y}{2}$, and $\frac{5y^2}{2}+y^2=126$;

whence, $y=\pm 6$, and $x=\pm 15$.

(5) Extracting the square root of each term of the proportion (Art. 276), we have

$$x+y:x-y::8:1;$$

(Art. 274), $2x:2y::9:7$; whence, $x=\frac{9y}{7}$.

By substitution $\frac{9y^2}{7}=63$.

Whence, $y=\pm 7$, and $x=\pm 9$.

(6) Writing b in the form $\frac{b}{1}$, the equation gives the proportion

$a+\sqrt{a^2-x^2} : a-\sqrt{a^2-x^2} : : 1 : b,$

(Art. 275), $2a : 2\sqrt{a^2-x^2} : : b+1 : 1-b,$

or $a : \sqrt{a^2-x^2} : : b+1 : 1-b,$

(Art. 276), $a^2 : a^2-x^2 : : (b+1)^2 : (1-b)^2.$

(Art. 274), $a^2 : a^2-(a^2-x^2) : : (b+1)^2 : (b+1)^2-(b-1)^2,$

or $a^2 : x^2 : : (b+1)^2 : 4b;$

whence, $x^2(b+1)^2=4a^2b,$

$$x^2=\frac{4a^2b}{(b+1)^2}, \text{ and } x=\pm\frac{2a\sqrt{b}}{b+1}.$$

(7) The equation gives the proportion

$\sqrt{a+x}+\sqrt{a-x} : \sqrt{a+x}-\sqrt{a-x} : : b : 1,$

(Art. 275), $2\sqrt{a+x} : 2\sqrt{a-x} : : b+1 : b-1,$

(Art. 276), $a+x : a-x : : (b+1)^2 : (b-1)^2,$

(Art. 275), $2a : 2x : : 2b^2+2 : 4b,$

or, $a : x : : b^2+1 : 2b;$

whence, $x=\frac{2ab}{b^2+1}$.

(8) Let $x=$ the greater number, and $y=$ the less. Then,

$x^3-y^3 : (x-y)^3 : : 61 : 1$, and $xy=820$.

(Art. 259), $x^2+xy+y^2 : x^2-2xy+y^2 : : 61 : 1,$

$x^2+320+y^2 : x^2-640+y^2 : : 61 : 1,$

(Art. 267), $x^2+320+y^2=61x^2-39040+61y^2.$

$60x^2+60y^2=39360.$

$x^2+y^2=656.$

From this, and the eq. $xy=320$, we obtain $x=20$, and $y=16$.

VARIATION.

Article 290.

Note.—The solutions to these examples are given for the same reason as those following Article 278, not because they are difficult, but because to many Teachers they will be new.

(3) Since y varies as x, let $y=mx$; then, since if $x=2$, $y=4a$, we have $4a=2m$, or $m=2a$; $\therefore y=2ax$.

(4) Since y varies as $\frac{1}{x}$, let $y=\frac{m}{x}$; then, since if $x=\frac{1}{2}$, $y=8$, we have $8=\frac{m}{\frac{1}{2}}$, or $m=4$; $\therefore$ $y=\frac{4}{x}$.

(5) Here, we have $y=v+z$, where $v\propto x$, and $z\propto\frac{1}{x^2}$.

Let $v=mx$, and $z=\frac{n}{x^2}$; then, $y=mx+\frac{n}{x^2}$.

Since $y=6$ when $x=1$, we have $6=m+n$, (1)

and " $y=5$ when $x=2$, " " $5=2m+\frac{n}{4}$. (2)

From equations (1) and (2), we readily find $m=2$ and $n=4$; hence, $y=2x+\frac{4}{x^2}$.

(6) Here, we have $y=a+v+z$, where a is constant, $v\propto x$, and $z\propto x^2$.
Let $v=mx$, and $z=nx^2$;
then, $y=a+mx+nx^2$.

$$\therefore\quad \begin{aligned} 6&=a+m+n, &(1)\\ 11&=a+2m+4n, &(2)\\ 18&=a+3m+9n. &(3)\end{aligned}$$

From the eqs. (1), (2), (3), by elimination (Art. 158), we find $a=3$, $m=2$, $n=1$; hence, $y=3+2x+x^2$.

(7) Since $s\propto t^2$ when f is constant; and $s\propto f$ when t is constant, therefore, when both vary, it is evident from Art. 283 (3), that $s\propto ft^2$;
then, let $s=mft^2$;
but since $2s=f$, or $s=\frac{1}{2}f$ when $t=1$, therefore,
$\frac{1}{2}f=mf1^2$;
whence, $m=\frac{1}{2}$, and $s=\frac{1}{2}ft^2$.

It is proper to observe, that all the preceding examples admit f proof.

Variation is of considerable use in Natural Philosophy, and hough not so easily understood as other parts of Proportion, is orthy the careful study of the learner.

Article 294.

Note.—The learner who wishes to understand the subject thoroughly, should derive each of the formulæ on page 256, by taking the two equations at the beginning of this article, and from them finding the value of the quantity marked "Required." We shall illustrate the method of doing this by the solution of two of the most difficult cases, Nos. 2 and 14.

Formula 2. Taking the equations

$$l=a+(n-1)d, \qquad (1)$$

and $$S=(a+l)\frac{n}{2}, \qquad (2)$$

we have given a, d, and S, and it is required to find l.

The first step is to eliminate n. This may be done by finding the value of n from each of the equations, and putting these values equal to each other.

Eq. (1) gives $n=\dfrac{l-a+d}{d}=\dfrac{l-a}{d}+1.$

Eq. (2) gives $n=\dfrac{2S}{l+a}$;

therefore, $\dfrac{l-a}{d}+1=\dfrac{2S}{l+a}$

Clearing, $l^2-a^2+dl+ad=2dS$,

$$l^2+dl+\frac{d^2}{4}=2dS+\left(a^2-ad+\frac{d^2}{4}\right)$$

$$=2dS+(a-\tfrac{1}{2}d)^2,$$

$$l+\frac{d}{2}=\pm\sqrt{\{2dS+(a-\tfrac{1}{2}d)^2\}},$$

$$l=-\tfrac{1}{2}d\pm\sqrt{\{2dS+(a-\tfrac{1}{2}d)^2\}}.$$

Formula 14. Here, we have the same formulæ, and the same quantities a, d, and S given, to find n.

Finding the value of l in eq. (2), and substituting it in (1), we have $a+(n-1)d=\dfrac{2S-na}{n}$;

clearing and reducing, $n^2+\dfrac{2a-d}{d}n=\dfrac{2S}{d}$,

$$n^2+\frac{2a-d}{d}n+\frac{(2a-d)^2}{4d^2}=\frac{(2a-d)^2+8dS}{4d^2};$$

whence, $n=\pm\frac{\sqrt{(2a-d)^2+8dS}-2a+d}{2d}$.

(10) Here, $d=-\frac{7}{6}$, and a, d, and n are given to find S.

$$S=\tfrac{1}{2}n\{1-\tfrac{7}{6}(n-1)\}=\tfrac{1}{12}n\{6-7(n-1)\}=\frac{n}{12}(13-7n).$$

(11) Here, $d=-\frac{1}{n}$, and we have a, d, and n given, to find S.

$$S=\tfrac{1}{2}n\left\{\frac{2(n-1)}{n}-\frac{1}{n}(n-1)\right\}=\tfrac{1}{2}n\left\{\frac{n-1}{n}\right\}=\frac{n-1}{2}.$$

(12) Here, $a=16\frac{1}{12}$, $d=16\frac{1}{12}\times2=32\frac{1}{6}$, and $n=30$, to find l and S.

Formula 1 gives* $l=16\frac{1}{12}+(30-1)32\frac{1}{6}=948\frac{11}{12}$.

$S=(l+a)\frac{n}{2}=(948\frac{11}{12}+16\frac{1}{12})\frac{30}{2}=14475.$

(13) Since there are 200 stones, there are 200 terms; therefore, $n=200$; and since the person travels $20+20=40$ yards, or 120 feet for the first stone; therefore, $a=120$.

Since the stones are 2 feet apart, he must travel over *twice* this distance to reach each successive stone; therefore, $d=4$. Applying formula 5, we have

$S=\frac{200}{2}\{2(120)+(200-1)4\}=100(1036)$

$=103600$ feet $=19$ m. 4 fur., 640 feet.

(15) Here, $a=3$, $e=18$, and $m=4$,

$d=\frac{e-a}{m+1}=\frac{18-3}{4+1}=3$; hence, the means are

$3+3=6$, 9, 12, 15.

(16) Here, $a=1$, $e=-1$, and $m=9$,

$d=\frac{e-a}{m+1}=\frac{-1-1}{9+1}=-\frac{1}{5}$,

$1-\frac{1}{5}=\frac{4}{5}$, $\frac{4}{5}-\frac{1}{5}=\frac{3}{5}$, &c.

(17) Here, $a=19$, $d=-2$, and $S=91$; and it is required to find n, which may be done by formula 14,

where $n=\frac{\pm\sqrt{(2a-d)^2+8dS}-2a+d}{2d}$;

$$\text{Hence, } n=\frac{\pm\sqrt{(38+2)^2-16\times 91}-38-2}{-4}$$

$$=\frac{\pm 12-40}{-4}=\mp 3+10=+13, \text{ or } +7.$$

Hence, the sum of either 13 terms, or 7 terms, will be equal to 91. To explain the reason of this, let the first 13 terms of the series be written thus,

No. of term, 1, 2, 3, 4, 5, 6, 7, 8, 9, 10, 11, 12, 13.
Terms 19, 17, 15, 13, 11, 9, 7, 5, 3, 1, —1—3, —5.

Here, we see that the sum of the first 7 terms is 91, and the sum of 13 terms is the same.

(18) Here, $a=.034$, $d=.0344-.034=.0004$, and $S=2.748$. Substituting these values in formula 14, we have

$$n=\frac{\pm\sqrt{(.068-.0004)^2+.0087936}-.068+.0004}{.008}$$

$$=\frac{\pm .1156-.0676}{.008}=+60.$$

(19) Let $x=$ the first term, and $y=$ the common difference then, $x+y=$ second term, and $x+x+y=2x+y=4$; fifth term $=a+(n-1)d=x+(5-1)y=x+4y=9$.

From these equations, we readily find $x=1$ and $y=2$; hence, the series is 1, 3, 5, 7, 9, &c.

(20) Let $x=$ the first term, and $y=$ the common difference; then, the series is
x, $x+y$, $x+2y$, $x+3y$, $x+4y$;
whence, $x+(x+y)=2x+y=18$,
and $(x+2y)+(x+3y)+(x+4y)=3x+9y=12$.

From these equations, we find $x=10$, and $y=-2$. It is now required to find n, having given the first term $=10$, the common difference -2, and the sum of the series 28.

$$\text{By formula 14, } n=\frac{\pm\sqrt{(20+2)-448}-20-2}{-4}=\frac{\mp 6-22}{-4}$$

$$=\mp 1\tfrac{1}{2}+5\tfrac{1}{2}=4, \text{ or } 7.$$

The series is 10, 8, 6, 4, 2, 0, —2, &c.

Here, we readily perceive why the sum of 4 terms is the same as that of 7.

(21) Here, $a=1$, and $d=2$, to find the sum of r terms, and also of $2r$ terms.

From formula 5, we find the sum of

r terms $=\frac{1}{2}r\{2+(r-1)2\}=r^2$,

of $2r$ terms $=\frac{1}{2}\times 2r\{2+(2r-1)2\}=4r^2$.

$\therefore\ 4r^2:r^2::x:1$; whence, $r^2x=4r^2$, and $x=4$.

(22) Let $x=$ the number of days the 1st travels before he is overtaken by the 2d. It is then required to find the sum of x terms of the arithmetical series whose first term a, is 1, and common difference $d=1$.

$$S=\tfrac{1}{2}n\{2a+(n-1)d\}=\frac{x}{2}\{2+(x-1)\}=\tfrac{1}{2}x^2+\tfrac{1}{2}x.$$

The 2d travels $(x-5)$ days, at the rate of 12 miles a day; hence, the whole distance he travels is represented by $12(x-5)$.

$\therefore\ \frac{1}{2}x^2+\frac{1}{2}x=12(x-5)$, or $x^2-23x=-120$.

Whence, $x=8$ or 15, and $x-5=3$ or 10.

$\therefore$ The 2d travels $12\times3=36$ miles, or $12\times10=120$ miles.

The 2d traveler overtakes the 1st at the end of 3 days, when each has traveled 36 miles; the 2d then passes the 1st, but as the 1st increases his speed each day, at the end of the 10th day he overtakes the 2d, and they are thus twice together.

This example furnishes a beautiful illustration of the manner in which the different roots of an equation correspond to the several circumstances of the problem.

GEOMETRICAL PROGRESSION.

Article 300.

NOTE.—All the formulæ in this Article are derived from the two equations

$$l=ar^{n-1}, \qquad (1)$$

$$\text{and } S=\frac{ar^n-a}{r-1}=\frac{rl-a}{r-1}, \qquad (2)$$

by supposing any three of the quantities to be known, and then finding the values of the other two.

In general, the formulæ are very easily found, but where n is large, the resulting numerical equation is hard to solve, and can only be understood by the learner, after he becomes acquainted with the numerical solution of equations. HIGHER ALGEBRA, Art. 428 to 444.

After the pupil becomes acquainted with exponential equations, Art. 382, 383, he will find no difficulty in obtaining the last four formulæ, 17 to 20.

To illustrate the method of finding these formulæ from the two preceding equations, we shall find l, formula 4.

From (1) $a=\dfrac{l}{r^{n-1}}$,

" (2) $a=rl-S(r-1)$.

Placing these values of a equal to each other, we find

$$l=\frac{S(r^n+r^{n-1})}{r^n-1}=\frac{(r-1)Sr^{n-1}}{r^n-1}.$$

(1) $r=2$, $r^{n-1}=2^7=128$; $ar^{n-1}=5\times128=640$.

(2) $r=\frac{1}{2}$, $r^{n-1}=(\frac{1}{2})^6=\frac{1}{64}$; $ar^{n-1}=54\times\frac{1}{64}=\frac{27}{32}$.

(3) $r=2\frac{1}{4}\div3\frac{3}{8}=\frac{2}{3}$, $r^{n-1}=(\frac{2}{3})^5=\frac{32}{243}$;
$ar^{n-1}=\frac{27}{8}\times\frac{32}{243}=\frac{4}{9}$.

(4) $r=-\frac{14}{21}=-\frac{2}{3}$, $(-\frac{2}{3})^6=\frac{64}{729}$, $\frac{64}{729}\times-21=-\frac{448}{243}$.

(5) $r=\frac{1}{2}\div\frac{1}{3}=\frac{3}{2}$, $r^{n-1}=(\frac{3}{2})^{n-1}=\dfrac{3^{n-1}}{2^{n-1}}$; $ar^{n-1}=\frac{1}{3}\times\dfrac{3^{n-1}}{2^{n-1}}=\dfrac{3^{n-2}}{2^{n-1}}$.

(9) Here, $r=3$, and $l=n^{th}$ term $=1\times3^{n-1}=3^{n-1}$,

$$S=\frac{rl-a}{r-1}=\frac{3\times3^{n-1}-1}{3-1}=\tfrac{1}{2}(3^n-1).$$

(10) Here, $r=-2$, and l, or n^{th} term $=1\times(-2)^{n-1}=\mp2^{n-1}$ according as n is odd or even.

$$S=\frac{rl-a}{r-1}=\frac{-2\times(\mp2^{n-1})-1}{-2-1}=\tfrac{1}{3}(1\mp2^n).$$

(11) $r=-\dfrac{y}{x}$, l, or n^{th} term $=x\left(-\dfrac{y}{x}\right)^{n-1}=\dfrac{x\left(-\dfrac{y}{x}\right)^n}{-\dfrac{y}{x}}$

$$=\frac{x^2\left(-\dfrac{y}{x}\right)^n}{-y}.$$

$$S=\frac{rl-a}{r-1}=\frac{\dfrac{-\dfrac{y}{x}\times x^2\left(-\dfrac{y}{x}\right)^n}{-y}-x}{-\dfrac{y}{x}-1}=\frac{x\left(-\dfrac{y}{x}\right)^n-x}{-\dfrac{y}{x}-1}=$$

$$\frac{x-x\left(-\frac{y}{x}\right)^n}{\frac{x+y}{x}}=\frac{x^2-x^2\left(-\frac{y}{x}\right)^n}{x+y}=\frac{x^2}{x+y}\left\{1-\left(-\frac{y}{x}\right)^n\right\}$$

(12) Comparing the given quantities with those in formula 13, we have $a=4$, $l=12500$, and $n=6$, to find r.

$$r=\sqrt[n-1]{\frac{l}{a}}=\sqrt[5]{\frac{12500}{4}}=\sqrt[5]{3125}=5.$$

$$S=\frac{rl-a}{r-1}=\frac{12500\times5-4}{5-1}=15624.$$

(13) Here, $a=\frac{2}{3}$, and $r=\frac{1}{2}$; $S=\frac{a}{1-r}=\frac{\frac{2}{3}}{1-\frac{1}{2}}=\frac{4}{3}.$

(14) Here, $a=9$, and $r=\frac{2}{3}$; $S=\frac{9}{1-\frac{2}{3}}=\frac{9}{\frac{1}{3}}=27.$

(15) Here, $a=\frac{2}{3}$, and $r=-\frac{1}{2}$; $S=\frac{\frac{2}{3}}{1+\frac{1}{2}}=\frac{4}{9}.$

(16) Here, $a=a$, and $r=\frac{b}{a}$; $S=\frac{a}{1-\frac{b}{a}}=\frac{a^2}{a-b}.$

(17) Let $x=$ the 1st term, and $y=$ the ratio; then, $x+xy=2\frac{2}{3}$, and $S=3=\frac{x}{1-y}$, from the formula $S=\frac{a}{1-r}$. From these equations, we find $y=+\frac{1}{3}$ or $-\frac{1}{3}$, and $x=2$ or 4; hence, there are two series, the 1st being $2+\frac{2}{3}+\frac{2}{9}+$, &c., and the 2d, $4-\frac{4}{3}+\frac{4}{9}-$, &c.

(19) From formula (1), $l=ar^{n-1}$, or $96=3r^5$; $\therefore$ $r^5=32$, and $r=2$.

(20) Here, $m=2$, and $r=\sqrt[m+1]{\frac{l}{a}}=\sqrt[3]{\frac{2}{\frac{16}{27}}}=\sqrt[3]{\frac{27}{8}}=\frac{3}{2}.$

$\therefore$ $\frac{16}{27}\times\frac{3}{2}=\frac{8}{9}$, and $\frac{8}{9}\times\frac{3}{2}=\frac{4}{3}$, are the means.

(21) Here, $m=7$, and $r=\sqrt[8]{\frac{13122}{2}}=\sqrt[4]{\sqrt[2]{6561}}=\sqrt[4]{81}=3.$

$\therefore$ the means are $2\times3=6$, $6\times3=18$, &c.

Article 301.

CIRCULATING DECIMALS

(1) Here, $a=\frac{63}{100}=\frac{63}{10^2}$, $r\ \frac{1}{100}=\frac{1}{10^2}$,

$S=\frac{.63}{1-\frac{1}{100}}=\frac{.63}{.99}=\frac{63}{99}=\frac{7}{11}$.

Or, thus, $S=\ .63636363....$

$100S=63.63636363....$

$99S=63.$

$S=\frac{63}{99}=\frac{7}{11}$.

(2) Here, $S=.54123123123....$

$100000S=54123.123123....$

$100S=\ 54.123123....$

$99900S=54069.$

$S=\frac{54069}{99900}=\frac{18023}{33300}$.

HARMONICAL PROGRESSION.

Article 303.

(3) Inverting the terms 3 and 12, they become $\frac{1}{3}$ and $\frac{1}{12}$.

Let us now insert two arithmetic means between $\frac{1}{3}$ and $\frac{1}{12}$, and the reciprocals of these will be the harmonic means between 3 and 12.

See example 14, page 258. $a=\frac{1}{12}$, $b=\frac{1}{3}$, and $m=2$;

$\frac{b-a}{m+1}=\frac{\frac{1}{3}-\frac{1}{12}}{2+1}=\frac{3}{12}\div 3=\frac{1}{12}$,

$\frac{1}{12}+\frac{1}{12}=\frac{2}{12}=\frac{1}{6}$; hence, 6 is one of the harmonic means.

$\frac{1}{6}+\frac{1}{12}=\frac{3}{12}=\frac{1}{4}$; hence, 4 is the other harmonic mean.

(4) 2 and $\frac{1}{5}$ inverted become $\frac{1}{2}$ and 5. Let us now insert two arithmetic means between $\frac{1}{2}$ and 5.

$\frac{b-a}{m+1}=\frac{5-\frac{1}{2}}{3}=1\frac{1}{2}$;

$\frac{1}{2}+1\frac{1}{2}=2$; hence, $\frac{1}{2}$ is one of the harmonic means.

$2+1\frac{1}{2}=3\frac{1}{2}$; hence, $\frac{1}{3\frac{1}{2}}=\frac{2}{7}$ is the other.

(5) $\frac{1}{2}$ and $\frac{1}{12}$ inverted become 2 and 12; let us now insert 4 arithmetic means between 2 and 12.

$\frac{b-a}{m+1}=\frac{12-2}{4+1}=\frac{10}{5}=2$; hence, we have for the arithmetic means, 4, 6, 8, 10, and for the harmonic means,

$\frac{1}{4}, \frac{1}{6}, \frac{1}{8}, \frac{1}{10}$.

(6) Since a, b, c, are in arithmetical progression, we have $a-b=b-c$; and since b, c, d, are in harmonical progression, we have $\frac{1}{b}, \frac{1}{c}$, and $\frac{1}{d}$ in arithmetical progression.

$\therefore \frac{1}{c}-\frac{1}{b}=\frac{1}{d}-\frac{1}{c}$; or, by reducing the fractions on each side to a common denominator,

$$\frac{b-c}{bc}=\frac{c-d}{cd}.$$

Multiplying by c, $\frac{b-c}{b}=\frac{c-d}{d}$;

hence, (Art. 283,) $b:b-c::d:c-d$;

but $b-c=a-b$, $\therefore b:a-b::d:c-d$.

By Inversion (Art. 271), $a-b:b::c-d:d$.

By Composition (Art. 273), $a:b::c:d$, which was required to be proved.

PROBLEMS IN ARITHMETICAL AND GEOMETRICAL PROGRESSION.

Article 304.

(3) Let $x-y$, x, and $x+y$, be the numbers;

then, $x-y+x+x+y=3x=30$, and $x=10$;

also, $(x-y)^2+x^2+(x-y)^2=3x^2+2y^2=308$.

By substituting the value of x, we find $y=2$; hence, $x-y=8$, $x=10$, and $x+y=12$, are the numbers.

(4) Let $x-3y$, $x-y$, $x+y$, and $x+3y$, be the numbers;

then, $x-3y+x-y+x+y+x+3y=4x=26$, and $x=6\frac{1}{2}$;

also, $(x-3y)(x+3y)(x-y)(x+y)=880$,

or $(x^2-9y^2)(x^2-y^2)=880$,

or $x^4-10x^2y^2+9y^4=880$.

Substituting the value of x, and reducing, we find $y=\frac{3}{2}$.

heuce, the numbers are 2, 5, 8, 11.

(5) Let x= the first term, and y= the ratio; then, x, xy, xy^2, represent the terms, and

$$x+xy+xy^2=31, \quad (1)$$
$$x+xy:x+xy^2::3:13,$$
$$\text{or } \frac{x+xy^2}{x+xy}=\frac{1+y^2}{1+y}=\frac{13}{3}. \quad (2)$$

From (2) we find $y=5$, and by substituting this in (1), we find $x=1$; therefore, the numbers are 1, 5, and 25.

(6) Let $x-y$, x, and $x+y$, represent the numbers; then,

$$(x-y)^2+x^2+(x+y)^2=3x^2+2y^2=83, \quad (1)$$
$$x^2-(x-y)(x+y)=x^2-(x^2-y^2)=y^2=4. \quad (2)$$

From (2) $y=2$, and by substituting this value in (1), we find $x=5$; hence, the numbers are 3, 5, 7.

(7) Let $x-3y$, $x-y$, $x+y$, and $x+3y$, represent the numbers; then, $(x-3y)(x+3y)=x^2-9y^2=27$, (1)

$$(x-y)(x+y)=x^2-y^2=35. \quad (2)$$

From these equations, we easily find $y=1$, and $x=6$; hence, the numbers are 3, 5, 7, 9.

(8) Let $x-y$, x, and $x+y$, represent the numbers; then, $(x-y)+x+(x+y)=3x=18$, and $x=6$; also, $2x-2y$, $3x$, and $6x+6y$ are in geometrical progression.

$$\therefore\ 2(x-y)(x+y)6=9x^2,$$
$$\text{or } 12(x^2-y^2)=9x^2;$$

whence, $2y=x$, and $y=3$;

therefore, the numbers are $6-3=3$, 6, and $6+3=9$.

(9) Let $x-1$, x, and $x+1$, represent the numbers; then, $(x-1)^4+x^4+(x+1)^4=3x^4+12x^2+2=962$; whence, $x=4$, and the numbers are 3, 4, 5.

(10) Let $x-3y$, $x-y$, $x+y$, and $x+3y$, represent the numbers; then, $(x-3y)(x-y)(x+y)(x+3y)=(x-3y)(x+3y)$ $(x-y)(x+y)=(x^2-9y^2)(x^2-y^2)=x^4-10x^2y^2+9y^4=840.$

But since the common difference between the numbers is 1, therefore, $2y=1$, and $y=\frac{1}{2}$; substituting this value of y, and reducing, we find $x=5\frac{1}{2}$; hence, the numbers are 4, 5, 6, 7.

Or, let $x-\frac{3}{2}$, $x-\frac{1}{2}$, $x+\frac{1}{2}$, and $x+\frac{3}{2}$ represent the numbers.

(11) Let $x-3y$, $x-y$, $x+y$, and $x+3y$, represent the three numbers; then,

$(x-3y)(x-y)(x+y)(x+3y)=x^4-10x^2y^2+9y^4=280,$ (1)
and $(x-3y)^2+(x-y)^2+(x+y)^2+(x+3y)^2=166,$
or $4x^2+20y^2=166,$ (2)
$\therefore\ x^2=41\frac{1}{2}-5y^2.$
Let $41\frac{1}{2}=a$; then, $x^4=a^2-10ay^2+25y^4$.
Substituting the values of x^4 and x^2 in equation (1), and reducing, we have $84y^4-830y^2=-\frac{5769}{4}$.
Whence, $y=1\frac{1}{2}$, and by substitution x becomes $5\frac{1}{2}$; whence, the numbers are $5\frac{1}{2}-3(1\frac{1}{2})=1$, $5\frac{1}{2}-1\frac{1}{2}=4$, $5\frac{1}{2}+1\frac{1}{2}=7$, &c.

(12) Let $x-4y$, $x-3y$, $x-2y$, $x-y$, x, $x+y$, $x+2y$, $x+3y$, and $x+4y$, represent the numbers; then, their sum $=9x=45$; whence, $x=5$;
also, the sum of their squares $=9x^2+60y^2=285$, from which, by substituting the value of x, we find $y=1$; hence, the numbers are 1, 2, 3, &c., to 9.

(13) Let $x-3y$, $x-2y$, $x-y$, x, $x+y$, $x+2y$, and $x+3y$, represent the numbers; then, their sum $=7x=35$; whence, $x=5$; also, the sum of their cubes $=7x^3+84xy^2=1295$, from which, by substituting the value of x, we find $y=1$; hence, the numbers are 2, 3, &c., to 8.

(14) Let x and y represent the numbers; then,

$$\frac{x+y}{2}:\sqrt{xy}::5:4,$$

or $x+y:2\sqrt{xy}::5:4;$

(Art. 276), $x^2+2xy+y^2:4xy::25:16,$

(Art. 274, Note), $x^2-2xy+y^2:x^2+2xy+y^2::9:25,$

(Art. 276), $x-y : x+y ::3:5,$

(Art. 275), $2x : 2y ::8:2,$

or $x : y ::4:1.$

This theorem may also be proved by multiplying together the means and extremes of the first proportion, and finding the value of x in terms of y, by which we find $x=4y$ or $\frac{1}{4}y$.

The converse of the preceding proposition is true; that is, if one of two numbers is four times the other, then their arithmetic mean is to their geometric mean as 5 to 4. Thus, let a and $4a$ be two numbers, then $2\frac{1}{2}a$ is their arithmetic mean, and $2a$ their geometric mean, and $2\frac{1}{2}a:2a::5:4$.

(15) Let x^2, xy, and y^2, represent the numbers; then,

$x^2+xy+y^2=7,$ (1)

$\frac{1}{x^2}+\frac{1}{xy}+\frac{1}{y^2}=\frac{7}{4}.$ (2)

Multiplying both members of equation (2) by x^2y^2, we have $x^2+xy+y^2=\frac{7}{4}x^2y^2$; (3)
therefore, $\frac{7}{4}x^2y^2=7$; whence, $x^2y^2=4$, and $xy=2$.
Substituting the value of xy in (1), we find $x^2+y^2=5$; then, from this, and $xy=2$, we readily find $x=2$ and $y=1$: hence, the numbers are 4, 2, and 1.

(16) Let $\frac{x^2}{y}$, x, y, and $\frac{y^2}{x}$, represent the numbers;

then, $\frac{x^2}{y}+y=10$, (1) $x+\frac{y^2}{x}=30$. (2)

Clearing these equations of fractions, by multiplying (1) by y, and (2) by x, we have
$x^2+y^2=10y$, and
$x^2+y^2=30x$;
whence, $10y=30x$, and $y=3x$.

Substituting this value of y in either of the equations (1) and (2), we find $x=3$; hence, $y=9$, and the numbers are 1, 3, 9, 27.

(17) Let x, xy, xy^2, xy^3, be the numbers; then,
$x+xy^3=35$, and $xy+xy^2=30$.
Dividing one equation by the other;

$$\frac{x+xy^3}{xy+xy^2}=\frac{35}{30}, \text{ or } \frac{1+y^3}{y+y^2}=\frac{7}{6}.$$

But $1+y^3$ is divisible by $1+y$, and $y+y^2=y(1+y)$.

$$\therefore \frac{1+y^3}{y+y^2}=\frac{(1+y)(1-y+y^2)}{y(1+y)}=\frac{1-y+y^2}{y}=\frac{7}{6};$$

whence, $6y^2-13y=-6$, and $y=\frac{3}{2}$ or $\frac{2}{3}$.

$$\text{And } x=\frac{30}{y+y^2}=8 \text{ or } 27.$$

Hence, the numbers are 8, 12, 18, 27.

(18) Let x, xy, xy^2, xy^3, be the numbers when increased;
$\therefore$ $x-2$, $xy-4$, xy^2-8, xy^3-15, are in arithmetical progression; hence, 1st + 3d = 2d $\times$ 2; and 2d + 4th = 3d $\times$ 2;
$\therefore$ $(x-2)+(xy^2-8)=2(xy-4)$;
or $x-2xy+xy^2=2$; $\therefore$ $x(1-2y+y^2)=2$; (1)
also, $(xy-4)+(xy^3-15)=2(xy^2-8)$;
or $xy-2xy^2+xy^3=3$; $\therefore$ $xy(1-2y+y^2)=3$. (2)
Dividing equation (2) by (1), we have

$$\frac{xy(1-2y+y^2)}{x(1-2y+y^2)}=\frac{3}{2}, \text{ or } y=\frac{3}{2};$$

whence, $x(1-3+\frac{9}{4})=2$.

$\therefore\ x=8,\ xy=12,\ xy^2=18$, and $xy^3=27$;

and subtracting 2, 4, 8, and 15 from these numbers, the remainders, 6, 8, 10, 12, are the numbers required.

(19) Let x, xy, xy^2, be the numbers;

then, $x\times xy\times xy^2=x^3y^3=64$,

$$xy=\sqrt[3]{64}=4;$$

also, $x^3+x^3y^3+x^3y^6=584$,

$$x^3+x^3y^6=584-x^3y^3=520.$$

From the equation $xy=4$, we have $x=\frac{4}{y}$.

Substituting this value of x in the last equation, we have

$$\frac{64}{y^3}+64y^3=520.$$

Dividing by 8, $\frac{8}{y^3}+8y^3=65$.

Clearing, $8y^6-65y^3=-8$;

whence, (Art. 242,) $y^3=8$ or $\frac{1}{8}$, and $y=2$ or $\frac{1}{2}$.

Therefore, $x=2$ or 8, and the numbers are 2, 4, 8.

PERMUTATIONS AND COMBINATIONS

Articles 305 and 309.

(1) (Art. 306), $P_2=n(n-1)=5(5-1)=20$;

$$P_3=n(n-1)(n-2)=5\times4\times3=60;$$

$$P_4=n(n-1)(n-2)(n-3)=5\times4\times3\times2=120$$

(2) (Art. 308), $C_2=\frac{n(n-1)}{1\times2}=\frac{5\times4}{1\times2}=10$;

$$C_3=\frac{n(n-1)(n-2)}{1\times2\times3}=\frac{5\times4\times3}{1\times2\times3}=10;$$

$$C_4=\frac{n(n-1)(n-2)(n-3)}{1\times2\times3\times4}=\frac{5\times4\times3\times2}{1\times2\times3\times4}=5;$$

$$C_5=\frac{n(n-1)(n-2)(n-3)(n-4)}{1\times2\times3\times4\times5}$$

$$=\frac{5\times4\times3\times2\times1}{1\times2\times3\times4\times5}=1.$$

(3) (Art. 306*a*), $P_r=P_3=1\times2\times3=6$.
Thus, NOT, NTO, ONT, OTN, TNO, TON.
$P_5=1\times2\times3\times4=24$.

(4) This is a case of permutations, when all the letters are taken together (Art. 306*a*).
Therefore, $P_6=1\times2\times3\times4\times5\times6=720$.

(5) This is similar to the preceding.
Therefore, $P_7=1\times2\times3\times4\times5\times6\times7=5040$.

(6) The whole number of arrangements is evidently equal to the sum of the different permutations of six letters taken 1 together, 2 together, and so on.

$P_1=n=$ 6
$P_2=n(n-1)=6\times5=$ 30
$P_3=n(n-1)(n-2)=6\times5\times4=$ 120
$P_4=n(n-1)(n-2)(n-3)=6\times5\times4\times3=$ 360
$P_5=n(n-1)(n-2)(n-3)(n-4)=6\times5\times4\times3\times2=$ 720
$P_6=n(n-1)(n-2)(n-3)(n-4)(n-5)=6\times5\times4\times3\times2\times1=$ 720

Ans. 1956

(7) Here, the number of different products will evidently be equal to the number of combinations of 4 things taken 2 together.

Therefore, $C_2=\frac{n(n-1)}{1\times2}=\frac{4\times3}{1\times2}=6$.

Let the learner verify this result by finding the different products; they are 12, 15, 18, 20, 24, 30.

(8) The number of permutations of n things taken 4 together is $P_4=n(n-1)(n-2)(n-3)$;
taken 3 together, is $P_3=n(n-1)(n-2)$;
therefore, $n(n-1)(n-2)(n-3)=6n(n-1)(n-2)$.
Dividing each member by $n(n-1)(n-2)$, we have
$n-3=6$, or $n=9$.

(9) $C_1=n=$ 4

$C_2=\frac{n(n-1)}{1\times2}=\frac{4\times3}{1\times2}=$ 6

$C_3=\frac{n(n-1)(n-2)}{1\times2\times3}=\frac{4\times3\times2}{1\times2\times3}=$ 4

$C_4=\frac{n(n-1)(n-2)(n-3)}{1\times2\times3}=\frac{4\times3\times2\times1}{1\times2\times3\times4}=$ . . 1

Ans. 15

The learner may easily verify this result by taking the coins, or by finding the different sums that can be formed of the numbers 1, 3, 5, 10; the sums are

1, 3, 5, 10; 4, 6, 11, 8, 13, 15; 9, 14, 16, 18; 19.

(10) Here, it will be necessary to find the different combinations of six things taken singly, two together, three together, four together, five together, and six together.

$C_1 = n = \ldots\ldots\ldots\ldots 6$

$C_2 = \frac{n\times(n-1)}{1\times2} = \frac{6\times5}{1\times2} = \ldots\ldots\ldots 15$

$C_3 = \frac{n(n-1)(n-2)}{1\times2\times3} = \frac{6\times5\times4}{1\times2\times3} = \ldots\ldots 20$

$C_4 = \frac{n(n-1)(n-2)(n-3)}{1\times2\times3\times4} = \frac{6\times5\times4\times3}{1\times2\times3\times4} = \ldots\ldots 15$

$C_5 = \frac{n(n-1)(n-2)(n-3)(n-4)}{1\times2\times3\times4\times5} = \frac{6\times5\times4\times3\times2}{1\times2\times3\times4\times5} = \ldots 6$

$C_6 = \frac{n(n-1)(n-2)(n-3)(n-4)(n-5)}{1\times2\times3\times4\times5\times6} = \frac{6\times5\times4\times3\times2\times1}{1\times2\times3\times4\times5\times6} = 1$

Ans. 63

In this solution, we notice an illustration of the principle of Art. 309. Thus the number of combinations of 6 things taken 1 together, is the same as when taken (6—1), or 5 together; the number, when taken 2 together, is the same as when taken (6—2), or 4 together.

(11) He may vote for 1 candidate only, or for any 2, or for any 3; hence, the whole number of ways in which he can vote will be equal to the number of combinations of four things taken *singly*, of four things taken *two* together, and of four things taken *three* together; thus,

$C_1 = n = \ldots\ldots\ldots\ldots 4$

$C_2 = \frac{n(n-1)}{1\times2} = \frac{4\times3}{1\times2} \ldots\ldots\ldots 6$

$C_3 = \frac{n(n-1)(n-2)}{1\times2\times3} = \frac{4\times3\times2}{1\times2\times3} = \ldots\ldots 4$

Total number of ways $= \ldots\ldots\ldots 14$

(12) A different guard may be posted as often as there are different combinations of four men out of 16.

$$C_4 = \frac{n(n-1)(n-2)(n-3)}{1\times2\times3\times4} = \frac{16\times15\times14\times13}{1\times2\times3\times4} = 1820.$$

To find the number of times any particular man will be on guard, it is merely necessary to find the different combinations of $(4-1)=3$ men that can be formed out of $(16-1)=15$ men, since the reserved man may be combined with each combination of 3 men, giving a combination of 4 men.

$$C_3=\frac{n(n-1)(n-2)}{1\times2\times3}=\frac{15\times14\times13}{1\times2\times3}=455.$$

(13) To find the number of peals that may be rung with 5 bells out of 8, find the number of different combinations of 5 things out of 8; then each combination will give as many changes as there are permutations of 5 bells, and the whole number of changes will be equal to the number of combinations multiplied by the number of permutations in each combination.

$$C_5=\frac{n(n-1)(n-2)(n-3)(n-4)}{1\times2\times3\times4\times5}=\frac{8\times7\times6\times5\times4}{1\times2\times3\times4\times5}=56;$$

$$P_5=1\times2\times3\times4\times5=120;$$

$$56\times120=6720.$$

The number of changes with the whole peal will evidently be equal to the number of permutations of 8 things taken all together.

$$P_8=1\times2\times3\times4\times5\times6\times7\times8=40320.$$

(14) The number of different combinations of 2 consonants out of 17, is $\frac{n(n-1)}{1\times2}=\frac{17\times16}{1\times2}=136.$

Each of these combinations may be united with each of the 5 vowels, giving $136\times5=680$ different combinations of 2 consonants and 1 vowel; now, each of these combinations of 3 letters will give $1\times2\times3=6$ permutations; therefore, the whole number of words will be $680\times6=4080$.

REMARK.—The term "different' is sometimes used in the preceding solutions in connection with combinations; this is not intended, however, to change the meaning of the word combinations, as given in the Algebra (Art. 308), but merely to render it more emphatic.

BINOMIAL THEOREM,

WHEN THE EXPONENT IS A POSITIVE INTEGER.

Article 313.

(2) By comparing the quantities with those in the formula (Art. 310, Cor. 3), we find $n=10$, $n-r+1=6$, $a=x$, and $x=y$.

Since $n-r+1=6$, we have $10-r+1=6$, and $r=5$; hence, $n-r+2=10-5+2=7$, and $r-1=4$; therefore, the coëfficient of the rth term, that is, the term in which the exponent of the leading letter is 6, is

$$\frac{n(n-1)(n-2)(n-3)}{1\times2\times3\times4}=\frac{10\times9\times8\times7}{1\times2\times3\times4}=210, \quad \textit{Ans.}$$

The coëfficient, however, is most readily found by writing out the whole development, thus,

$(x+y)^{10}=x^{10}+10x^9y+45x^8y^2+120x^7y^3+210x^6y^4+$, &c.

(3) If instead of a, x, n, and r, we substitute c^2, $-d^2$, 12, and 5 in the formula, Cor. 3, Art. 310, we have

$$\frac{12\times11\times10\times9}{1\times2\times3\times4}(c^2)^8(-d^2)^4=495c^{16}d^8.$$

(4) Comparing the quantities with those in the formula, Cor. 3, Art. 310, we have $a=a^3$, $x=3ab$, $n=9$, and $r=7$.

Therefore, the 7th term is $\dfrac{9\times8\times7\times6\times5\times4}{1\times2\times3\times4\times5\times6}(a^3)^3(3ab)^6$

$=84a^9\times729a^6b^6=61236a^{15}b^6$.

(5) Since the exponent of the binomial is 12, there will be 13 terms (Art. 310, Cor. 4); hence, the middle term will be the 7th, and $a=a^m$, $x=x^n$, $n=12$, and $r=7$, (Art. 310, Cor. 3); therefore, the middle term

$$=\frac{12\times11\times10\times9\times8\times7}{1\times2\times3\times4\times5\times6}(a^m)^6(x^n)^6=924a^{6m}x^{6n}.$$

(6) (Art. 310, Cor. 3), $a=1$, $x=x$, $n=11$, $r=8$;

$$\therefore \text{ 8th term }=\frac{11\times10\times9\times8\times7\times6\times5}{1\times2\times3\times4\times5\times6\times7}(1)^4(x)^7=330x^7.$$

(7) Comparing this with the general expansion of $a+x$, Art. 310, we have $a=3ac$, $x=-2bd$, and $n=5$; and we have

$$(3ac-2bd)^5=(3ac)^5+5(3ac)^4(-2bd)$$
$$+10(3ac)^3(-2bd)^2+10(3ac)^2(-2bd)^3+5(3ac)(-2bd)^4$$
$$+(-2bd)^5=243a^5c^5-810a^4c^4bd+1080a^3c^3b^2d^2$$
$$-720a^2c^2b^3d^3+240acb^4d^4-32b^5d^5.$$

(8) $$(a+2b-c)^3=\{(a+2b)-c\}^3=(a+2b)^3-3(a+2b)^2c$$
$$+3(a+2b)c^2-c^3=a^3+6a^2b+12ab^2+8b^3$$
$$-3a^2c-12abc-12b^2c+3ac^2+6bc^2-c^3.$$

(9) Since the coëfficients in the expansion of $(a+x)^n$ do not contain either a or x, they will be the same when $a=1$, or $x=1$, or both a and x at the same time $=1$. (See Art. 310, Cor. 6).

For the sake of brevity, let the coëfficients of the expansion of $(1+x)^n$ be represented by A_1, A_2, A_3, &c.; then,

$(1+x)^n=1+A_1x+A_2x^2+A_3x^3+A_4x^4+A_5x^5+$, &c.

Writing $-x$, instead of x,

$(1-x)^n=1-A_1x+A_2x^2-A_3x^3+A_4x^4-A_5x^5+$, &c.

Now, if x be made $=1$, then, since $(1-1)^n=0$, we have

$1-A_1+A_2-A_3+A_4-A_5+$, &c., $=0$.

$\therefore\ 1+A_2+A_4+A_6+$, &c., $=A_1+A_3+A_5+$, &c.

That is, the sum of the coëfficients of the odd terms is equal to the sum of the coëfficients of the even terms.

INDETERMINATE COEFFICIENTS; BINOMIAL THEOREM WHEN THE EXPONENT IS FRACTIONAL OR NEGATIVE; SERIES.

INDETERMINATE COEFFICIENTS.

Article 318.

(1) Let $\dfrac{1+2x}{1-3x}=A+Bx+Cx^2+Dx^3+Ex^4+$, &c.

Clearing of fractions, we have

$1+2x=A+(B-3A)x+(C-3B)x^2+(D-3C)x^3+$, &c.,

from which, by equating the coëfficients of the same powers of x,

$$A=1;$$
$$B-3A=2;\text{ whence, } B=5;$$
$$C-3B=0;\text{ whence, } C=15;$$
$$D-3C=0;\text{ whence, } D=45,\text{ \&c.}$$
$$\therefore \frac{1+2x}{1-3x}=1+5x+15x^2+45x^3+,\text{ \&c.}$$

(2) Let $\dfrac{1+2x}{1-x-x^2}=A+Bx+Cx^2+Dx^3+Ex^4+$, &c.

Clearing, $1+2x=A+(B-A)x+(C-A-B)x^2$
$+(D-B-C)x^3+$, &c.

Therefore, (Art. 314), $A=1$;

$$B-A=2;\text{ whence, } B=3;$$
$$C-A-B=0;\text{ whence, } C=4;$$
$$D-B-C=0;\text{ whence, } D=7;$$
$$\therefore \frac{1+2x}{1-x-x^2}=1+3x+4x^2+7x^3+11x^4+,\text{ \&c.}$$

Here, we easily perceive that the law is, that the coëfficient of any term is equal to the sum of the coëfficients of the two preceding terms.

(3) Let $\dfrac{1+x}{(1-x)^3}=A+Bx+Cx^2+Dx^3+Ex^4+$, &c.

Clearing, by multiplying both sides by $(1-x)^3$,

$1+x=A+(B-3A)x+(3A-3B+C)x^2$
$+(3B-A-3C+D)x^3+(3C-B-3D+E)x^4+$, &c.

Therefore, (Art. 314), $A=1$;

$$B-3A=1;\text{ whence, } B=4=2^2;$$
$$3A-3B+C=0;\text{ whence, } C=9=3^2;$$
$$3B-A-3C+D=0;\text{ whence, } D=16=4^2;$$
$$3C-B-3D+E=0;\text{ whence, } E=25=5^2,\text{ \&c}$$

$\therefore$ the series is $1^2+2^2x+3^2x^2+4^2x^3+5^2x^4+$, &c.

(4) Let $\sqrt{1-x}=A+Bx+Cx^2+Dx^3+Ex^4+Fx^5+$, &c.

Squaring both members,

$1-x=A^2+2ABx+(2AC+B^2)x^2+(2AD+2BC)x^3$
$+(2AE+2BD+C^2)x^4+$, &c.; $\therefore$

(Art. 314), $A^2=\ 1$; whence, $A=1$;

$$2AB=-1;\text{ whence, } B=-\tfrac{1}{2};$$
$$2AC+B^2=\ 0;\text{ whence, } C=-\frac{1}{8}=-\frac{1}{2.4};$$
$$2AD+2BC=\ 0;\text{ whence, } D=-\frac{1}{16}=-\frac{3}{2.4.6}$$

$$2AE+2BD+C^2=0;\ \text{whence, } E=-\frac{5}{128}=-\frac{3.5}{2.4.6.8};$$

$$\therefore \text{ the series is } 1-\frac{x}{2}-\frac{x^2}{2.4}-\frac{3x^3}{2.4.6}-\frac{3.5x^4}{2.4.6.8}-, \ \&c$$

(5) If we assume $(1+x+x^2)$ equal to the preceding series, $A+Bx+$, &c., and square both members, the coëfficients of the different powers of x will be the same as in the preceding solution. By equating the corresponding coëfficients, we have

$$A^2=1;\ \text{whence, } A=1;$$
$$2AB=1;\ \text{whence, } B=\tfrac{1}{2};$$
$$2AC+B^2=1;\ \text{whence, } C=\tfrac{3}{8};$$
$$2AD+2BC=0;\ \text{whence, } D=-\tfrac{3}{16};\ \&c.$$

Therefore, the series is $1+\frac{x}{2}+\frac{3x^2}{8}-\frac{3x^3}{16}+$, &c.

(6) Since $x-x^2=x(1-x)$, let $\frac{1+x}{x-x^2}=\frac{A}{x}+\frac{B}{1-x}$.

Reducing the fractions to a common denominator, we have

$$\frac{1+x}{x-x^2}=\frac{A(1-x)+Bx}{x(1-x)};$$

or $1+x=A+(B-A)x$;

whence, $A=1$, and $B-A=1$, or $B=2$.

Therefore, $\frac{1+x}{x-x^2}=\frac{1}{x}+\frac{2}{1-x}$.

(7) Since $x^2-7x+12=(x-4)(x-3)$,

let $\frac{x+1}{x^2-7x+12}=\frac{A}{x-4}+\frac{B}{x-3}$.

Therefore, $\frac{x+1}{x^2-7x+12}=\frac{A(x-3)+B(x-4)}{(x-4)(x-3)}$

$=\frac{(A+B)x-(3A+4B)}{(x-4)(x-3)}$;

$x+1=(A+B)x-(3A+4B)$.

Therefore, $A+B=1$, and $-3A-4B=1$;

whence, $A=5$, and $B=-4$.

Therefore, $\frac{x+1}{x^2-7x+12}=\frac{5}{x-4}-\frac{4}{x-3}$.

(8) $(x^2-1)(x-2)=(x-2)(x-1)(x+1)$.

Let $\dfrac{x^2}{(x^2-1)(x-2)}=\dfrac{A}{x-2}+\dfrac{B}{x-1}+\dfrac{C}{x+1}$

$$=\frac{A(x^2-1)+B(x-2)(x+1)+C(x-2)(x-1)}{(x-2)(x-1)(x+1)};$$

$\therefore\ x^2=(A+B+C)x^2-(B+3C)x+(2C-A-2B)$.

Solving these equations, we find $A=\frac{4}{3}$, $B=-\frac{1}{2}$, $C=\frac{1}{6}$;

$$\therefore\ \frac{x^2}{(x^2-1)(x-2)}=\frac{4}{3(x-2)}-\frac{1}{2(x-1)}+\frac{1}{6(x+1)}.$$

BINOMIAL THEOREM,

WHEN THE EXPONENT IS FRACTIONAL OR NEGATIVE.

Article 320.

(2) Here, $(n+1)\dfrac{b}{a+b}=(\frac{5}{2})\dfrac{\frac{9}{10}}{1+\frac{9}{10}}=\frac{5}{2}\times\frac{9}{10}\times\frac{10}{19}=\frac{45}{38}$; $\therefore\ r>1$; hence, the 2d term is the greatest.

(3) Here, $(n+1)\dfrac{b}{a+b}=(8+1)\dfrac{\frac{5}{2}}{3+\frac{5}{2}}=9\times\frac{5}{2}\times\frac{2}{11}=\frac{45}{11}=4\frac{1}{11}$.

The *first* whole number, greater than $4\frac{1}{11}$, is 5; therefore, the 5th term is the greatest.

(4) Here, $(n+1)\dfrac{b}{a+b}=7\times\dfrac{\frac{5}{3}}{\frac{2}{3}+\frac{5}{3}}=\dfrac{7}{1}\times\dfrac{5}{3}\times\dfrac{3}{7}=5$. Hence, $r=5$; therefore, the greatest terms are the 5th and 6th.

Article 321.

(1) Here, $a=1$, $b=-x$, $n=-1$.

Therefore, $(1-x)^{-1}=1-1\times1\times-x-\dfrac{1(-1-1)}{1.2}x^2$

$$-\frac{1(-1-1)(-1-2)}{1.2.3}(-x)^3+,\ \&c.,$$

$$=1+x+x^2+x^3+x^4+,\ \&c.$$

(2) Here, $a=1$, $b=-x$, $n=-2$.

Therefore, $(1-x)^{-2}=1-2\times1\times-x-\frac{2(-2-1)}{1.2}(-x)^2$

$$-\frac{2(-2-1)(-2-2)}{1.2.3}(-x)^2+, \text{\&c.},$$

$$=1+2x+3x^2+4x^3+, \text{\&c.}$$

(3) To develop this expression, expand the part in the parenthesis, and multiply by a^2.

Comparing $(a+x)^{-2}$ with $(a+b)^n$, we have

$a=a$, $b=x$, and $n=-2$.

Therefore, $(a+x)^{-2}=a^{-2}-2\times a^{-3}x-\frac{2(-2-1)}{1.2}a^{-4}x^2$

$$-\frac{2(-3)(-4)}{1.2.3}a^{-5}x^3+, \text{\&c.},$$

$$=\frac{1}{a^2}-\frac{2x}{a^3}+\frac{3x^2}{a^4}-\frac{4x^3}{a^5}+, \text{\&c.}$$

$$a^2(a+x)^{-2}=1-\frac{2x}{a}+\frac{3x^2}{a^2}-\frac{4x^3}{a^3}+, \text{\&c.}$$

Or, since $\frac{a^2}{(a+x)^2}=\left(1+\frac{x}{a}\right)^{-2}$, expand the last form.

(4) Here, $a=1$, $b=-x^3$, $n=\frac{1}{3}$.

Therefore, $(1-x^3)^{\frac{1}{3}}=1-\frac{1}{3}\times1\times x^3+\frac{\frac{1}{3}(\frac{1}{3}-1)}{1.2}(-x^3)^2$

$$+\frac{\frac{1}{3}(-\frac{2}{3})(-\frac{5}{3})}{1.2.3}(-x^3)^3-, \text{\&c.},$$

$$=1-\frac{x^3}{3}-\frac{x^6}{9}-\frac{5x^9}{81}-, \text{\&c.}$$

(5) Here, $a=a^2$, $b=x$, $n=\frac{1}{2}$.

$\therefore (a^2+x)^{\frac{1}{2}}=(a^2)^{\frac{1}{2}}+\frac{1}{2}(a^2)^{-\frac{1}{2}}x+\frac{\frac{1}{2}(\frac{1}{2}-1)}{1.2}(a^2)^{-\frac{3}{2}}x^2$

$$+\frac{\frac{1}{2}(-\frac{1}{2})(-\frac{3}{2})}{1.2.3}(a^2)^{-\frac{5}{2}}x^3+\frac{\frac{1}{2}(-\frac{1}{2})(-\frac{3}{2})(-\frac{5}{2})}{1.2.3.4}(a^2)^{-\frac{7}{2}}x^4+, \text{\&c}$$

$$=a+\frac{x}{2a}-\frac{x^2}{8a^3}+\frac{x^3}{16a^5}-\frac{5x^4}{128a^7}+, \text{\&c.}$$

In making these reductions, the pupil must notice that

$$\frac{1}{2}(a^2)^{-\frac{1}{2}}x=\frac{x}{2(a^2)^{\frac{1}{2}}}=\frac{x}{2a},$$

$$\frac{\frac{1}{2}(\frac{1}{2}-1)}{1.2}(a^2)^{-\frac{3}{2}}x^2=-\frac{x^2}{8(a^2)^{\frac{3}{2}}}=-\frac{x^2}{8a^3};$$

$$\frac{\frac{1}{2}(-\frac{1}{2})(-\frac{3}{2})}{1.2.3}(a^2)^{-\frac{5}{2}}x^3=\frac{x^3}{16(a^2)^{\frac{5}{2}}}=\frac{x^3}{16a^5}, \text{ \&c.}$$

Or, since $\sqrt{a^2+x}=(a^2+x)^{\frac{1}{2}}=a\left(1+\frac{x}{a^2}\right)^{\frac{1}{2}}$, expand the part in parenthesis, and multiply by a.

(6) Here, $a=a^3$, $b=-x$, $n=\frac{1}{3}$.

$$\therefore\ (a^3-x)^{\frac{1}{3}}=(a^3)^{\frac{1}{3}}+\tfrac{1}{3}(a^3)^{-\frac{2}{3}}\times -x+\frac{\frac{1}{3}(-\frac{2}{3})}{1.2}(a^3)^{-\frac{5}{3}}(-x)^2$$

$$+\frac{\frac{1}{3}(-\frac{2}{3})(-\frac{5}{3})}{1.2.3}(a^3)^{-\frac{8}{3}}(-x)^3+\frac{\frac{1}{3}(-\frac{2}{3})(-\frac{5}{3})(-\frac{8}{3})}{1.2.3.4}(a^3)^{-\frac{11}{3}}(-x)^4$$

$$+, \text{ \&c.}, =a-\frac{x}{3a^2}-\frac{x^2}{9a^5}-\frac{5x^3}{81a^8}-\frac{10x^4}{243a^{11}}-, \text{ \&c.}$$

Or, put $(a^3-x)^{\frac{1}{3}}=a\left(1-\frac{x}{a^3}\right)^{\frac{1}{3}}$, and expand as in Ex. 5th.

(7) Here, $a=1$, $b=2x$, $n=\frac{1}{2}$.

$$\therefore\ (1+2x)^{\frac{1}{2}}=1+\tfrac{1}{2}(2x)+\frac{\frac{1}{2}(-\frac{1}{2})}{1.2}(2x)^2+\frac{\frac{1}{2}(-\frac{1}{2})(-\frac{3}{2})}{1.2.3}(2x)^3$$

$$+\frac{\frac{1}{2}(-\frac{1}{2})(-\frac{3}{2})(-\frac{5}{2})}{1.2.3.4}(2x)^4+, \text{ \&c.}$$

$$=1+x-\tfrac{1}{2}x^2+\tfrac{1}{2}x^3-\tfrac{5}{8}x^4+, \text{ \&c.}$$

(8) Here, $a=a^2$, $b=-x^2$, $n=\frac{1}{2}$.

$$\therefore\ (a^2-x^2)=(a^2)^{\frac{1}{2}}+\tfrac{1}{2}(a^2)^{-\frac{1}{2}}\times -x^2+\frac{\frac{1}{2}(-\frac{1}{2})}{1.2}(a^2)^{-\frac{3}{2}}(-x^2)^2$$

$$+\frac{\frac{1}{2}(-\frac{1}{2})(-\frac{3}{2})}{1.2.3}(a^2)^{-\frac{5}{2}}(-x^2)^3+\frac{\frac{1}{2}(-\frac{1}{2})(-\frac{3}{2})(-\frac{5}{2})}{1.2.3.4}(a^2)^{-\frac{7}{2}}$$

$$(-x^2)^4+, \text{ \&c.},$$

$$=a-\frac{x^2}{2a}-\frac{x^4}{8a^3}-\frac{x^6}{16a^5}-\frac{5x^8}{128a^7}-, \text{ \&c.}$$

Or, put $\sqrt{a^2-x^2}=a\sqrt{1+\frac{x^2}{a^2}}=a\left(1+\frac{x^2}{a^2}\right)^{\frac{1}{2}}$, expand the part in parenthesis and multiply by a.

(9) $\sqrt[3]{a+x}=\sqrt[3]{\left\{a\left(1+\frac{x}{a}\right)\right\}}=\sqrt[3]{a}\sqrt[3]{\left(1+\frac{x}{a}\right)}.$

Comparing $\sqrt[3]{\left(1+\frac{x}{a}\right)}$ with $(a+b)^n$, we have $a=1$.

$b=\frac{x}{a}$, $n=\frac{1}{3}$.

$$\therefore \sqrt[3]{\left(1+\frac{x}{a}\right)}=1+\tfrac{1}{3}\frac{x}{a}+\frac{\frac{1}{3}(-\frac{2}{3})}{1.2}\frac{x^2}{a^2}+\frac{\frac{1}{3}(-\frac{2}{3})(-\frac{5}{3})}{1.2.3}\frac{x^3}{a^3}$$

$$+\frac{\frac{1}{3}(-\frac{2}{3})(-\frac{5}{3})(-\frac{8}{3})}{1.2.3.4}\frac{x^4}{a^4}+, \text{\&c.},$$

$$=1+\frac{x}{3a}-\frac{x^2}{9a^2}+\frac{5x^3}{81a^3}-\frac{10x^4}{243a^4}+, \text{\&c.}$$

$$\therefore \sqrt[3]{a+x}=\sqrt[3]{a}\left(1+\frac{x}{3a}-\frac{x^2}{9a^2}+\frac{5x^3}{81a^3}-\frac{10x^4}{243a^4}+, \text{\&c.}\right)$$

(10) $(a^3+x^3)^{\frac{1}{3}}=\left\{a^3\left(1+\frac{x^3}{a^3}\right)\right\}^{\frac{1}{3}}=a\left(1+\frac{x^3}{a^3}\right)^{\frac{1}{3}}.$

Comparing $\left(1+\frac{x^3}{a^3}\right)^{\frac{1}{3}}$ with $(a+b)^n$, we have $a=1$, $b=\frac{x^3}{a^3}$, $n=\frac{1}{3}$.

$$\therefore \left(1+\frac{x^3}{a^3}\right)^{\frac{1}{3}}=1+\tfrac{1}{3}\frac{x^3}{a^3}+\frac{\frac{1}{3}(-\frac{2}{3})}{1.2}\frac{x^6}{a^6}+\frac{\frac{1}{3}(-\frac{2}{3})(-\frac{5}{3})}{1.2.3}\frac{x^9}{a^9}+, \text{\&c.}$$

$$=1+\frac{x^3}{3a^3}-\frac{2x^6}{3.6a^6}+\frac{2.5x^9}{3.6.9a^9}-, \text{\&c.}$$

$$\therefore (a^3+x^3)^{\frac{1}{3}}=a\left(1+\frac{x^3}{3a^3}-\frac{2x^6}{3.6a^6}+\frac{2.5x^9}{3.6.9a^9}-, \text{\&c.}\right)$$

(11) $\sqrt[3]{8+1}=\sqrt[3]{\{8(1+\frac{1}{8})\}}=2\sqrt[3]{(1+\frac{1}{8})}$. By comparing this with example 9, we find that $a=8$, $\sqrt[3]{a}=2$, and $x=1$. We may therefore obtain the development merely by substituting $\frac{1}{8}$ for $\frac{x}{a}$, in the development of $\sqrt[3]{a+x}$, or by the method pursued in the solution of that example.

(12) This is the same as example 10, except that x^3 is minus instead of plus: the development will therefore be the same, except that all the terms of the expansion after the first term will be minus.

(13) $(a^3-x^3)^{\frac{2}{3}}=\left\{a^3\left(1-\frac{x^3}{a^3}\right)\right\}^{\frac{2}{3}}=a^2\left(1-\frac{x^3}{a^3}\right)^{\frac{2}{3}};$

$$\therefore \frac{a^3}{(a^3-x^3)^{\frac{2}{3}}}=\frac{a^3}{a^2\left(1-\frac{x^3}{a^3}\right)^{\frac{2}{3}}}=a\left(1-\frac{x^3}{a^3}\right)^{-\frac{2}{3}}.$$

Comparing $\left(1-\frac{x^3}{a^3}\right)^{-\frac{2}{3}}$ with $(a+b)^n$, we have $a=1$, $b=-\frac{x^3}{a^3}$, $n=-\frac{2}{3}$.

$$\therefore \left(1-\frac{x^3}{a^3}\right)^{-\frac{2}{3}}=1-\tfrac{2}{3}\times-\frac{x^3}{a^3}-\frac{\frac{2}{3}(-\frac{2}{3}-1)}{1.2}\left(-\frac{x^3}{a^3}\right)^2$$

$$-\frac{\frac{2}{3}(-\frac{5}{3})(-\frac{8}{3})}{1.2.3}\left(-\frac{x^3}{a^3}\right)^3-, \text{ \&c.,}$$

$$=1+\frac{2}{3}\cdot\frac{x^3}{a^3}+\frac{2.5x^6}{3.6a^6}+\frac{2.5.8x^9}{3.6.9a^9}+, \text{ \&c.}$$

$$\therefore a\left(1-\frac{x^3}{a^3}\right)^{-\frac{2}{3}}=a+\frac{2}{3}\cdot\frac{x^3}{a^2}+\frac{2.5x^6}{3.6a^5}+\frac{2.5.8x^9}{3.6.9a^8}+, \text{ \&c.}$$

Article 323.

(1) $\sqrt{9+1}=\sqrt{9(1+\frac{1}{9})}=3\sqrt{(1+\frac{1}{9})}$. (See Formula, Art. 322.)

$$\sqrt{1+\tfrac{1}{9}}=1+\tfrac{1}{2}\times\tfrac{1}{9}-\frac{1}{2^3}\times\frac{1}{9^2}+\frac{1}{2^4}\times\frac{1}{9^3}-\frac{5}{2^6}\times\frac{1}{9^4}+, \text{ \&c.}$$

$=1+.055555-.001543+.000085$
$-.000005+$, &c., $=1.054092$,

and $1.054092\times3=3.16227+$.

(2) $\sqrt[3]{27-8}=\sqrt[3]{27(1-\frac{1}{9})}=3\sqrt[3]{(1-\frac{1}{9})}$.

The development of $(1-\frac{1}{9})^{\frac{1}{3}}$ is the same as that of $(1+\frac{1}{9})^{\frac{1}{3}}$, except that all the terms after the first are negative. To get the result accurately requires that we should calculate five terms of the series after the first. These carried to nine places of decimals are

$-.037037037-.001371742-.000084675$
$-.000006272-.000000511-$, &c.

Subtracting these from 1, and multiplying the remainder by 3, we have $\sqrt[3]{24}=2.8844992+$.

(3) $\sqrt{128-20}=\sqrt[7]{128(1-\frac{5}{32})}=2\sqrt[7]{1-\frac{5}{32}}$.

In calculating the value of each term, the shortest method is to find it from the preceding term. Thus, by considering the formula, Art. 322, we notice that each term in the development after the first, is equal to the preceding term, multiplied by two factors, one of which is $\frac{b}{a^n}$, and the others successively $\frac{1}{n}$, $\frac{n-1}{2n}$, $\frac{2n-1}{3n}$, $\frac{3n-1}{4n}$, $\frac{4n-1}{5n}$, and so on; therefore, calling the terms A, B, C, and so on, we have

$\sqrt[7]{1-\frac{5}{32}}=1-\frac{1}{7}.\frac{5}{32}A-\frac{3}{7}.\frac{5}{32}B-\frac{13}{21}.\frac{5}{32}C-\frac{5}{7}.\frac{5}{32}D$
$-\frac{27}{35}.\frac{5}{32}E-$, &c. $=1-.0223214-.0014947-.0001446$
$-.0000161-.0000019=.9760213$, and $.9760213\times2$
$=1.95204+$.

DIFFERENTIAL METHOD OF SERIES.

Article 325.

(2) Here, $n=2$, $a=1$, $b=4$, $c=9$.

$\therefore\ D_2=1-2\times4+\dfrac{2(1)9}{1.2}=1-8+9=2.$

(3) Here, $n=3$, $a=1$, $b=3$, $c=6$, $d=10$.

$\therefore\ D_3=-1+3\times3-\dfrac{3(2)6}{1.2}+\dfrac{3(2)(1)10}{1.2.3}=-1+9-18+10$
$=0.$

(4) Here, $n=5$, $a=1$, $b=3$, $c=9$, $d=27$, $e=81$, $f=243$.

$\therefore\ D_5=-1+15-90+270-405+243=32.$

(5) Here, $n=5$, $a=1$, $b=\frac{1}{2}$, $c=\frac{1}{4}$, $d=\frac{1}{8}$, $e=\frac{1}{16}$, $f=\frac{1}{32}$.

$\therefore\ D_5=-1+2\frac{1}{2}-\dfrac{5.4}{1.2}.\frac{1}{4}+\dfrac{5.4.3}{1.2.3}.\frac{1}{8}-\dfrac{5.4.3.2}{1.2.3.4}.\frac{1}{16}$
$+\dfrac{5.4.3.2.1}{1.2.3.4.5}.\frac{1}{32}=-1+2\frac{1}{2}-2\frac{1}{2}+1\frac{1}{4}-\frac{5}{16}+\frac{1}{32}=\frac{1}{4}-\frac{5}{16}$
$+\frac{1}{32}=-\frac{1}{32}.$

Article 326.

(3) Here, $a=1$, $D_1=3$, $D_2=2$, and $D_3=0$. Therefore,

15th term $=1+(15-1)3+\dfrac{14.13}{1.2}\times2=1+42+182=225$

n^{th} term $=1+(n-1)3+\dfrac{(n-1)(n-2)}{1.2}\times2=n^2.$

(4) Here, $a=1$, $D_1=4$, $D_2=6$, $D_3=4$, $D_4=1$, $D_5=0$.

$\therefore\ 12^{th}$ term $=1+11\times4+\dfrac{11.10}{1.2}\times6+\dfrac{11.10.9}{1.2.3}\times4$
$+\dfrac{11.10.9.8}{1.2.3.4}\times1=1+44+330+660+330=1365.$

(5) Here, $a=1$, $D_1=2$, $D_2=1$, $D_3=0$.

$\therefore$ n^{th} term $=1+(n-1)2+\dfrac{(n-1)(n-2)}{1.2}=\dfrac{n^2+n}{2}$

$=\dfrac{n(n+1)}{2}$.

(6) Multiplying the factors together, the terms are 70, 252, 594, 1144, 1950, and so on.

Here, $a=70$, $D_1=182$, $D_2=160$, $D_3=48$, $D_4=0$.

$\therefore$ 9th term $=70+8\times182+\dfrac{8\times7}{1.2}\times160+\dfrac{8.7.6}{1.2.3}\times48$

$=70+1456+4480+2688=8694$.

(7) Here, the terms are 2, 12, 30, 56, and so on; hence, $a=2$, $D_1=10$, $D_2=8$, $D_3=0$.

$\therefore$ n^{th} term $=2+(n-1)10+\dfrac{(n-1)(n-2)}{2}\times8$

$=2+10n-10+4n^2-12n+8=4n^2-2n$.

Article 327.

(3) Here, $a=1$, $D_1=2$, $D_2=1$, $D_3=0$.

$\therefore$ Sum of n terms $=n+\dfrac{n(n-1)}{1.2}\times2+\dfrac{n(n-1)(n-2)}{1.2.3}\times1$

$=\dfrac{6n+6n^2-6n+n^3-3n^2+2n}{1.2.3}=\dfrac{n^3+3n^2+2n}{1.2.3}$

$=\dfrac{n(n+1)(n+2)}{1.2.3}$.

(4) Here, $a=3$, $D_1=8$, $D_2=12$, $D_3=6$, $D_4=0$. Therefore,

Sum of 20 terms $=20\times3+\dfrac{20.19}{1.2}\times8+\dfrac{20.19.18}{1.2.3}\times12$

$+\dfrac{20\times19\times18\times17}{1.2.3.4}\times6=60+1520+13680+29070$

$=44330$.

(5) Here, the terms are 6, 24, 60, 120, 210, and so on; hence, $a=6$, $D_1=18$, $D_2=18$, $D_3=6$, and $D_4=0$.

$\therefore$ Sum of 20 terms $=20\times6+\dfrac{20\times19}{1.2}\times18$

$+\dfrac{20\times19\times18}{1.2.3}\times18+\dfrac{20\times19\times18\times17}{1.2.3.4}\times6=120+3420$

$+20520+29070=53130$.

(6) Here, $a=1$, $D_1=7$, $D_2=12$, $D_3=6$, $D_4=0$.

$\therefore$ Sum of n terms $=n+\frac{n(n-1)}{1.2}\times7+\frac{n(n-1)(n-2)}{1.2.3}$
$\times12+\frac{n(n-1)(n-2)(n-3)}{1.2.3.4}\times6=\frac{4n}{4}+\frac{14n^2-14n}{4}$
$+\frac{8n^3-24n^2+16n}{4}+\frac{n^4-6n^3+11n^2-6n}{4}$
$=\frac{n^4+2n^3+n^2}{4}=\frac{n^2}{4}(n^2+2n+1)=[\frac{1}{2}n(n+1)]^2$.

(7) We must find this series by making $n=1, 2, 3$, and so on; thus, if $n=1$, the first term is 1; if $n=2$, the second term is 16; if $n=3$, the third term is 63; in like manner, we find the fourth term is 160, the fifth term 325, and so on. Hence, we find $a=1$, $D_1=15$, $D_2=32$, $D_3=18$, $D_4=0$.

$\therefore$ Sum of 25 terms $=25+\frac{25.24}{1.2}\times15+\frac{25.24.23}{1.2.3}\times32$
$+\frac{25.24.23.22}{1.2.3.4}\times18=25+4500+73600+227700=305825$.

PILING BALLS AND SHELLS.

Article 332.

(3) Comparing the number 15 with Formula B in Art. 332, we have $n=15$.

$\therefore$ number $=\frac{n(n+1)(2n+1)}{6}=\frac{15\times16\times31}{6}=1240$.

(4) See Formula C, Art. 332, $l=52$, and $n=34\frac{1}{6}$;
$n(n+1)(3l-n+1)=\frac{34}{6}\times35\times(156-34+1)=\frac{17}{3}\times35$
$\times123=17\times35\times41=24395$.

(5) Number of balls in a complete triangular pile of which each side of the base is 25, is (Art. 332),
$\frac{1}{6}n(n+1)(n+2)=\frac{25}{6}\times26\times27=25\times13\times9=2925$.
Since the number of balls in a side of the top course is 13, the number in a side of the pile that is wanting is 12; hence, the number in this pile is $\frac{12}{6}\times13\times14=364$.
Therefore, $2925-364=2561$, the number required.

(6) Number in the pile considered as complete, (Art. 332),

$=\frac{n}{6}(n+1)(n+2)=\frac{38}{6}\times39\times40=19\times13\times40=9880.$

Since there are 15 courses, and the number of balls is one less in each course than in the next preceding course; therefore, $38-15=23$ is the number of balls in a side of the incomplete pile, and the number in this pile is

$\frac{23}{6}\times24\times25=23\times4\times25=2300.$

Therefore, $9880-2300=7580$, the number required.

(7) Number in the pile considered as complete (Art. 332),

$=\frac{n}{6}(n+1)(2n+1)=\frac{44}{6}\times45\times89=22\times15\times89=29370.$

Number of balls in the side of a pile that is wanting is 21, and the number in the incomplete pile is

$\frac{21}{6}\times22\times43=7\times11\times43=3311.$

Therefore, $29370-3311=26059$, the number in the incomplete square pile.

(8) $\sqrt{1521}=39=$ number of balls in a side of the base course,

$\sqrt{169}=13=$ " " " " " top "

$\frac{39}{6}\times40\times79=13\times20\times79=20540$, the number of balls in the pile considered as complete.

$13-1=12$, the number of balls in a side of the base of the pile that is wanting; and $\frac{12}{6}\times13\times25=650.$

Therefore, $20540-650=19890$, the number of balls in the incomplete pile.

(9) Here, we have the equation (Art. 332),

$\frac{1}{6}n(n+1)(3l-n+1)=6440,$

in which $n=20$, to find l.

Therefore, $\frac{20}{6}\times21(3l-19)=6440,$

$$70(3l-19)=6440,$$

$$3l-19=92, \text{ and } l=37.$$

$37\times20=740$, the number of balls in the base.

(10) Here, we have the proportion

$\frac{1}{6}n(n+1)(n+2):\frac{1}{6}n(n+1)(2n+1)::6:11.$

Placing the product of the means equal to the product of the extremes, and canceling $\frac{1}{6}n(n+1)$ on each side, we have $12n+6=11n+22$;

whence, $n=16$, the number of balls in a side of the base of each.

$\frac{1}{6}n(n+1)(n+2)=\frac{16}{6}\times17\times18=816=$ balls in tr. pile,

$\frac{1}{6}n(n+1)(2n+1)=\frac{16}{6}\times17\times33=1496=$ " " sq. pile.

(11) Since the number of balls in each side increases by 1 as we descend, and since there are 7 courses below the upper one; therefore, $36+7=43$, and $17+7=24$, are the number of balls in the longer and shorter sides of the lower course.

$\frac{1}{6}n(n+1)(3l-n+1)=\frac{24}{6}\times25(129-24+1)=10600$, the number of balls in the pile considered as complete. It is evident that 35 and 16 are the number of balls in the longer and shorter sides of the pile that is wanting. hence, the number of balls in this pile, is

$\frac{16}{6}\times17(105-16+1)=4080$.

$\therefore$ $10600-4080=6520$, the number of balls in the incomplete pile.

INTERPOLATION OF SERIES.

Article 335.

(1) Since the 4th differences vanish, we have (Art. 325), $e-4d+6c-4b+a=0$, where $a=3$, $c=15$, $d=30$, and $e=55$, to find b.

$\therefore$ $55-4\times30+6\times15-4b+3=0$; whence, $b=7$.

Having the terms of the series, viz.: 3, 7, 15, 30, 55, we readily find the first terms of the several orders of differences (Art. 325) to be $D_1=4$, $D_2=4$, $D_3=3$, and $D_4=0$; therefore, by making $n=6$, 7, and 8 successively, and substituting the values of D_1, D_2, and D_3 in the formula

$$a+(n-1)D_1+\frac{(n-1)(n-2)}{1.2}D_2+\frac{(n-1)(n-2)(n-3)}{1.2.3}D_3,$$

we obtain the 6th, 7th, and 8th terms. Thus,

the 6th term is $3+5\times4+5\times4\times2+\frac{5\times4\times3}{1\times2\times3}\times3$

$=3+20+40+30=93$.

The 7th term is $3+6\times4+6\times5\times2+\frac{6\times5\times4}{1\times2\times3}\times3=3+24+60+60=147$.

The 8th term is $3+7\times4+7\times6\times2+\frac{7\times6\times5}{1\times2\times3}\times3=3+28+84+105=220$.

(2) Let $x=$ the 5th term; then, writing down the terms, and finding the respective orders of differences, we have

11 , 18 , 30 , 50 , x , 132 , 209,
7 , 12 , 20 , $x-50$, $132-x$, 77 ,
5 , 8 , $x-70$, $182-2x$, $x-55$,
3 , $x-78$, $252-3x$, $3x-237$,
$x-81$, $330-4x$, $6x-489$,
$411-5x$, $10x-819$,
$15x-1230$.

Therefore, $15x-1230=0$, and $x=82$.

Or thus, since the 6th differences vanish, or become 0, it is merely necessary to find the first term of the 6th order, by means of the Formula, Art. 325, by calling $n=6$, $a=11$, $b=18$, &c.; thus,

$$z-nb+\frac{n(n-1)}{1.2}c-\frac{n(n-1)(n-2)}{1.2.3}d$$
$$+\frac{n(n-1)(n-2)(n-3)}{1.2.3.4}x-\frac{n(n-1)(n-2)(n-3)(n-4)}{1.2.3.4.5}f$$
$$+\frac{n(n-1)(n-2)(n-3)(n-4)(n-5)}{1.2.3.4.5.6}g=0;$$

$$\therefore 11-6\times18+\frac{6\times5}{2}\times30-\frac{6\times5\times4}{2\times3}\times50+\frac{6\times5\times4\times3}{2\times3\times4}x$$
$$-\frac{6\times5\times4\times3\times2}{2\times3\times4\times5}\times132+\frac{6\times5\times4\times3\times2\times1}{1\times2\times3\times4\times5\times6}\times209=0;$$

$11-108+450-1000+15x-792+209=0$;
whence, $15x=1230$, and $x=82$.

(3) Calling the respective given logarithms, a, b, d and e, since c is wanting, we have, by the formula, Art. 325, $e-4d+6c-4b+a=0$.
From this equation, by substituting the values of a. b, d, and e, we readily find $c=2.0128372$.

(4)

Nos.	Cube Roots.	1st Diff.	2d Diff.	Mean of 2d Diff.
60	3.91487	4302		
62	3.95789	4211	—91	—89
64	4.	4124	—87	
66	4.04124			

Here, $p'=\frac{1}{2}$, $d=4211$, $d'=-89$, (Art. 335), and
$$p'\left(d+\frac{p'-1}{2}d'\right)=\tfrac{1}{2}\left(4211+\frac{\frac{1}{2}-1}{2}\times-89\right)=\tfrac{1}{2}(4211+22)$$
$=2116$; and $3.95789+.02116=3.97905$.

(5) Let a^2, $(a+1)^2$, $(a+2)^2$, &c., be a series of squares, and let them be developed, and their differences be taken as below:

$$a^2,\ a^2+2a+1,\ a^2+4a+1,\ a^2+6a+9,\ \text{\&c.},$$
$$2a+1,\quad 2a+3,\quad 2a+5,\ \text{\&c.},$$
$$2,\quad 2,\ \text{\&c.}$$

The second differences are constant, and a table of squares may be found as follows:

Let us commence with $50^2=2500$ and $51^2=2601$, whose difference is 101; then, since the second differences are constant and equal to 2, the difference between the squares of 51 and 52 will be $101+2=103$, and this added to 2601 will give the square of 52; and so on, as in the following table:

$2500=50^2$	$2809=53^2$
101	107
$2601=51^2$	$2916=54^2$
103	109
$2704=52^2$	$3025=55^2$
105	111
$2809=53^2$	$3136=56^2$.

In a manner nearly similar, a table of cube numbers may be computed.

INFINITE SERIES.

Article 338.

(2) Since $q=1$, $p=1$, and $n=1, 2, 3$, &c.

$$\therefore \left\{\begin{matrix} 1+\frac{1}{2}+\frac{1}{3}+\frac{1}{4}+, \text{\&c., ad inf.} \\ -(\frac{1}{2}+\frac{1}{3}+\frac{1}{4}+, \text{\&c.,) ad inf.} \end{matrix}\right\} =1= \text{sum.}$$

(3)
$$\left\{\begin{matrix} 1+\frac{1}{2}+\frac{1}{3}+\frac{1}{4}\cdot\cdot\cdot\cdot\frac{1}{n} \\ -\left(\frac{1}{2}+\frac{1}{3}+\frac{1}{4}\cdot\cdot\frac{1}{n}+\frac{1}{n+1}\right) \end{matrix}\right\} =1-\frac{1}{n+1}=\frac{n}{n+1}$$

(4) Since $q=1$, $p=3$, and $n=1, 2, 3$, &c.

$$\therefore \left\{\begin{matrix} 1+\frac{1}{2}+\frac{1}{3}+\frac{1}{4}+\frac{1}{5}+, \text{\&c.,} \\ -(\frac{1}{4}+\frac{1}{5}+\frac{1}{6}+\frac{1}{7}+\frac{1}{8}+, \text{\&c.)} \end{matrix}\right\} =1+\frac{1}{2}+\frac{1}{3}=1\frac{5}{6},$$

and $\frac{1}{p}^{th}$ of this sum $=\frac{11}{18}=$ sum required.

(5) Since $q=1$, $p=2$, and $n=1, 2, 3$, &c.

$$\therefore \left\{ \begin{array}{l} 1+\frac{1}{2}+\frac{1}{3}+\frac{1}{4}+\frac{1}{5}+, \text{\&c.,} \\ \quad -(\frac{1}{3}+\frac{1}{4}+\frac{1}{5}+, \text{\&c.}) \end{array} \right\} = 1+\frac{1}{2} = \frac{3}{2},$$

and $\frac{1}{p}$th of this sum $=\frac{1}{2}$ of $\frac{3}{2}=\frac{3}{4}$.

(6) To find the series let $n=1, 2, 3, 4$, &c., successively; then, the terms are

$$\frac{1}{1.5}+\frac{1}{2.6}+\frac{1}{3.7}+\frac{1}{4.8}+, \text{\&c.}$$

Also, $q=1$, and $p=4$.

$$\therefore \left\{ \begin{array}{l} 1+\frac{1}{2}+\frac{1}{3}+\frac{1}{4}+\frac{1}{5}+\frac{1}{6}+, \text{\&c.,} \\ \quad -(\frac{1}{5}+\frac{1}{6}+, \text{\&c.}) \end{array} \right\} = 1+\frac{1}{2}+\frac{1}{3}+\frac{1}{4} = \frac{25}{12}$$

and $\frac{1}{p}$th of this sum $=\frac{1}{4}$ of $\frac{25}{12}=\frac{25}{48}$.

(7) Dividing each term of this series by 2, it becomes

$$\frac{1}{2}+\frac{1}{2.3}+\frac{1}{3.4}+\frac{1}{4.5}+, \text{\&c.}$$

The sum of this series has been found (see example 2,) to be 1, therefore the sum of the given series is $1\times2=2$.

(8) Multiplying each term of this series by 3×4, or 12, it becomes $\frac{1}{2}+\frac{1}{2.3}+\frac{1}{3.4}+$, &c., the sum of which has been found to be 1; therefore, the sum of the series is $1\div12=\frac{1}{12}$.

RECURRING SERIES.

Article 343.

(2) Here, $A=1$, $B=6x$, $C=12x^2$, $D=48x^3$, $E=120x^4$, &c. Making $x=1$, and substituting in the formula, (Art. 341), we have $p=\frac{12\times48-6\times120}{12\times12-6\times48}=1$, $q=\frac{12\times120-48\times48}{12\times12-6\times48}=6$.

(Art. 343), $S=\frac{A+B-Apx}{1-px-qx^2}=\frac{1+6x-x}{1-x-6x^2}=\frac{1+5x}{1-x-6x^2}$.

(3) Here, $A=1$, $B=2x$, $C=3x^2$, $D=4x^3$, $E=5x^4$.
Making $x=1$, and applying formula (Art. 341), we have

$$p=\frac{3\times4-2\times5}{3\times3-2\times4}=2,\ q=\frac{3\times5-4\times4}{3\times3-2\times4}=-1.$$

(Art. 343), $S=\frac{A+B-Apx}{1-px-qx^2}=\frac{1+2x-2x}{1-2x+x^2}=\frac{1}{(1-x)^2}$.

(4) Here, $A=\frac{a}{c}$, $B=-\frac{abx}{c}$, $C=\frac{ab^2x^2}{c^3}$, $D=-\frac{ab^3x^3}{c^4}$, &c.

If we make $x=1$, and apply the formula, (Art. 341), we shall find $p=-\frac{b}{c}$, and $q=0$, but the scale of relation is easily seen to be $-\frac{b}{c}$, since if any coëfficient is multiplied by this quantity it will give the coëfficient of the next following term.

$$(\text{Art. } 343),\ S=\frac{A+B-Apx}{1-px}=\frac{\frac{a}{c}-\frac{abx}{c^2}+\frac{abx}{c^2}}{1+\frac{bx}{c}}=\frac{a}{c+bx}.$$

(5) Here, $A=0$, $B=x$, $C=x^2$, &c., and the scale of relation is 1, that is $p=1$, and $q=0$.

Therefore, $S=\frac{A+B-Apx}{1-px}=\frac{0+x-0}{1-x}=\frac{x}{1-x}$.

(6) Here, $A=0$, $B=x$, $C=-x^2$, &c., and the scale of relation is -1, that is, $p=-1$, and $q=0$.

Therefore, $S=\frac{A+B-Apx}{1-px}=\frac{0+x-0}{1+x}=\frac{x}{1+x}$.

(7) Here, $A=1$, $B=3x$, $C=5x^2$, $D=7x^3$, $E=9x^4$, &c.
Making $x=1$, and applying the formula (Art. 341), we have $p=\frac{5\times7-3\times9}{5\times5-3\times7}=2$, $q=\frac{5\times9-7\times7}{5\times5-3\times7}=-1$.

(Art. 343), $S=\frac{A+B-Apx}{1-px-qx^2}=\frac{1+3x-2x}{1-2x+x^2}=\frac{1+x}{(1-x)^2}$.

(8) Here, $A=1$, $B=4x$, $C=9x^2$, $D=16x^3$, $E=25x^4$, &c.
Making $x=1$, and applying the formula, (Art. 341), the values of p and q thus found will not reproduce the series; hence, we must apply the equations in Art. 342, and find the values of p, q, and r, when $x=1$. These equations give

$$16=9p+4q+r;$$
$$25=16p+9q+4r;$$
$$36=25p+16q+9r.$$

From these equations, we find $p=3$, $q=-3$, and $r=1$.

We shall now extend the principle of Art. 343 to finding the sum of an infinite recurring series when the scale of relation consists of three terms.

The 1st term $A=A$;
the 2d " $B=B$;
the 3d " $C=C$;
the 4th " $D=Cpx+Bqx^2+Arx^3$;
the 5th " $E=Dpx+Cqx^2+Brx^3$;
the 6th " $F=Epx+Dqx^2+Crx^3$;
&c., = &c.

Now, if S represent the required sum, by adding together the corresponding members of these equations, and observing that $C+D+E+$, &c., $=S-A-B$; $B+C+D+$, &c., $=S-A$, we have

$$S=A+B+C+(S-A-B)px+(S-A)qx^2+Srx^3;$$

whence, $S=\dfrac{A+B+C-(A+B)px-Aqx^2}{1-px-qx^2-rx^3}$.

Substituting in this formula the values of A, B, C, and of p, q, and r, we have

$$S=\frac{1+4x+9x^2-3x-12x^2+3x^2}{1-3x+3x^2-x^3}=\frac{1+x}{(1-x)^3}.$$

REVERSION OF SERIES.

Article 346.

(1) Comparing the series with the formula (Art. 344), we have $a=+1$, $b=-1$, $c=+1$, $d=-1$, &c.;
hence, by substitution, we have

$$x=\frac{1}{1}y-\frac{-1}{1}y^2+\frac{2-1}{1}y^3-\frac{-1+5-5}{1}y^4+, \text{ \&c.,}$$
$$=y+y^2+y^3+y^4+, \text{ \&c.}$$

(2) Here, $a=1$, $b=1$, $c=1$, $d=1$, &c.

$$\therefore\ x=\frac{1}{1}y-\frac{1}{1}y^2+\frac{2-1}{1}y^3-\frac{1-5+5}{1}y^4+, \text{ \&c.}$$
$$=y-y^2+y^3-y^4+, \text{ \&c.}$$

(3) Comparing the coëfficients with those of the series in Art. 346, we have $a=2$, $b=3$, $c=4$, $d=5$, &c.

$$\therefore\ x=\frac{1}{2}y-\frac{3}{16}y^3+\frac{27-8}{128}y^5-, \text{ \&c.,}$$
$$=\tfrac{1}{2}y-\tfrac{3}{16}y^3+\tfrac{19}{128}y^5-, \text{ \&c.}$$

(4) Applying the formula, (Art. 345), we have

$a'=1$, $a=-2$, and $b=3$.

$$\therefore\ x=-\frac{1}{2}(y-1)+\frac{3}{8}(y-1)^2-\frac{18-0}{32}(y-1)^3+, \&c.,$$

$$=-\tfrac{1}{2}(y-1)+\tfrac{3}{8}(y-1)^2-\tfrac{9}{16}(y-1)^3+, \&c.$$

(5) See formula, Art. 344. Here, $a=1$, $b=\frac{1}{2}$, $c=\frac{1}{6}$, $d=\frac{1}{24}$, &c.

$$\therefore\ x=\frac{1}{1}y-\frac{\frac{1}{2}}{1}y^2+\frac{\frac{1}{2}-\frac{1}{6}}{1}y^3-\frac{\frac{1}{24}-\frac{5}{12}+\frac{5}{8}}{1}y^4, \&c.,$$

$$=y-\tfrac{1}{2}y^2+\tfrac{1}{3}y^3-\tfrac{1}{4}y^4+, \&c.$$

(6) Let $x=Ay+By^2+Cy^3+$, &c.

then, $x^2=A^2y^2+2ABy^3+$, &c.;

$x^3=\qquad A^3y^3+$, &c.

Substituting these values for x, x^2, x^3, . . in the second member of the given equation, and transposing the first member, we have

$$0=\left.\begin{matrix}gA\\-1\end{matrix}\right|y+\left.\begin{matrix}gB\\hA^2\\-a\end{matrix}\right|y^2+\left.\begin{matrix}gC\\+2hAB\\+\ kA^3\\-b\end{matrix}\right|y^3+\ldots$$

Hence, $Ag-1=0$, $A^2h+Bg-a=0$,

$A^3k+2ABh+gC-b=0$;

whence, $A=\frac{1}{g}$, $B=\frac{1}{g}(a-A^2h)=\frac{1}{g}\left(a-\frac{h}{g^2}\right)=\frac{1}{g^3}(ag^2-h)$;

$$C=\frac{1}{g}(b-A^3k-2ABh)$$

$$=\frac{1}{g}\left\{b-\frac{k}{g^3}-\frac{2}{g}\cdot\frac{1}{g^3}(ag^2-h)h\right\}$$

$$=\frac{bg^4-kg-2h(ag^2-h)}{g^5},$$

$$\therefore\ x=\frac{y}{g}+\frac{(ag^2-h)y^2}{g^3}+\frac{[bg^4-kg-2h(ag^2-h)]y^3}{g^5}+, \&c.$$

CONTINUED FRACTIONS; LOGARITHMS; EXPONENTIAL EQUATIONS; INTEREST AND ANNUITIES.

CONTINUED FRACTIONS.

Article 356.

(1) Dividing the greater term by the less, the last divisor by the last remainder, and so on, the quotients are 3, 4, 5 and 6; hence, the integral fractions are $\frac{1}{3}$, $\frac{1}{4}$, $\frac{1}{5}$, and $\frac{1}{6}$, and the converging fractions are

$$\frac{1}{3},\ \frac{1\times4}{3\times4+1}=\frac{4}{13},\ \frac{4\times5+1}{13\times5+3}=\frac{21}{68},\ \frac{21\times6+4}{68\times6+13}=\frac{130}{421}.$$

The 2d and 3d examples are worked in a similar manner.

(4) Making 3900 the numerator, and 10963 the denominator of a fraction, and proceeding as in the preceding examples, the successive quotients, that is the denominators of the respective integral fractions, are 2, 1, 4, 3, 2, 2, 1, 30; hence, the 1st approximate fraction is $\frac{1}{2}$, the 2d,

$$\frac{1\times1}{2\times1+1}=\frac{1}{3};\ \text{the 3d,}\ \frac{1\times4+1}{3\times4+2}=\frac{5}{14};\ \text{and so on.}$$

(5) Making 4900 the numerator, and 11283 the denominator of a fraction, and proceeding as above, we find the successive quotients to be 2, 3, 3, 3, 2, 7, 1, 1, 1, 2; hence, the approximating fractions are $\frac{1}{2}$; $\frac{1\times3}{2\times3+1}=\frac{3}{7}$;

$$\frac{3\times3+1}{7\times3+2}=\frac{10}{23};\ \frac{10\times3+3}{23\times3+7}=\frac{33}{76};\ \frac{33\times2+10}{76\times2+23}=\frac{76}{175},\ \&c.$$

(6) Making 1 the numerator, and 3.1415926 the denominator of a fraction, or 10000000 and 31415926, and dividing the greater by the less, the less by the remainder, and so on, the quotients are 3, 7, 15, 1, 243, &c. Operating in like manner with 1, and 3.1415927, the quotients are 3, 7, 15, 1, 354, &c.; then finding the approximating fractions corresponding to these quotients, we have $\frac{1}{3}$;

$$\frac{1\times7}{3\times7+1}=\frac{7}{22};\ \frac{7\times15+1}{22\times15+3}=\frac{106}{333};\ \frac{106\times1+7}{333\times1+22}=\frac{113}{355}.$$

The ratio of 113 to 355, that is, $\frac{355}{113}=3.1415929+$; and since the true ratio lies between 3.141526, and 3.1415927, and since the difference between 3.1415929 and 3.1415926 is .0000003; therefore $\frac{113}{355}$ expresses the part that the diameter is of the circumference to within less than .0000003.

(7) 5 hrs., 48 min., 49 sec., =20929 seconds,

24 hrs., = 86400 "

Operating with these numbers as before, we find the successive quotients to be 4, 7, 1, 3, 1, 16, 1, 1, 15; and from these, the converging fractions are readily found.

(8) Dividing the greater term by the less, the less by the remainder, and so on, the quotients are 1, 1, 2, 1, 1, 1, 3, 2, 1, 1, 2, 3; and the successive converging fractions found from these are $\frac{1}{1}$, $\frac{1}{2}$, $\frac{3}{5}$, $\frac{4}{7}$, $\frac{7}{12}$, $\frac{11}{19}$, $\frac{40}{69}$, &c.; whence, $\frac{11}{19}$ is the required fraction.

(9) In solving this example, it is most convenient to consider 1 as the numerator, and 27.321661 the denominator, and then invert the resulting converging fractions. Dividing 27.321661 by 1, or 27321661 by 1000000, as in the preceding examples, the quotients are 27, 3, 9, 5, 2, &c.; these give for approximating fractions $\frac{1}{27}$, $\frac{3}{82}$, $\frac{28}{765}$, $\frac{143}{3907}$, &c., hence, the required ratios are $\frac{27}{1}$, $\frac{82}{3}$, $\frac{765}{28}$, $\frac{3907}{143}$, &c.

(10) Referring to Art. 353, we have $a=1$;

hence, $\sqrt{2}=1+\cfrac{1}{2+\cfrac{1}{2+\cfrac{1}{2+,\ \&c.}}}$

The integral fractions are	$\frac{1}{2}$, $\frac{1}{2}$, $\frac{1}{2}$, $\frac{1}{2}$, &c.
The converging fractions are	$\frac{1}{2}$, $\frac{2}{5}$, $\frac{5}{12}$, $\frac{12}{29}$, &c.
Adding 1 to each of these, we have	$\frac{3}{2}$, $\frac{7}{5}$, $\frac{17}{12}$, $\frac{41}{29}$, &c.

(11) Referring to Art. 353, we have $a=2$, and $2a=4$

hence, $\sqrt{4+1}=2+\cfrac{1}{4+\cfrac{1}{4+\cfrac{1}{4+\cfrac{1}{4+,\ \&c.}}}}$

The int. fractions are	$\frac{1}{4}$, $\frac{1}{4}$, $\frac{1}{4}$, $\frac{1}{4}$, $\frac{1}{4}$, &c.
The conv. fractions are	$\frac{1}{4}$, $\frac{4}{17}$, $\frac{17}{72}$, $\frac{72}{305}$, $\frac{305}{1292}$, &c.
Adding 2 to each of these, we have	$\frac{9}{4}$, $\frac{38}{17}$, $\frac{161}{72}$, $\frac{682}{305}$, $\frac{2889}{1292}$, &c.

Now the fourth fraction being in an even place is *less* than the true value, and the fifth being in an odd place is *greater* than the true value; therefore, $\sqrt{5}$ is greater than $\frac{682}{305}$, and less than $\frac{2889}{1292}$.

(12) Since $8^1=8$, and $8^2=64$, x lies between 1 and 2; hence, let $x=1+\dfrac{1}{y}$.

$\therefore\ 8^{1+\frac{1}{y}}=32$, or $8\times 8^{\frac{1}{y}}=32$, or $8^{\frac{1}{y}}=\frac{32}{8}=4$;

or $8=4^y$, by raising both members to the y power.

Now, since $4^1=4$, and $4^2=16$, the value of y lies between 1 and 2; hence, let $y=1+\dfrac{1}{z}$.

Therefore, $4^{1+\frac{1}{z}}=8$, or $4\times 4^{\frac{1}{z}}=8$, or $4^{\frac{1}{z}}=2$;

raising both members to the z power, we have

$2^z=4$; whence, $z=2$.

Therefore, $x=1+\cfrac{1}{1+\cfrac{1}{2}}=1+\dfrac{2}{3}=\dfrac{5}{3}$.

(13) $3^x=25$; $3^2=9$, and $3^3=27$.

Therefore, $x=2+\dfrac{1}{x'}$.

$3^{2+\frac{1}{x'}}=15$, or $3^2\times 3^{\frac{1}{x'}}=15$, or $3^{\frac{1}{x'}}=\frac{15}{9}=\frac{5}{3}$.

Since $3^{\frac{1}{x'}}=\frac{5}{3}$, we have $(\frac{5}{3})^{x'}=3$. By trial, we find $x'>2$ and <3; therefore, put $x'=2+\dfrac{1}{x''}$;

Therefore, $(\frac{5}{3})^{2+\frac{1}{x''}}=3$, or $(\frac{5}{3})^2\times(\frac{5}{3})^{\frac{1}{x''}}=3$;

whence, $(\frac{5}{3})^{\frac{1}{x''}}=\frac{27}{25}$, or $(\frac{27}{25})^{x''}=\frac{5}{3}$.

Here, $x''=6+\dfrac{1}{x'''}$; $\therefore\ x=2+\cfrac{1}{2+\cfrac{1}{6+}}$, &c.;

hence, the approximating fraction to be added to 2, is $\frac{1}{2}$, or $\frac{6}{13}$;

$\frac{6}{13}=2.46+$, which is true to within $(\frac{1}{13})^2=\frac{1}{169}$.

This method of finding the value of x is more curious than useful, as the same thing may be accomplished directly, and with but little labor, by means of logarithms.

Thus, $x=\dfrac{\log.\ 15}{\log.\ 3}=\dfrac{1.1760913}{.4771213}=2.465$ nearly.

LOGARITHMS.

Article 366.

(1) The result in this example follows directly from Art. 360, the pupil, however, may prove the principle generally in the case of three factors; thus,

$a^x = N$ . . . . (1),

$a^{x'} = N'$ . . . . (2),

$a^{x''} = N''$ . . . . (3).

Multiplying equations (1), (2), and (3) together, we have

$a^x \times a^{x'} \times a^{x''} = a^{x+x'+x''} = NN'N''$.

But, by the definition of logarithms, if we consider a the base of the system, then x, x', and x'' are the logarithms of N, N′, and N″, and $(x+x'+x'')$ is the logarithm of $NN'N''$; hence, the sum of the logarithms of three numbers is equal to the logarithm of their product.

(2) By Art. 361, log. $\left(\frac{abc}{de}\right) =$ log. $(abc) -$ log. (de); but log. $(abc) =$ log. $a +$ log. $b +$ log. c; and log. $(de) =$ log. $d +$ log. e; hence, log. $\left(\frac{abc}{de}\right) =$ log. $a +$ log. $b +$ log. c $-$(log. $d +$ log. e) $=$ log. $a +$ log. $b +$ log. $c -$ log. $d -$ log. e.

(3) By Art. 360, log. $(a^m . b^n . c^p .) =$ log. $a^m +$ log. $b^n +$ log. c^p; but (Art. 362), log. $a^m = m$ log. a, log. $b^n = n$ log. b, and log. $c^p = p$ log. c.

$\therefore$ log. $(a^m . b^n . c^p) = m$ log. $a + n$ log. $b + p$ log. c.

(4) Log. $\left(\frac{a^m . b^n}{c^p}\right) =$ log. $(a^m . b^n) -$ log. $c^p = m \times$log. a $+ n \times$log. $b - p$ log. c.

(5) $a^2 - x^2 = (a+x)(a-x)$, and log. $(a^2 - x^2)$ $=$ log. $\{(a+x)(a-x)\} =$ log. $(a+x) +$ log. $(a-x)$.

(6) Since log. $(a^2 - x^2) =$ log. $(a+x) +$ log. $(a-x)$,

$\frac{1}{2}$ log. $(a^2 - x^2) = \frac{1}{2}$ log. $(a+x) + \frac{1}{2}$ log. $(a-x)$,

but, (Art. 363), $\frac{1}{2}$ log. $(a^2 - x^2) =$ log. $(a^2 - x^2)^{\frac{1}{2}}$ or log. $\sqrt{a^2 - x^2}$;

$\therefore$ log. $\sqrt{a^2 - x^2} = \frac{1}{2}$ log. $(a+x) + \frac{1}{2}$ log. $(a-x)$.

(7) $a^3 \times \sqrt[4]{a^3} = a^3 \times a^{\frac{3}{4}} = a^{\frac{15}{4}}$; and log. $\left(a^{\frac{15}{4}}\right) = \frac{15}{4}$ log. a, or $3\frac{3}{4}$ log. a.

(8) $\frac{\sqrt{a^2-x^2}}{(a+x)^2} = \frac{\sqrt{a^2-x^2}}{\sqrt{(a+x)^4}} = \sqrt{\frac{(a+x)(a-x)}{(a+x)(a+x)^3}} = \sqrt{\frac{a-x}{(a+x)^3}}$;

log. $\frac{a-x}{(a+x)^3}$ = log. $(a-x)$ — log. $(a+x)^3$,

= log. $(a-x)$ — 3 log. $(a+x)$;

hence, log. $\sqrt{\frac{a-x}{(a+x)^3}}$; or log. $\frac{\sqrt{a^2-x^2}}{(a+x)^2}$

$=\frac{1}{2}$ {log. $(a-x)$ — 3 log. $(a+x)$};

or $=\frac{1}{2}$ log. $(a-x)$ — $\frac{3}{2}$ log. $(a+x)$; but the first form is the best.

Article 370.

(1) Since $14=2\times7$, ∴ log. 14 = log. 2 + log. 7;
Since $15=3\times5$, ∴ log. 15 = log. 3 + log. 5;
Since $16=2^4$, ∴ log. 16 = (log. 2) × 4;
Since $18=3^2\times2$, ∴ log. 18 = (log. 3) × 2 + log. 2;
Since $20=2^2\times5$, ∴ log. 20 = (log. 2) × 2 + log. 5;
Since $21=3\times7$, ∴ log. 21 = log. 3 + log. 7;
Since $24=2^3\times3$, ∴ log. 24 = (log. 2) × 3 + log. 3;
Since $25=5^2$, ∴ log. 25 = (log. 5) × 2;
Since $27=3^3$, ∴ log. 27 = (log. 3) × 3;
Since $28=2^2\times7$, ∴ log. 28 = (log. 2) × 2 + log. 7;
Since $30=3\times10$, ∴ log. 30 = log. 3 + log. 10.

(2) The numbers will evidently be those that can be formed by multiplying together any two or more of the factors 2, 3, 5, 7, either of which may be taken more than once if necessary; thus,

2^5, 5×7, $3^2\times2^2$, $2^3\times5$, $2\times3\times7$, $3^2\times5$, $2^4\times3$, 7^2, $5^2\times2$, $3^3\times2$, $2^3\times7$, $2^2\times3\times5$, $3^2\times7$, 2^6, $2\times5\times7$, $2^3\times3^2$, $5^2\times3$, $2^4\times5$, 3^4, $2^2\times3\times7$, $3^2\times2\times5$, $2^5\times3$, $7^2\times2$.

Article 377.

Remark.—The pupil will find the logarithm of 2, as given in all the tables in common use, to be .30103000; from this he may perhaps infer that there is some defect in the calculations in this article in the Algebra. On the contrary, however, the result there given, as far as it is carried, is absolutely correct, the logarithm of 2 to 20 places of decimals being .30102999566398119521. (See Hutton's Tables.)

(1) To find the logarithm of 3,

$$\text{Log. P} = \text{log. } 2 \ldots\ldots = .30102999;$$

$$\frac{2A}{2P+1} = \frac{.86858896}{5} \ldots\ldots = .17371779; \text{ (B)}$$

$$\frac{B}{3(2P+1)^2} = \frac{.17371779}{3\times5^2} \ldots\ldots = .00231623; \text{ (C)}$$

$$\frac{3C}{5(2P+1)^2} \ldots\ldots = .00005559; \text{ (D)}$$

$$\frac{5D}{7(2P+1)^2} \ldots\ldots = .00000159; \text{ (E)}$$

$$\frac{7E}{9(2P+1)^2} \ldots\ldots = .00000005; \text{ (F)}$$

$$\therefore \text{ Common log. of } 3 \ldots\ldots = .47712124.$$

(2) To find the logarithm of 5.

$$\text{Here, P} = 4, \text{ and log. P} = 2 \text{ log. } 2 \ldots = .60205999;$$

$$\frac{2A}{2P+1} = \frac{.86858896}{9} \ldots\ldots = .09650988; \text{ (B)}$$

$$\frac{B}{3(2P+1)^2} = \frac{.09650988}{3\times9^2} \ldots\ldots = .00039716; \text{ (C)}$$

$$\frac{3C}{5(2P+1)^2} \ldots\ldots = .00000294; \text{ (D)}$$

$$\frac{5D}{7(2P+1)^2} \ldots\ldots = .00000003; \text{ (E)}$$

$$\text{Log. } 5 \ldots\ldots = .69897000.$$

The last figure of the term E is taken to the nearest unit.

It is not necessary, however, except as an exercise, to calculate the common logarithm of 5, since $5=\frac{10}{2}$, and log. 5= log. 10— log 2=1— log. 2.

(3) To find the logarithm of 7.

$$\text{Here, P}=6, \text{ and log. } 6 = \text{ log. } 2 + \text{ log. } 3 = .77815123;$$

$$\frac{2A}{2P+1} = \frac{.86858896}{13} \ldots\ldots = .06681453; \text{ (B)}$$

$$\frac{B}{3(2P+1)^2} = \frac{.06681453}{3\times13^2} \ldots\ldots = .00013178; \text{ (C)}$$

$\frac{3C}{5(2P+1)^2}$ . . . . =.00000047; (D)

Log. 7 . . . . =.84509801.

(4) To find the logarithm of 11.

Here, P=10, and log. P . . . . . . =1.00000000;

$\frac{2A}{2P+1}=\frac{.86858896}{21}$ . . . . = .04136138; (B)

$\frac{B}{3(2P+1)^2}$ . . . . = .00003126; (C)

$\frac{3C}{5(2P+1)^2}$ . . . . = .00000004; (D)

Log. 11 . . . . =1.04139268.

Article 379.

(1) 1st. No system of logarithms can have a negative base, since the odd powers of a negative number are negative, and therefore the positive numbers corresponding to the odd powers of the base would not be represented.

2d. The base of a system of logarithms can not be 1, for the simple reason that every power of 1 is 1.

(2) Calling A and A′ the moduli of two different systems, whose logarithms are denoted by log. and log.′; if B and C are two numbers, from Art. 376, we have

log. B : log.′ B : : A : A′,

log. C : log.′ C : : A : A′,

whence, log. B : log. C : : log.′ B : log.′ C,

or $\frac{\log. C}{\log. B}=\frac{\log.' C}{\log.' B}$; that is,

The logarithms of the same numbers, in two different systems, have the same ratio to each other.

Example. The ratio of the common logarithm of 2 to that of 10, is $\frac{1.00000}{.30103}=3.321928$; and the ratio of the Naperian logarithm of 2 to that of 10, is $\frac{2.302585}{.693147}=3.321928$.

(3) Let N and N+1 be two consecutive numbers, the difference of their logarithms, taken in any system, will be log. (N+1)— log. N.

But (Art. 351), log. (N+1)— log. N= log. $\left(\frac{N+1}{N}\right)$

$=$ log. $\left(1+\frac{1}{N}\right)$, a quantity which approaches to the logarithm of 1 (which is zero, Art. 367,) in proportion as $\frac{1}{N}$ decreases, that is, as N increases. Hence,

The difference of the logarithms of two consecutive numbers is less as the numbers themselves are greater.

Example. The difference of the logarithms of 9 and 10 is 1—.9542425=.0457575; and the difference of the logarithms of 999 and 1000, is 3—.9995655=.0004345.

EXPONENTIAL EQUATIONS.

Article 383.

(2) $20^x=100$, ∴ x log. 20= log. 100,

whence, $x=\frac{\text{log. } 100}{\text{log. } 20}=\frac{2.000000}{1.301030}=1.53724.$

(3) Since $2^2=4$, and $3^3=27$, we easily see that x lies between 2 and 3, and that it is near the former. We also readily find that it is less than 2.2; then, let us assume 2 and 2.2 for the two numbers.

First Supposition.	*Second Supposition.*
$x=2$; log. 2=.301030	$x=2.2$; log. 2.2=.342423
x log. x . . =.601060	x log. x . . . =.753330
true no. log. 5=.698970	true no. log. 5 =.698970
Error . . —.097910	Error . . . +.054360

Difference of results =.152270; diff. assumed nos. =.2;
As .152270 : .2 : : .05436 : .0713, correction.
2.2—.0713=2.1287.

By trial, we find that x is greater than 2.12, and less than 2.13; therefore, let 2.12 and 2.13 be two new assumed numbers.

First Supposition.	*Second Supposition.*
$x=2.12$; log. 2.12=.326336	$x=2.13$; log. 2.13=.328380
x log. x . . . . =.691832	x log. x . . . . =.699449
true no. 698970	true no. 698970
Error . . . —007138	Error . . . +.000479

Diff. of results $=.007617$; diff. of assumed nos. $=.01$
As $.007617 : .01 :: .000479 : .000628$ correction.
Hence, $x=2.13-.000628=2.129372$ nearly.

(4) Log. $2=0.301030$, and $0.301030\times 64=19.265920$, which is the logarithm of the number expressing the 64th power of 2; and since the index is 19, the number of places of figures will be $19+1=20$. (Art. 35£)

(5) $a^{bx+d}=c$,
$(bx+d)$ log. $a=$ log. c;
or, bx log. $a=$ log. $c-d$ log. a;
whence, $x=\frac{\text{log. } c-d.\text{ log. } a}{b.\text{ log. } a}$.

(6) $a^{mx}.b^{nx}=c$,
log. $(a^{mx}.b^{nx})=$ log. c;
but log. $(a^{mx}.b^{nx})=mx$ log. $a+nx$ log. b;
therefore, mx log. $a+nx$ log. $b=$ log. c;
or, $x(m$ log. $a+n$ log. $b)=$ log. c;
whence, $x=\frac{\text{log. } c}{m\text{ log. } a+n\text{ log. } b}$.

(7) From the equation $m^{x-y}=n$, we have
$(x-y)$ log. $m=$ log. n, or x log. $m-y$ log. $m=$ log. n,
dividing by log. m; $x-y=$ log. $n\div$ log. $m=$ log. $\frac{n}{m}$;
from this, and the equation $x+y=a$, by adding and divic ing by 2, we find $x=\frac{1}{2}(a+$ log. $n\div$ log. $m)$,
or $x=\frac{1}{2}\left(a+\text{log. }\frac{n}{m}\right)$.
By subtracting and dividing by 2, we find
$y=\frac{1}{2}(a-$ log. $n\div$ log. $m)=\frac{1}{2}\left(a-\text{log. }\frac{n}{m}\right)$.

(8) First, log. $2000=$ log. $(1000\times 2)=$ log $1000+$ log. $2=3+$ log. 2, and $2^x.3^z=2000$;
log. $(2^x.3^z)=$ log. $2000=3+$ log. 2;
log. $(2^x.3^z)=$ log. 2^x+ log. $3^z=x.$ log. $2+z.$ log. 3;
therefore, $x.$ log. $2+z.$ log. $3=3+$ log. 2;
and $3z=5x$, or $z=\frac{5x}{3}$;

hence, $x. \log. 2+\frac{5x}{3}. \log. 3=3+\log. 2$;

or $3 \log. 2.x+5 \log. 3.x=3(3+\log. 2)$;

whence, $x=\frac{3(3+\log. 2)}{3 \log. 2+5 \log. 3}$;

and $z=\frac{5x}{3}=\frac{5(3+\log. 2)}{3 \log. 2+5 \log. 3}$.

(9) Let $a^x=z$; then $a^{2x}=z^2$, and the equation becomes
$z^2-2z=8$, or $z^2-2z+1=9$;
whence, $z=\pm 3+1=4$, or -2.
Therefore, $a^x=4$, or -2;
hence, $x \log. a=\log. 4$, or $\log. (-2)$, but the last is inadmissible (Art. 369); also, $4=2^2$, and $\log. 4=2 \log. 2$;
therefore, $x. \log. a=2 \log. 2$, and $x=\frac{2 \log. 2}{\log. a}$.

(10) Let $2^x=z$; then, $2^{2x}=z^2$, and $z^2+z=12$.
From the equation $z^2+z=12$, we find $z=+3$, the negative value being omitted (Art. 369);
therefore, $2^x=3$, and $x \log. 2=\log. 3$;
whence, $x=\frac{\log. 3}{\log. 2}=\frac{.477121}{.301030}=1.58496$.

(11) Let $a^x=z$; then, $z+\frac{1}{z}=b$, or $z^2-bz=-1$;
whence, z or $a^x=\frac{b}{2}\pm\frac{1}{2}\sqrt{b^2-4}=\frac{1}{2}(b\pm\sqrt{b^2-4})$;
therefore, $x \log. a=\log. \frac{1}{2}(b\pm\sqrt{b^2-4})$;
whence, $x=\frac{\log. \frac{1}{2}(b\pm\sqrt{b^2-4})}{\log. a}$.

(12) Here, $x^y=y^x$ (1), and $x^3=y^2$ (2).
Extracting the y root of both members of eq. (1), and the cube root of both members of eq. (2), we have
$x=y^{\frac{x}{y}}$, and $x=y^{\frac{2}{3}}$;
therefore, $y^{\frac{x}{y}}=y^{\frac{2}{3}}$; whence, $\frac{x}{y}=\frac{2}{3}$, and $x=\frac{2}{3}y$:
hence, $\frac{2}{3}y=y^{\frac{2}{3}}$; divide each member by $y^{\frac{2}{3}}$;
$\frac{2}{3}y^{\frac{1}{3}}=1$, or $y^{\frac{1}{3}}=\frac{3}{2}$.
Cubing each side, $y=(\frac{3}{2})^3=\frac{27}{8}=3\frac{3}{8}$;
$x=\frac{2}{3}y=\frac{2}{3}$ of $\frac{27}{8}=\frac{9}{4}=2\frac{1}{4}$.

(13) Here, $(a^2-b^2)^{2(x-1)}=(a-b)^{2x}$.

Extracting the square root of both members, we have

$(a^2-b^2)^{(x-1)}=(a-b)^x$;

whence, $(x-1)\log.(a^2-b^2)=x\log.(a-b)$;

but $\log.(a^2-b^2)=\log.[(a+b)(a-b)]=\log.(a+b)+\log.(a-b)$.

$\therefore (x-1)\{\log.(a+b)+\log.(a-b)\}=x\log.(a-b)$;

or $x\log.(a+b)+x\log.(a-b)-\log.(a+b)-\log.(a-b)=x\log.(a-b)$.

Omitting $x\log.(a-b)$ on each side, and transposing,

$x\log.(a+b)=\log.(a+b)+\log.(a-b)$;

whence, $x=1+\dfrac{\log.(a-b)}{\log.(a+b)}$.

(14) $(a^4-2a^2b^2+b^4)^{x-1}=\{(a^2-b^2)^2\}^{x-1}=(a^2-b^2)^{2x-2}$

$=\dfrac{(a^2-b^2)^{2x}}{(a^2-b^2)^2}$; and $(a-b)^{2x}(a+b)^{-2}=\dfrac{(a-b)^{2x}}{(a+b)^2}$;

therefore, $\dfrac{(a^2-b^2)^{2x}}{(a^2-b^2)^2}=\dfrac{(a-b)^{2x}}{(a+b)^2}$.

Extracting the square root of both members, we have

$\dfrac{(a^2-b^2)^x}{a^2-b^2}=\dfrac{(a-b)^x}{a+b}$;

but $(a^2-b^2)^x=\{(a+b)(a-b)\}^x=(a+b)^x(a-b)^x$:

therefore, $\dfrac{(a+b)^x(a-b)^x}{(a+b)(a-b)}=\dfrac{(a-b)^x}{a+b}$.

Dividing both members by $(a-b)^x$, and multiplying by $a+b$, we have $\dfrac{(a+b)^x}{a-b}=1$, or $(a+b)^x=a-b$;

whence, $x\log.(a+b)=\log.(a-b)$,

and $x=\dfrac{\log.(a-b)}{\log.(a+b)}$.

(15) Here, $x^y=y^x$ (1), and $x^p=y^q$ (2).

From (1) $x^{\frac{y}{x}}=y$, and from (2) $x^{\frac{p}{q}}=y$;

$\therefore\ x^{\frac{y}{x}}=x^{\frac{p}{q}}$, and $\dfrac{y}{x}=\dfrac{p}{q}$; or $\dfrac{x^{\frac{p}{q}}}{x}=\dfrac{p}{q}$;

$\therefore\ x^{\frac{p}{q}-1}=\dfrac{p}{q}$, or $x^{\frac{p-q}{q}}=\dfrac{p}{q}$; $\therefore\ x=\left(\dfrac{p}{q}\right)^{\frac{q}{p-q}}$;

$y=\dfrac{p}{q}x=\dfrac{p}{q}\left(\dfrac{p}{q}\right)^{\frac{q}{p-q}}=\left(\dfrac{p}{q}\right)^{\frac{q}{p-q}+1}=\left(\dfrac{p}{q}\right)^{\frac{p}{p-q}}$.

(21) Let $x^2-4x+5=z$, then $3^z=1200$, and z log. 3 = log. 1200,

whence, $z=\frac{\text{log. } 1200}{\text{log. } 3}=\frac{3.079181}{.477121}=6.4536$.

Therefore, $x^2-4x+5=6.4536$;

$x^2-4x+4=5.4536$;

$x-2=\pm 2.33$,

$x=2\pm 2.33=4.33$, or -0.33.

INTEREST AND ANNUITIES.

Article 386.

(2) $1+r=1.06$ and log. 1.06 . . . . = .025306

$.025306\times 100=t$ log. $(1+r)$. . . . . =2.530600

log. P= log. 1 . . . . =0.000000

log. A= log. (339.30) . . . . =2.530600

(3) This example is similar to the preceding; if we multiply .025306 by 1000, the product is 25.306000, which is the log. of the amount, and as the index is 25, the corresponding natural number will contain $25+1=26$ figures. (Art. 358.)

(4) See Art. 386, Cor. 3. For 5%, R=1.05; for 6%, R=1.06; for 7%, R=1.07; for 8%, R=1.08.

For 5%, $t=\frac{\text{log. } 2}{\text{log. } 1.05}=\frac{.301030}{.021189}=14.2066$ yrs;

for 6%, $t=\frac{\text{log. } 2}{\text{log. } 1.06}=\frac{.301030}{.025306}=11.8956$ yrs;

for 7%, $t=\frac{\text{log. } 2}{\text{log. } 1.07}=\frac{.301030}{.029384}=10.2447$ yrs;

for 8%, $t=\frac{\text{log. } 2}{\text{log. } 1.08}=\frac{.301030}{.033424}=9.0064$ yrs.

(5) See Art. 386, Cor. 3. Here, $m=10$, and R=1.05.

Therefore, $t=\frac{\text{log. } 10}{\text{log. } 1.05}=\frac{1.000000}{.021189}=47.19$ yrs.

(6) Let $x=$ the sum; then (Art. 386), $M=P.R^t$, and $P=x.R^t$,

whence, $\frac{M}{P}=\frac{P.R^t}{x.R^t}=\frac{P}{x}$, and $\therefore x=\frac{P^2}{M}$.

Article 387.

(2) Here, A=13000000, P=11000000, and t=10.

$$\begin{array}{lr} \text{Log. A} = & 7.113943 \\ \text{Log. P} = & \underline{7.041393} \\ \text{Divide by 10,} & 10)\underline{0.072550} \\ \text{Log. }(1+r)1.016 & 0.007255 \end{array}$$

To find the number corresponding to the log. 0.007255, we look in a larger table than the one given (p. 326), and find it 1.016; $\therefore$ r=1.016—1=.016 nearly.

To find in what time the population will be doubled, we have, (Art. 386, Cor. 3.) $t=\frac{\log. 2}{\log. 1.016}=\frac{.301030}{.006894}=43.66$ years, the log. of the denominator being taken from a book of tables.

Article 388.

Log. P′= log. 1000—20 log. (1.05)=3—20×0.021189 =3—.423780=2.576220, and the number corresponding is 376.89= present worth. Subtracting this from 1000, we have for the Compound Discount $623.11.

Article 390.

(1) We have $m=a\,\frac{(1+r)^t-1}{r}$.

Taking the logarithm of 1.06 $(1+r)$, multiplying it by 20 (t) and finding the corresponding number, we have 3.20713546. Subtracting 1 from this and dividing by .06, we obtain 36.785591. This multiplied by 120(a) gives $4414.27, *Ans.*

(2) Let x, y, z, denote the three shares; then, we shall have $x+y+z=\text{P}$. Also, $x\times \text{R}^a=y\times \text{R}^b=z\times \text{R}^c$, as the equations of condition.

$\therefore$ $y=\text{R}^{a-b}x$, and $z=\text{R}^{a-c}x$.

Whence, $x+\text{R}^{a-b}x+\text{R}^{a-c}x=\text{P}$.

$$x=\frac{\text{P}}{1+\text{R}^{a-b}+\text{R}^{a-c}}.$$

(3) We have $m=aR\frac{R^t-1}{R-1}=100\times1.06\frac{(1.06)^{10}-1}{1.06-1}$.

Taking the log. of 1.06, multiplying it by 10, finding the corresponding number, subtracting 1 from it, and dividing by .06, we obtain 13.1808. Multiplying this by 100 $\times$1.06=106, gives \$1397.16, *Ans.*

Article 391.

(1) We have $p=\frac{a}{R-1}\left(1-\frac{1}{R^t}\right)=\frac{250}{.05}\left(1-\frac{1}{(1.05)^{30}}\right)$

$=\frac{250}{.05}(.76862254)=\$3843.1135$, *Ans.*

(2) From Cor., $p=\frac{a}{r}=\frac{600}{.06}=\$10000$, *Ans.*

Article 392.

(1) Here, $p=\frac{a}{rR^n}\left(1-\frac{1}{R^t}\right)=\frac{112.50}{.04(1.04)^{10}}\left(1-\frac{1}{(1.04)^{20}}\right)$

$=\frac{112.50}{.05920976}(1-.45638697)$

$=\frac{112.50}{.05920976}(.54361303)=\$1032.877$, *Ans.*

(2) We have $p=\frac{a}{rR^n}=\frac{1000}{.06(1.06)^{15}}$

$=\frac{1000}{.1437942}=\$6954.40$, *Ans.*

(3) The amount of a\$ at compound interest for n years, r being the rate per cent., is $a(1+r)^n$.

The amount of an annuity of b\$, for the same period, at the same rate, is $b\frac{(1+r)^n-1}{r}$ (Arts. 386 and 390).

$\therefore b\frac{(1+r)^n-1}{r}=a(1+r)^n$;

or, $b(1+r)^n-b=ra(1+r)^n$;

or, $b(1+r)^n-ra(1+r)^n=b$;

or, $(b-ra)(1+r)^n=b$; (1)

or, $\log. (b-ra)+n \log. (1+r)=\log. b$;

$$n \log. (1+r)=\log. b-\log. (b-ra).$$

$$n=\frac{\log. b-\log. (b-ra)}{\log. (1+r)}.$$

(4) Taking eq. (1) in the last problem, we have

$b(1+r)^n-ra(1+r)^n=b$;

$b(1+r)^n-b=ra(1+r)^n$;

$$b=\frac{ra(1+r)^n}{(1+r)^n-1}=\frac{8000\times.06(1.06)^8}{(1.06)^8-1}=\frac{480\times(1.06)^8}{(1.06)^8-1}$$

This example is not in a suitable form for logarithmic computation, on account of the subtractive term in the denominator. It may, however, be solved by logarithms indirectly, thus:

Add together the log. of 480, and 8 times the log. of 1.06, and find the corresponding number for a dividend. For a divisor, take 8 times the log. of 1.06, find the corresponding number, and diminish it by unity. The quotient will be the annual payment or b. Thus,

Log. 480 . . .	= 2.681241
8 times log. 1.06	= 0.202448
Cor. No. 765.05 .	= 2.883689

Dividing 765.05 by the number corresponding to 8 times the log. of 1.06 diminished by unity, which is .593853, we have $1288.286, *Ans.*

From the formulas deduced (Arts. 385 to 392), rules may easily be deduced applicable to Arithmetic, but the processes will generally be more tedious when logarithms are not employed.

From eq. (1) in Prob. 3 above, we find $(1+r)^n=\frac{b}{b-ar}$, which would require the solution of an exponential equation to find n without the use of logarithms. The last problem, however, which presents a practical case in Banking, may be easily solved arithmetically according to the following rule:

For a dividend, multiply the interest on the given sum for one year by the amount of one dollar for one year raised to a power equal to the number of annual payments.

For a divisor, take the amount of one dollar raised to a power equal to the number of payments, and diminish it by unity.

The quotient will be the annual payment.

By another process, the following formula may be deduced for the last problem:

$$b=\frac{aR^8}{1+R+R^2+R^3+R^4+R^5+R^6+R^7}.$$

GENERAL THEORY OF EQUATIONS.

Article 396.

Note.—Although the *Synthetic Method of Divison* is not explained till Art. 409, page 366, yet we shall employ it, instead of the common method, on account of its conciseness. The Teacher who prefers to use the Synthetic method, can require his pupils to study Art. 409, before commencing the theory of equations.

(1) $1-11+23+35\ \underline{|-1}$, since $x+1$ is the divisor

$\underline{\quad -1+12-35}$

$1-12+35+0$

Ans. $x^2-12x+35=0$.

(2) $1-9+26-24\ \underline{|+3}$, since $x-3$ is the divisor.

$\underline{\quad +3-18+24}$

$1-6+\ 8+0$

$\therefore\ x^2-6x+8=0$; whence (Art. 231), $x=4$ or 2.

(3) $1+2-41-42+360\ \underline{|+3}$, since $x-3$ is a divisor.

$\underline{\quad +3+15-\ 78-360}$

$1+5-26-120+0\quad \underline{|-4}$, since $x+4$ is a divisor.

$\underline{\quad -4-\ 4+120}$

$1+1-30+0$

$\therefore\ x^2+x-30=0$, and (Art. 231), $x=5$, or -6.

Article 398.

(2) $x=\ 2,\ \therefore\ x-2=0,$

$x=\ 3,\ \therefore\ x-3=0,$

$x=-5,\ \therefore\ x+5=0.$

$\therefore\ (x-2)(x-3)(x+5)=x^3-19x+30=0.$

(3) $x=\ \ 0$, $\therefore$ $x-0=0$,
$x=-1$, $\therefore$ $x+1=0$,
$x=\ \ 2$, $\therefore$ $x-2=0$,
$x=-5$, $\therefore$ $x+5=0$.
$\therefore$ $(x-0)(x+1)(x-2)(x+5)=x^4+4x^3-7x^2-10x-0$

(4) $x=1+\sqrt{2}$, $\therefore$ $x-1-\sqrt{2}=0$,
$x=1-\sqrt{2}$, $\therefore$ $x-1+\sqrt{2}=0$,
$x=2+\sqrt{3}$, $\therefore$ $x-2-\sqrt{3}=0$,
$x=2-\sqrt{3}$, $\therefore$ $x-2+\sqrt{3}=0$.
$\therefore$ $(x-1-\sqrt{2})(x-1+\sqrt{2})(x-2-\sqrt{3})(x-2+\sqrt{3})$
$=(x^2-2x-1)(x^2-4x+1)=x^4-6x^3+8x^2+2x-1=0$.

(5) It has been shown, Art. 398, that the coëfficient of the fourth term is equal to the sum of the products of all the roots taken three and three with their signs changed. The roots with their signs changed are $+2$, $+1$, -1, -3 -4, and the sum of their products taken three and three is $(2\times1\times-1)+(2\times1\times-3)+(2\times1\times-4)$
$+(2\times-1\times-3)+(2\times-1\times-4)+(2\times-3\times-4)$
$+(1\times-1\times-3)+(1\times-1\times-4)+(1\times-3\times-4)$
$+(-1\times-3\times-4)=-2-6-8+6+8+24+3+4+12-12$
$=29$; and since x^5 appears in the first term, $29x^2$ is the fourth term.

Article 400.

(1) Since $x^3+3x^2-10x-24=0$, is the same as $x^3-3x^2-10x+24=0$, with the signs of the alternate terms changed, and since the roots of the latter are 2, -3, and 4, therefore (Art. 400), the roots of the former are -2, $+3$, -4.

Article 401.

(1) Dividing the given equation by $x+6=x-(-6)$, the quotient is $x^2-6x+10=0$, of which the roots are $3+\sqrt{-1}$, and $3-\sqrt{-1}$.

(2) Since one root is $2-\sqrt{3}$, therefore (Art. 401, Cor. 1), $2+\sqrt{3}$, is another root.

$(x-2+\sqrt{3})(x-2-\sqrt{3})=x^2-4x+1$, and dividing the given equation by this, the quotient is $x-3$; hence,

$$x-3=0, \text{ and } x=+3.$$

(3) Since $-\frac{1}{2}(3+\sqrt{-31})$ is one root of the given equation; therefore (Art. 401), $-\frac{1}{2}(3-\sqrt{-31})$ is another root. $[x+\frac{1}{2}(3+\sqrt{-31})][x+\frac{1}{2}(3-\sqrt{-31})]=x^2+x(3)+\frac{1}{4}[9-(-31)]=x^2+3x+10$, and dividing the given equation by this, the quotient is x^2-3x-4; hence,

$$x^2-3x-4=0, \text{ and } x=4 \text{ or } -1.$$

(4) Since $+\sqrt{2}$ is one root of the given equation; therefore, (Art. 410, Cor. 2), $-\sqrt{2}$ is another root, and three of the binomial factors of the given equation are

$$(x-\sqrt{2})(x+\sqrt{2})(x-3)=x^3-3x^2-2x+6.$$

Dividing the given equation by this, the quotient is $x^2-7x+10$; hence, $x^2-7x+10=0$; from which $x=2$, and 5.

Article 403.

(2) If we substitute 5 for x in the equation $x^3-5x^2-x+1=0$, we have $-4=0$, and if we substitute 6 for x, we have $+31=0$; and since the results have contrary signs, one root lies between 5 and 6, that is, 5 is the first figure of one of the roots.

TRANSFORMATION OF EQUATIONS.

Article 405.

(2) Here, $x^4+7x^2-4x+3=0$; let $x=\frac{y}{3}$; then,

$\frac{y^4}{81}+\frac{7y^2}{9}-\frac{4y}{3}+3=0$; multiply by 81, to clear of fractions, $y^4+63y^2-108y+243=0$.

(3) Here, $x^4+2x^3-7x-1=0$; let $x=\frac{y}{5}$; then.

$$\frac{y^4}{625}+\frac{2y^3}{125}-\frac{7y}{5}-1=0;\text{ clearing of fractions,}$$
$y^4+10y^3-875y-625=0$.

(4) Here, $x^3-3x^2+4x+10=0$; let $x=2y$; then, $8y^3-12y^2+8y+10=0$; dividing by 2, $4y^3-6y^2+4y+5=0$.

(5) Here, $x^3-2x^2+\frac{1}{3}x-10=0$; let $x=\frac{1}{3}y$; then,
$$\frac{y^3}{27}-\frac{2y^2}{9}+\frac{1}{3}y-10=0;\text{ clearing of fractions,}$$
$y^3-6y^2+3y-270=0$.

Article 407.

(1) Here, $x^3-7x+7=0$; let $y=x-1$; then, $x=y+1$. $\therefore\ (y+1)^3-7(y+1)+7=0$, or $y^3+3y^2-4y+1=0$.

(2) Here, $x^4-3x^3-15x^2+49x-12=0$; let $y=x-3$; then, $x=y+3$; $\therefore\ (y+3)^4-3(y+3)^3-15(y+3)^2+49(y+3)-12=0$; or, by developing and reducing, $y^4+9y^3+12y^2-14y=0$.

(3) Here, $x^3-6x^2+8x-2=0$, and $x=y+2$. $\therefore\ (y+2)^3-6(y+2)^2+8(y+2)-2=0$, or reducing, $y^3-4y-2=0$.

Article 410.

(4) Let $y=x-3$; then, it is required to divide the given equation, and the successive quotients, by $x-3$.

$$\begin{array}{llll}
1 & \pm 0 & -27 & -36 \quad (+3, \text{ since the divisor is } x-3, \\
 & +3 & +9 & -54 \\ \hline
 & +3 & -18 & -90 \quad \therefore\ -90 = 1^{st}\ \text{R} \\
 & +3 & +18 & \\ \hline
 & +6 & +0 & \therefore\ 0 = 2^{d}\ \text{R.} \\
 & +3 & & \\ \hline
 & +9 & \multicolumn{2}{l}{\therefore\ +9 = 3^{d}\ \text{R.} \quad \textit{Ans.},\ y^3+9y^2-90=0.}
\end{array}$$

(5)

1	−18	− 32	+ 17	+ 9	(+5, since the divisor is $x-5$,
	+ 5	− 65	− 485	−2340	
	−13	− 97	− 468	−2331 ∴ −2331 = 1st R.	
	+ 5	− 40	− 685		
	− 8	−137	−1153 ∴ −1153 = 2d R.		
	+ 5	− 15			
	− 3	−152 ∴ −152 = 3d R.			
	+ 5				
	+ 2 ∴ +2 = 4th R.				

Ans., $y^4+2y^3-152y^2-1153y-2331=0$.

(6) We shall first diminish the roots by 1, then by .2, indicating the remainders after each transformation by stars.

1	−6	+7.4	+ 7.92	−17.872	− .79232 (+1.2
	+1	−5	+ 2.4	+10.32	−7.552
	−5	+2.4	+10.32	− 7.552	−8.34432*
	+1	−4	− 1.6	+ 8.72	+ .34432
	−4	−1.6	+ 8.72	+ 1.168*	−8*
	+1	−3	− 4.6	+ .5536	
	−3	−4.6	+ 4.12*	+ 1.7216	
	+1	−2	− 1.352	+ .2784	
	−2	−6.6*	+ 2.768	+ 2.0000*	
	+1	− .16	− 1.376		
	−1*	−6.76	+ 1.392		
	+.2	− .12	− 1.392		
	−.8	−6.88	+ 0.000*		
	+.2	− .08			
	−.6	−6.96			
	+.2	− .04			
	−.4	−7*			
	+.2				
	−.2				
	+.2				
	0*				

Ans., $y^5-7y^3+2y-8=0$

(7) Here, $A=-6$, $n=3$, ∴ $r=2$; hence, $x=y+2$, or $y=x-2$.

$$\begin{array}{rrrrl}
1 & -6 & +7 & -2 & \text{(+2, since the divisor is } x-2. \\
 & +2 & -8 & -2 & \\ \hline
 & -4 & -1 & -4 & \therefore -4 = 1^{st}\text{ R.} \\
 & +2 & -4 & & \\ \hline
 & -2 & -5 & & \therefore -5 = 2^{d}\text{ R.} \\
 & +2 & & & \\ \hline
 & 0 & & & \therefore 0 = 3^{d}\text{ R.} \quad \textit{Ans.},\ y^3-5y-4=0.
\end{array}$$

(8) Here, $A=-6$, $n=3$, $\therefore r=2$;
hence, $x=y+2$, or $y=x-2$.

$$\begin{array}{rrrrl}
1 & -6 & +12 & +19 & \text{(+2, since the divisor is } x-2. \\
 & +2 & -8 & +8 & \\ \hline
 & -4 & +4 & +27 & \therefore +27 = 1^{st}\text{ R.} \\
 & +2 & -4 & & \\ \hline
 & -2 & 0 & & \therefore 0 = 2^{d}\text{ R.} \\
 & +2 & & & \\ \hline
 & 0 & & & \therefore 0 = 3^{d}\text{ R.} \quad \textit{Ans.},\ y^3+27=0.
\end{array}$$

(9) Here, $A=-6$, $B=+9$, $n=3$,
$\frac{1}{2}n(n-1)r^2+(n-1)Ar+B=\frac{3}{2}(2)r^2+(2)\times-6r+9=0$,
or $r^2-4r+3=0$; whence, $r=3$, or 1;
hence, $x=y+3$, or $y+1$, and $y=x-3$, or $x-1$.

$$\begin{array}{rrrrl}
1 & -6 & +9 & -20 & \text{(+3, since the divisor is } x-3 \\
 & +3 & -9 & +0 & \\ \hline
 & -3 & 0 & -20 & \\
 & +3 & 0 & & \\ \hline
 & 0 & 0 & & \\
 & +3 & & & \\ \hline
 & +3 & & & \textit{Ans.},\ y^3+3y^2-20=0.
\end{array}$$

$$\begin{array}{rrrrl}
\text{Or } 1 & -6 & +9 & -20 & \text{(+1, since the divisor is } x-1. \\
 & +1 & -5 & +4 & \\ \hline
 & -5 & +4 & -16 & \\
 & +1 & -4 & & \\ \hline
 & -4 & 0 & & \\
 & +1 & & & \\ \hline
 & -3 & & & \textit{Ans.},\ y^3-3y^2-16=0.
\end{array}$$

(10) Here, $A=-4$, $B=5$, $n=3$.
$\frac{1}{2}n(n-1)r^2+(n-1)Ar+B=3r^2-8r+5=0$, and $r=\frac{5}{3}$ or 1
hence, $x=y+\frac{5}{3}$, or $y+1$, and $y=x-\frac{5}{3}$, or $x-1$.

$$\begin{array}{rrrrl}
1 & -4 & +5 & -2 & (+\tfrac{5}{3}, \text{ since the divisor is } x-\tfrac{5}{3}. \\
 & +\frac{5}{3} & -\frac{25}{9} & +\frac{50}{27}, & \\ \hline
 & -\frac{7}{3} & +\frac{10}{9} & -\frac{4}{27} & \\
 & +\frac{5}{3} & -\frac{10}{9} & & \\ \hline
 & -\frac{2}{3} & 0 & & \\
 & +\frac{5}{3} & & & \\ \hline
 & +1 & & &
\end{array}$$

Ans., $y^3+y^2-\frac{4}{27}=0$.

$$\begin{array}{rrrrl}
\text{or } 1 & -4 & +5 & -2 & (+1 \\
 & +1 & +3 & +2 & \\ \hline
 & -3 & +2 & 0 & \\
 & +1 & +2 & & \\ \hline
 & -2 & 0 & & \\
 & +1 & & & \\ \hline
 & -1 & & &
\end{array}$$

Ans., $y^3-y^2=0$.

EQUAL ROOTS

Article 414.

(2) Here, $x^3-2x^2-15x+36=0$,
$3x^2-4x-15=$ 1st derived polynomial, and the G. C. D. of this and the given equation (Art. 108), is $x-3$; hence, $x-3=0$, and $x=+3$; therefore, $+3$ and $+3$ are two roots of the given equation.

Dividing the given equation by $(x-3)(x-3)$, the quotient is $x+4$; hence, $x+4=0$, and $x=-4$.

(3) Here, $x^4-9x^2+4x+12=0$.
$4x^3-18x+4=$ 1st derived polynomial, and the G. C. D. of this and the given equation is $x-2$; hence, $x=+2$, and $+2$. Dividing the given equation by $(x-2)(x-2)$, the quotient is x^2+4x-3; hence, $x^2+4x-3=0$, from which we find $x=-1$, and -3.

(4) Here, $x^4-6x^3+12x^2-10x+3=0$.
$4x^3-18x^2+24x-10=$ 1st derived polynomial, and the G C. D. of this and the given equation is x^2-2x+1; but $x^2-2x+1=(x-1)^2$; therefore, the given equation has three roots, each equal to 1.

Dividing the given equation by $(x-1)(x-1)(x-1)$, the quotient is $x-3$; hence, $x-3=0$, and $x=3$.

The operation of dividing by $x-1$ should be performed by synthetic division on account of its brevity: thus.

1	−6	+12	−10	+3	(+1
	+1	−5	+7	−3	
	−5	+7	−3	0	
	+1	−4	+3		
	−4	+3	0		
	+1	−3			
	−3	0	Quotient $=x-3$.		

(5) Here, $x^4-7x^3+9x^2+27x-54=0$.
$4x^3-21x^2+18x+27=$ the first derived polynomial, and the G. C. D. of this and the given equation is x^2-6x+9; but $x^2-6x+9=(x-3)^2$; therefore, the equation has three roots, each equal to 3.

Dividing the given equation by $(x-3)(x-3)(x-3)$, the quotient is $x+2$; hence, $x+2=0$, and $x=-2$.

(6) Here, $x^4+2x^3-3x^2-4x+4=0$.
$4x^3+6x^2-6x-4=$ 1st derived polynomial, and the G. C. D of this and the given equation is $x^2+x-2=(x+2)(x-1)$; therefore, the equation contains two factors of the form $x+2$, and of the form $x-1$; hence, the four roots are -2, -2, $+1$, $+1$.

If the learner does not readily see that $x^2+x-2=(x+2)(x-1)$, let him place it equal to zero, and find the roots.

(7) Here, $x^4-12x^3+50x^2-84x+49=0$.
$4x^3-36x^2+100x-84=$ 1st derived polynomial, and the G. C. D. of this and the given equation is x^2-6x+7.

Placing this equal to zero, we find its roots are $3+\sqrt{2}$, and $3-\sqrt{2}$, that is, $x^2-6x+7=(x-3-\sqrt{2})(x-3+\sqrt{2})$; hence, the four binomial factors of the given equation are $(x-3-\sqrt{2})(x-3-\sqrt{2})(x-3+\sqrt{2})(x-3+\sqrt{2})$, and the four roots are $3+\sqrt{2}$, $3+\sqrt{2}$, $3-\sqrt{2}$, $3-\sqrt{2}$.

(8) Here, $x^5-2x^4+3x^3-7x^2+8x-3=0$.
$5x^4-8x^3+9x^2-14x+8=$ 1st derived polynomial, and the G. C. D. of this and the given equation is x^2-2x+1 $=(x-1)^2$; therefore, the equation has three roots, each equal to $+1$.

Dividing the given equation by $(x-1)(x-1)(x-1)$, the quotient is x^2+x+3; thus,

$$\begin{array}{rrrrrl}
1 & -2 & +3 & -7 & +8 & -3 \;(+1 \\
 & +1 & -1 & +2 & -5 & +3 \\
 & -1 & +2 & -5 & +3 & 0 = 1^{st} \text{ R.} \\
 & +1 & +0 & +2 & -3 & \\
 & 0 & +2 & -3 & 0 = 2^{d} \text{ R.} & \\
 & +1 & +1 & +3 & & \\
 & +1 & +3 & 0 = 3^{d} \text{ R.} & &
\end{array}$$

$\therefore x^2+x+3=0$, from which $x=-\frac{1}{2}\pm\frac{1}{2}\sqrt{-11}$.

As learners sometimes experience difficulty in finding the G. C. D. in this example, we will here give the operation.

Multiplying the given eq. by 5, the operation is as follows:

$$\begin{array}{rl}
5x^5-10x^4+15x^3-35x^2+40x-15 & |\underline{5x^4-8x^3+9x^2-14x+8} \\
\underline{5x^5-\ 8x^4+\ 9x^3-14x^2+\ 8x\quad} & \underline{(x-2} \\
-\ 2x^4+\ 6x^3-\ 21x^2+\ 32x-15 & \\
-10x^4+30x^3-105x^2+160x-75 & \text{Multiply the first} \\
\underline{-10x^4+16x^3-\ 18x^2+\ 28x-16} & \text{divisor by 14.} \\
+14x^3-\ 87x^2+132x-59 &
\end{array}$$

$$\begin{array}{rl}
70x^4-112x^3+126x^2-196x+112 & |\underline{14x^3-87x^2+132x-59} \\
\underline{70x^4-435x^3+660x^2-295x\quad} & \underline{(5x+323} \\
+323x^3-534x^2+\ 99x+112 & \\
\times \text{ by } 14,\quad 4522x^3-7476x^2+1386x+1568 & \\
\underline{4522x^3-28101x^2+42636x-19057} & \\
20625x^2-41250x+20625, & \\
\text{or } 20625(x^2-2x+1). &
\end{array}$$

x^2-2x+1 will be found to divide $14x^3-87x^2+132x-59$ and it is therefore the G. C. D. required.

(9) Here, $x^6+3x^5-6x^4-6x^3+9x^2+3x-4=0$.
$6x^5+15x^4-24x^3-18x^2+18x+3=$ 1st derived polynomial.
$30x^4+60x^3-72x^2-36x+18=$ 2^{d} derived polynomial.

We find the G. C. D. of the given equation and the first derived polynomial is x^3-x^2-x+1; if we put this equal to zero, it is easily seen that $x=1$; then, dividing by $x-1$, the quotient is x^2-1, of which the factors are $x+1$ and $x-1$; hence, $x^3-x^2-x+1=(x-1)(x-1)(x+1)=(x-1)^2(x+1)$; therefore, the given equation contains $x-1$ as a factor *three* times, and $x+1$ as a factor *twice;* hence, three roots of the equation are $+1$, $+1$, $+1$, and two roots -1, -1.

Dividing the given equation by $(x-1)^3(x+1)^2$, the quotient is $x+4$; hence, $x+4=0$, and $x=-4$.

Otherwise thus:

After finding the G. C. D. of the given equation, and its first derived polynomial, we may proceed to find the G. C. D. of the 1st and 2d derived polynomials, which is $x-1$; hence, since the 2d derived polynomial contains $x-1$ as a factor *once*, the 1st derived polynomial must contain it as a factor *twice*, and the given equation *three* times.

Also, by dividing x^3-x^2-x+1 by $(x-1)^2$, the quotient is $x+1$, which is therefore contained *twice* as a factor in the given equation. The operation of finding the G. C. D. of the 1st and 2d derived polynomials is quite tedious, but it enables us to determine that $x-1$ is a factor of x^3-x^2-x+1, without solving an equation of the third degree, the method of doing which has not yet been explained.

THEOREM OF STURM.

Article 427.

(3) Here, $X = x^3-2x^2-x+2$, and (Art. 411),
$X_1=3x^2-4x-1$.

Multiplying X by 3, to render the first term divisible by the first term of X_1 and proceeding according to Art. 108, we have for a remainder $-14x+16$. Canceling the factor $+2$, and changing the signs (Art. 420), we have $X_2=+7x-8$. Multiplying X_1 by 7 to render the first term divisible by the first term of X_2, and proceeding as before, the remainder is -81; hence, $X_3=+81$, and the series of functions is

$$X = x^3-2x^2-x+2$$
$$X_1=3x^2-4x-1$$
$$X_2=7x-8$$
$$X_3=+81$$

	X	X_1	X_2	X_3	
For $x=-\infty$ the signs are	$-$	$+$	$-$	$+$,	3 var. ∴ $k=3$,
$x=+\infty$ the signs are	$+$	$+$	$+$	$+$,	0 var. ∴ $k'=0$.

Therefore, $k-k'=2-1=1$, the number of real roots.

By substituting the whole numbers from -2 to $+3$, we find the roots are -1, $+1$, and $+2$.

(4) Here, $X = 8x^3-36x^2+46x-15$, and (Art. 411),

$X_1=24x^2-72x+46$, (or $12x^2-36x+23$).

Multiplying X by 3, and dividing by X_1, the first remainder is $-36x^2+92x-45$; multiplying this by 2, and continuing the division, the remainder is $-32x+48=16(-2x+3)$; hence, $X_2=2x-3$. Dividing X_1 by X_2 the remainder is -8; hence, $X_3=+8$, and the series of functions is

$$X = 8x^3-36x^2+46x-15$$
$$X_1=24x^2-72x+46$$
$$X_2= 2x-3$$
$$X_3=+8.$$

For $x=-\infty$ the signs are $- + - +$, 3 var. $\therefore$ $k=3$,

$x=+\infty$ the signs are $+ + + +$, 0 var. $\therefore$ $k'=0$.

Therefore, $k-k'=3-0=3$, the number of real roots.

By substituting the whole numbers, from 0 to 3, we find that one variation is lost in passing from 0 to 1, one from 1 to 2, and one from 2 to 3.

(5) Here, $X = x^3-3x^2-4x+11$, and (Art. 411),

$X_1=3x^2-6x-4$.

Multiplying X by 3, and dividing by X_1, the remainder is $-14x+29$; hence, $X_2=14x-29$. Multiplying X_1 by 14, and dividing by X_2, the first remainder is $+3x-56$, multiplying this by 14, and continuing the division, the remainder is -697; hence, $X_3=+697$ and the series of functions is

$$X = x^3-3x^2-4x+11$$
$$X_1= 3x^2-6x-4$$
$$X_2=14x-29$$
$$X_3=+697.$$

For $x=-\infty$ the signs are $- + - +$, 3 var. $\therefore$ $k=3$,

$x=+\infty$ the signs are $+ + + +$, 0 var. $\therefore$ $k'=0$.

Therefore, $k-k'=3-0=3$, the number of real roots.

By substituting the whole numbers from -2 to $+4$, we find that one variation is lost in passing from -2 to -1, one from $+1$ to $+2$, and one from $+3$ to $+4$.

(6) Here, $X=x^3-2x-5$, and $X_1=3x^2-2$.

Multiplying X by 3, and dividing by X_1, the remainder is $-4x-15$; hence, $X_2=4x+15$. Multiplying X_1 by 4, and dividing by

X_2, the first remainder is $-45x-8$; multiplying this by 4, and continuing the division, the remainder is $+643$; hence, $X_3=-643$ and the series of functions is

$$X = x^3-2x-5$$
$$X_1=3x^2-2$$
$$X_2=4x+15$$
$$X_3=-643.$$

For $x=-\infty$ the signs are $- + - -$, 2 var. $\therefore$ $k=2$,
$x=+\infty$ the signs are $+ + + -$, 1 var. $\therefore$ $k'=1$.

Therefore, $k-k'=2-1=1$, the number of real roots.

We also find that one variation is lost in passing from 2 to 3; therefore, the root lies between 2 and 3.

(7) Here, $X=x^3-15x-22$, and $X_1=3x^2-15$, or x^2-5.

Dividing X by $X_1=x^2-5$, the remainder is $-10x-22=2(-5x-11)$; hence, $X_2=+5x+11$. Multiplying X_1 by 5, and dividing by X_2, the first remainder is $-11x-25$; multiplying this by 5, and continuing the division, the remainder is -4; hence, $X_3=+4$, and the series of functions is

$$X = x^3-15x-22$$
$$X_1= x^2-5$$
$$X_2=5x+11$$
$$X_3=+4.$$

For $x=-\infty$ the signs are $- + - +$, 3 var. $\therefore$ $k=3$,
$x=+\infty$ the signs are $+ + + +$, 0 var. $\therefore$ $k'=0$.

Therefore, $k-k'=3-0=3$, the number of real roots.

By substituting the whole numbers from -3 to $+5$, we find that two variations are lost from -3 to -2, and one from $+4$ to $+5$; we also find that -2 is a root. For $x=-2\frac{1}{2}$ there are three variations, and for $x=-2\frac{1}{4}$ there are two variations; hence, one root lies between $-2\frac{1}{4}$ and $-2\frac{1}{2}$.

(8) Here, $X=x^4-4x^3-3x+23$, and $X_1=4x^3-12x^2-3$.

Multiplying X by 4, and dividing by X_1, the remainder is $-12x^2-9x+89$; hence, $X_2=+12x^2+9x-89$. Multiplying X_1 by 3, and dividing by X_2, the first remainder is $-45x^2+89x-9$; multiplying this by 4, and continuing the division, the remainder is $+491x-1371$; hence, $X_3=-491x+1371$. Multiplying X_2 by 491, and dividing by X_3, the first remainder is $20871x-43699$, multiplying this by 491, and continuing the division, the remainder is $+7157932$; hence, $X_4=-7157932$, and the series of functions is

$$X=x^4-4x^3-3x+23$$
$$X_1=4x^3-12x^2-3$$
$$X_2=12x^2+9x-89$$
$$X_3=-491x+1371$$
$$X_4=-7157932.$$

For $x=-\infty$ the signs are $+-++-$, 3 var. $\therefore$ k $=3$,
$x=+\infty$ the signs are $+++--$, 1 var. $\therefore$ k$'=1$.

Therefore, k$-$k$'=3-1=2$, the number of real roots.

By substituting the whole numbers from 1 to 4, we find that one variation is lost in passing from 2 to 3, and one from 3 to 4.

(9) Here, $X=x^4-2x^3-7x^2+10x+10$, and $X_1=4x^3-6x^2-14x+10$, or $2x^3-3x^2-7x+5$.

Multiplying X by 2, and dividing by X_1, the first remainder is $-x^3-7x^2+15x+20$; multiplying this by 2, and continuing the division, the remainder is $-17x^2+23x+45$; hence, $X_2=17x^2-23x-45$. Multiplying X_1 by 17, and dividing by X_2, the first remainder is $-5x^2-29x+85$, multiplying this by 17, and continuing the division, the remainder is $-608x+1220=4(-152x+305)$; hence, $X_3=152x-305$. Multiplying X_2 by 152, and dividing by X_3, the first remainder is $1689x-6840$, multiplying this by 152, and continuing the division, the remainder is -524535; hence, $X_4=+524535$, and the series of functions is

$$X=x^4-2x^3-7x^2+10x+10$$
$$X_1=2x^3-3x^2-7x+5$$
$$X_2=17x^2-23x-45$$
$$X_3=152x-305$$
$$X_4=+524535.$$

For $x=-\infty$ the signs are $+-+-+$, 4 var. $\therefore$ k $=4$,
$x=+\infty$ the signs are $+++++$, 0 var. $\therefore$ k$'=0$.

Therefore, k$-$k$'=4-0=4$, the number of real roots.

We also find that one variation is lost in passing from -3 to -2, one in passing from -1 to 0, and two in passing from $+2$ to $+3$.

(10) Here, $X=x^5-10x^3+6x+1$, and $X_1=5x^4-30x^2+6$.

Multiplying X by 5, and dividing by X_1, the remainder is $-20x^3+24x+5$; hence, $X_2=20x^3-24x-5$. Multiplying X_1 by 4, and dividing by X_2, the remainder is $-96x^2+5x+24$; hence, $X_3=96x^2-5x-24$. Multiplying X_2 by 24, and dividing by X_3, the first remainder is $25x^2-456x-120$; multiplying this by 96, and continuing the division, the remainder is $-43651x-10920$: hence, $X_4=43651x+10920$. Multiplying X_3 by 43651; and dividing by X_4, the first remainder is $-1266575x-1047624$; multiplying this by 43651, and continuing the division, the remainder is -1372624203024; hence, $X_5=+1372624203024$. It is not necessary, however, to obtain any thing more than the sign of the last function. The series of functions is

$$\begin{aligned}
X &= x^5-10x^3+6x+1\\
X_1 &= 5x^4-30x^2+6\\
X_2 &= 20x^3-24x-5\\
X_3 &= 96x^2-5x-24\\
X_4 &= 43651x+10920\\
X_5 &= +.
\end{aligned}$$

For $x=-\infty$ the signs are $-+-+-+$, 5 var. $\therefore$ $k=5$,
$x=+\infty$ the signs are $++++++$, 0 var. $\therefore$ $k'=0$.

Therefore, $k-k'=5-0=5$, the number of real roots.

By substituting the whole numbers from -4 to $+4$, we find that one variation is lost in passing from -4 to -3, two in passing from -1 to 0, one in passing from 0 to 1, and one in passing from 3 to 4.

RESOLUTION OF NUMERICAL EQUATIONS.

RATIONAL ROOTS

Article 429.

(2) Here, $x^3-7x^2+36=0$. $+1$ and -1 are not roots.
Limit of positive roots $=1+7=8$.
Changing the signs of the alternate terms (Art. 418), the equation becomes $x^3+7x^2\pm 0x-36=0$.
Therefore, limit of negative roots $=-(1+\sqrt[3]{36})$, or -5.
Last term $+36$.

Divisors, . . .	+6,	+4,	+ 3,	+ 2,	− 2,	− 3,	−4.
Quotients, . .	+6,	+9,	+12,	+18,	−18,	−12,	−9.
Add 0, ...	+6,	+9,	+12,	+18,	−18,	−12,	−9.
Quotients, . .	+1,	*,	+ 4,	+ 9,	+ 9,	+ 4,	*.
Add −7, . . .	−6,		− 3,	+ 2,	+ 2,	− 3.	
Quotients, . .	−1,		− 1,	+ 1,	− 1,	+ 1.	
Add +1, . . .	0,		0,	+ 2,	0,	+ 2.	

Hence, the roots are $+6$, $+3$, and -2.

(3) Here, $x^3-6x^2+11x-6=0$, and $+1$ is found to be a root
Limit of positive roots $=1+6=7$.

Limit of negative roots $=0$, since, when the signs of the alternate terms are changed, all the terms are positive; therefore, this equation has no positive root, and therefore the given equation has no negative root (Art. 402).

Last term -6.

Divisors, ...	$+6$,	$+3$,	$+2$.
Quotients, ...	-1,	-2,	-3.
Add $+11$, ...	$+10$,	$+9$,	$+8$.
Quotients, ...	*,	$+3$,	$+4$.
Add -6, ...		-3,	-2.
Quotients, ...		-1,	-1.
Add $+1$, ...		0,	0.

Hence, the roots are $+3$, $+2$, and 1.

(4) Here, $x^3+x^2-4x-4=0$, and -1 is found to be a root.
Limit of positive roots $1+\sqrt{4}=3$.
Limit of negative roots $-(1+4)=-5$.
Last term -4.

Divisors, ...	$+2$,	-2,	-4.
Quotients, ...	-2,	$+2$,	$+1$.
Add -4, ...	-6,	-2,	-3.
Quotients, ...	-3,	$+1$,	*.
Add $+1$, ...	-2,	$+2$.	
Quotients, ...	-1,	-1.	
Add $+1$, ...	0,	0.	

Therefore, the roots are $+2$, -2, -1.

(5) Here, $x^3-3x^2-46x-72=0$, and $+1$ and -1 are not roots.
Limit of positive roots 72, of negative roots $-(1+\sqrt{46})$, or -8.
Last term -72.

Divisors,
$+72$, $+36$, $+24$, $+18$, $+12$, $+9$, $+8$, $+6$, $+4$, $+3$, $+2$,
-2, -3, -4, -6, -8.

Quotients,
-1, -2, -3, -4, -6, -8, -9, -12, -18, -24, -36,
$+36$, $+24$, $+18$, $+12$, $+9$.

Add -46,
-47, -48, -49, -50, -52, -54, -55, -58, -64, -70, -82,
-10, -22, -28, -34, -37.

Quotients,

*, *, *, *, *, 6, *, *, —16, *, —41,

+ 5, *, + 7, *, *, *.

Add —3,

+ 2, + 4, — 9, —19, —44.

Quotients,

— 1, — 1, — 1, *, —22.

Add +1,

0, 0, 0, —21.

Therefore, the roots are —2, —4, +9.

(6) Here, $x^3-5x^2-18x+72=0$, and +1 and —1 are not roots. Limit of positive roots 1+18=19, of negative roots —72.

Last term +72.

Divisors,

+18, +12, + 9, + 8, + 6, + 4, + 3, + 2, — 2, — 3,

— 4, — 6, — 8, — 9, —12, —18, —24, —36, —72.

Quotients,

+ 4, + 6, + 8, + 9, +12, +18, +24, +36, —36, —24,

—18, —12, — 9, — 8, — 6, — 4, — 3, — 2, — 1.

Add —18,

—14, —12, —10, — 9, — 6, 0, + 6, +18, —54, —42,

—36, —30, —27, —26, —24, —22, —21, —20, —19.

Quotients,

*, — 1, *, *, — 1, 0, + 2, + 9, +27, +14,

+ 9, + 5, *, *, + 2, *, *, *, *.

Add —5,

*, — 6, *, *, — 6, — 5, — 3, + 4, +22, + 9,

+ 4, 0, *, *, — 3.

Quotients,

*, *, *, *, — 1, *, — 1, + 2, —11, — 8,

— 1, 0, *, *, *.

Add +1,

0, + 1, 0, 0, + 3, —10, — 2.

Therefore, +6, +3, and —4 are the roots.

(7) Here, $x^4-10x^3+35x^2-50x+24=0$, and +1 is found to be one of the roots (Art. 429, Cor. 1).

The limit of the positive roots is 24, and since when we change the signs of the alternate terms, all the terms are positive, this equation has no positive roots (Art. 402, Cor. 1); therefore, the given equation has no negative roots.

Last term +24.

Divisors,	+24,	+12,	+ 8,	+ 6,	+ 4,	+ 3,	+ 2.
Quotients,	+ 1,	+ 2,	+ 3,	+ 4,	+ 6,	+ 8,	+12.
Add —50,	—49,	—48,	—47,	—46,	—44,	—42,	—38.
Quotients,	*,	— 4,	*	*,	—11,	—14,	—19.
Add +35,		—31,			+24,	+21,	+16.
Quotients,		*,			+ 6,	+ 7,	+ 8.
Add —10,					— 4,	— 3,	— 2.
Quotients,					— 1,	— 1,	— 1.
Add +1,					0,	0,	0

Therefore, +4, +3, +2, and +1. are the roots.

(8) Here, $x^4+4x^3-x^2-16x-12=0$, and —1 is found to be a root.

Limit of positive roots $1+\sqrt{16}=5$; of negative roots $-(1+4)=-5$.

Last term —12.

Divisors,	+ 4,	+ 3,	+ 2,	— 2,	— 3,	— 4.
Quotients,	— 3,	— 4,	— 6,	+ 6,	+ 4,	+ 3.
Add —16,	—19,	— 20,	—22,	—10,	—12,	—13.
Quotients,	*,	*,	—11,	+ 5,	+ 4,	*.
Add —1,			—12	+ 4,	+ 3.	
Quotients,			— 6,	— 2,	— 1.	
Add +4,			— 2,	+ 2,	+ 3.	
Quotients,			— 1,	— 1,	— 1.	
Add +1,			0,	0,	0.	

Therefore, +2, —2, —3, and —1, are the roots.

(9) Here, $x^4-4x^3-19x^2+46x+120=0$, and +1 and —1 are found not to be roots.

Limit of the positive roots $1+19=20$; of the negative roots $-(1+\sqrt{46})$, or —8.

Last term +120.

Divisors,	+ 20,	+15,	+12,	+10,	+ 8,	+ 6,	+ 5,	+ 4,	+ 3,
	+ 2,	— 2,	— 3,	— 4,	— 5,	— 6,	— 8.		
Quotients,	+ 6,	+ 8,	+10,	+12,	+15,	+20,	+24,	+30,	+40,
	+ 60,	—60,	—40,	—30,	—24,	—20,	—15.		
Add +46,	+ 52,	+54,	+56,	+58,	+61,	+66,	+70,	+76,	+86,
	+106,	—14,	+ 6,	+16,	+22,	+26,	+31.		

Quotients, *, *, *, *, *, +11, +14, +19, *,
+ 53, + 7, — 2, — 4, *, *, *.
Add —19, ... — 8, — 5, 0,
+ 34, —12, —21, —23.
Quotients, ... *, — 1, 0,
+ 17, + 6, + 7, *.
Add —4, ... — 5, — 4,
— 13, + 2, + 3.
Quotients, ... — 1, — 1,
*, — 1, — 1.
Add +1, ... 0, 0,
0, 0.

Therefore, +5, +4, —2, and —3 are the roots.

(10) Here, $x^4+0x^3-27x^2+14x+120=0$, and +1 and —1 are not roots.

Limit of positive roots $1+\sqrt{27}$ or 7; of negative roots —(1+27) or 28.

Last term +120.

Divisors, + 6, + 5, + 4, + 3, + 2, — 2, — 3, — 4, — 5,
— 6, — 8, —10, —12, —15, —20, —24.
Quotients, +20, +24, +30, +40, +60, —60, —40, —30, —24,
—20, —15, —12, —10, — 8, — 6, — 5.
Add +14, +34, +38, +44, +54, +74, —46, —26, —16, —10,
— 6, — 1, + 2, + 4, + 6, + 8, + 9.
Quotients, *, *, +11, +18, +37, +23, *, + 4, + 2,
+ 1, *, *, *, *, *, *.
Add —27, ... —16, — 9, +10, — 4, —23, —25,
—26.
Quotients, ... — 4, — 3, + 5, + 2, *, + 5,
*.
Add 0, ... — 4, — 3, + 5, + 2, + 5.
Quotients, ... — 1, — 1, *, — 1, — 1.
Add +1, ... 0, 0, 0, 0.

Therefore, the roots are +4, +3, —2, and —5.

(11) Here, $x^4+x^3-29x^2-9x+180=0$, and +1 and —1 are not roots.

Limit of positive roots, $1+\sqrt{29}$, or 7; of negative roots, —(1+29)=—30.

Last term				+180.					
Divisors,	+ 6,	+ 5,	+ 4,	+ 3,	+ 2,	— 2,	— 3,	— 4,	— 5,
	— 6,	— 9,	—10,	—12,	—15,	—18,	—20,	—30.	
Quotients,	+30,	+36,	+45,	+60,	+90,	—90,	—60,	—45,	—36,
	—30,	—20,	—18,	—15,	—12,	—10,	— 9,	— 6.	
Add —9,	+21,	+27,	+36,	+51,	+81,	—99,	—69,	—54,	—45,
	—39,	—29,	—27,	—24,	—21,	—19,	—18,	—15.	
Quotients,	*,	*,	+ 9,	+17,	*,	*,	+23,	*,	+ 9,
	*,	*,	*,	+ 2,	*,	*,	*,	*.	
Add —29,	. . .	. . .	—20,	—12,			— 6,		—20,
				—27.					
Quotients,	. . .	. . .	— 5,	— 4,			+ 2,		+ 4,
				*.					
Add +1,	. . .	. . .	+ 4,	— 3,			+ 3,		+ 5.
Quotients,	. . .	. . .	— 1,	— 1,			— 1,		— 1.
Add +1,	. . .	. . .	0,	0,			0,		0.

Therefore, the roots are +4, +3, —3, and —5.

(12) Here, $x^3-2x^2-4x+8=0$, and +1 and —1 are not roots. Limit of positive roots, $1+\sqrt{4}=3$; of negative roots, $-(1+4)=-5$.

Last term	+8.		
Divisors, ...	+2,	—2,	—4.
Quotients, ...	+4,	—4,	—2.
Add —4, ...	0,	—8,	—6.
Quotients, ...	0,	+4,	*.
Add —2, ...	—2,	+2.	
Quotients, ...	—1,	—1.	
Add +1, ...	0,	0.	

∴ +2 and —2 are roots, and by dividing the given equation by $(x-2)(x+2)$, the quotient is $x-2$; hence, $x-2=0$ and $x=+2$; ∴ the equation has two equal roots, each of which is +2.

(13) Here, $x^3+3x^2-8x+10=0$, and +1 and —1 are not roots. Limit of positive roots, $1+\sqrt{8}$, or 4; of negative roots, $-(1+8)=-9$.

Last term	+10.		
Divisors, ...	+2,	— 2,	— 5.
Quotients, ...	+5,	— 5,	— 2.

Add -8, ...	-3,	-13,	-10.
Quotients, ...	*,	*,	$+2$.
Add $+3$, ...			$+5$.
Quotient, ...			-1.
Add $+1$, ...			0.

$\therefore$ -5 is a root, and dividing the given equation by $x-(-5)=x+5$ the quotient is x^2-2x+2; hence, $x^2-2x+2=0$, and $x=1\pm\sqrt{-1}$.

(14) Here, $x^4-9x^3+17x^2+27x-60=0$, and $+1$ and -1 are not roots.

Limit of positive roots, $1+9=10$; of negative roots, $-(1+\sqrt[3]{27})$, or -4.

Last term -60.

Divisors,	$+10$,	$+5$,	$+4$,	$+3$,	$+2$,	-2,	-3,	-4.
Quotients,	-6,	-12,	-15,	-20,	-30,	$+30$,	$+20$,	$+15$.
Add $+27$,	$+21$,	$+15$,	$+12$,	$+7$,	-3,	$+57$,	$+47$,	$+42$.
Quotients,	*,	$+3$,	$+3$,	*,	*,	*,	*,	*.
Add $+17$, . . .		$+20$,	$+20$.					
Quotients, . . .		$+4$,	$+5$.					
Add -9, . . .		-5,	-4.					
Quotients, . . .		-1,	-1.					
Add $+1$, . . .		0,	0.					

Therefore, $+5$ and $+4$ are roots, and by dividing the given equation by $(x-5)(x-4)$, the quotient is x^2-3; hence, $x^2=3$, and $x=\pm\sqrt{3}$; $\therefore$ the four roots are $+5$, $+4$, $+\sqrt{3}$, $-\sqrt{3}$.

(15) Here, $2x^3-3x^2+2x-3=0$.

Let $x=\dfrac{y}{2}$, then the transformed equation (Art. 405, Cor.) is $y^3-3y^2+4y-12=0$, and $+1$ and -1 are not roots.

Limit of positive roots, $1+3=4$, and since when the signs of the alternate terms are changed (Art. 400) all the terms are positive; therefore, the given equation has no negative roots.

Last term -12.

Divisors, ...	$+4$,	$+3$,	$+2$.
Quotients, ...	-3,	-4,	-6.
Add $+4$, ...	$+1$,	0,	-2.
Quotients, ...	*,	0,	-1.

Add -3, ... -3, -4.
Quotients, ... -1, -2.
Add $+1$, ... 0, -1.

Therefore, $+3$ is a root of the transformed equation, and dividing by $y-3$, the quotient is y^2+4; hence, $y^2+4=0$, and $y=\pm\sqrt{-4}=\pm2\sqrt{-1}$.

Therefore, $y=+3,\ +2\sqrt{-1},\ -2\sqrt{-1}$.

$$x=\frac{y}{2}=+\tfrac{3}{2},\ +\sqrt{-1},\ -\sqrt{-1}.$$

(16) Here, $3x^3-2x^2-6x+4=0$.

Let $x=\frac{y}{3}$; then, the transformed equation (Art. 405, Cor.) is $y^3-2y^2-18y+36=0$, and $+1$ and -1 are not roots.

Limit of positive roots, $1+18=19$; of negative roots, $-(1+\sqrt{18})$, or -6.

Last term $+36$.

Divisors,											
	$+18$,	$+12$,	$+9$,	$+6$,	$+4$,	$+3$,	$+2$	-2,	-3,	-4,	-6.
Quotients,											
	$+2$,	$+3$,	$+4$,	$+6$,	$+9$,	$+12$,	$+18$,	-18,	-12,	-9,	-6.
Add -18,											
	-16,	-15,	-14,	-12,	-9,	-6,	0,	-36,	-30,	-27,	-24.
Quotients,											
	*,	*,	*,	-2,	*,	-2,	0,	$+18$,	$+10$,	*,	$+4$.
Add -2,		. .		-4,		-4	-2,	$+16$,	$+8$,		$+2$.
Quotients,		. .		*,		*,	-1,	-8,	*,		*.
Add $+1$,		. . . .					0,	-7.			

$\therefore$ $+2$ is a root of the transformed equation, and dividing by $y-2$, the quotient is y^2-18; hence, $y^2-18=0$, and $y=\pm3\sqrt{2}$.

Therefore, $y=2,\ +3\sqrt{2},\ -3\sqrt{2}$.

$$x=\frac{y}{3}=\tfrac{2}{3},\ +\sqrt{2},\ -\sqrt{2}.$$

(17) Here, $8x^3-26x^2+11x+10=0$.

Let $x=\frac{y}{8}$; then, the transformed equation is $y^3-26y^2+88y+640=0$, and $+1$ and -1 are not roots

Limit of positive roots, $1+26=27$; of negative roots, $-(1+\sqrt[3]{640})$, or -10.

Last term $+640$.

Divisors,	+20,	+16,	+10,	+8,	+5,	+2,	−2,
	−5,	−8,	−10.				
Quotients,	+32,	+40,	+64,	+80,	+128,	+320,	−320,
	−128,	−80,	−64.				
Add +88,	+120,	+128,	+152,	+168,	+216,	+408,	−232,
	−40,	+8,	+24.				
Quotients,	+6,	+8,	*,	+21,	*,	+204,	−116
	+8,	−1,	*.				
Add −26,	−20,	−18,		−5,		+178,	−142,
	−18,	−27,	*.				
Quotients,	−1,	*,		*,		+89,	+71,
	*,	*.					
Add +1,	0,					+90,	+72.

Therefore, $+20$ is a root of the transformed equation, and by dividing by $x-20$, the quotient is $y^2-6y-32$; hence, $y^2-6y-32=0$, and $y=3\pm\sqrt{41}$.

Therefore, $y=+20$, and $3\pm\sqrt{41}$;

$$x=\frac{y}{8}=+\tfrac{5}{2}, \text{ or } \tfrac{1}{8}(3\pm\sqrt{41}).$$

(18) Here, $6x^4-25x^3+26x^2+4x-8=0$.

Let $x=\frac{y}{6}$; then, the transformed equation is $y^4-25y^3+156y^2+144y-1728=0$, and $+1$ and -1 are not roots.

Limit of positive roots, $1+25=26$; of negative roots, $-(1+\sqrt[3]{144})$, or -7.

Last term -1728.

Divisors,	+24,	+18,	+16,	+12,	+9,	+8,	+6,
	+4,	+3,	+2,	−2,	−3,	−4,	−6.
Quotients,	−72,	−96,	−108,	−144,	−192,	−216,	−288,
	−432,	−576,	−864,	+864,	+576,	+432,	+288.
Add +144,	+72,	+48,	+36,	0,	−48,	−72,	−144,
	−288,	−432,	−720,	+1008,	+720,	+576,	+432.
Quotients,	+3,	+2,	*,	0,	*,	−9,	−24,
	−72,	−144,	−360,	−504,	−240,	−144,	−72.
Add +156,	+159,	+158,		+156,		+147,	+132,
	+84,	+12,	−204,	−348,	−84,	+12,	+84.

Quotients,	*,	*,		+13,		*,	+22,
	+21,	+4,	−102,	+174,	+28.	−3,	−14.
Add −25,	. .	. .	. .	−12,			−3,
	−4,	−21,	−127,	+149,	+3,	−28,	−39.
Quotients,	. .	. .	. .	−1,			*,
	−1,	−7,	*,	*,	−1,	+7,	*
Add +1,	. .	. .	. .	0,			
	0,	−6,			0,	+8.	

Therefore, $y=+12$, $+4$, and -3; and by dividing by $(y-12)(y-4)(y+3)$, the quotient is $y-12$; hence, $y-12=0$, and $y=12$.

Therefore, $x=\frac{y}{6}=+2, +2, +\frac{2}{3}$, and $-\frac{1}{2}$.

(19) Here, $x^4-9x^3+\frac{45}{4}x^2+\frac{27}{2}x-\frac{81}{4}=0$.

Let $x=\frac{y}{2}$; then, the transformed equation is

$y^4-18y^3+45y^2+108y-324=0$.

Limit of positive roots, $1+18=19$; of negative roots, $-(1+\sqrt[3]{108})$, or -6.

Last term -324.

Divisors,	+ 18,	+ 12,	+ 9,	+ 6,	+ 4,	+ 3,	+ 2,
	− 2,	− 3,	− 4,	− 6.			
Quotients,	− 18,	− 27,	− 36,	− 54,	− 81,	−108,	−162,
	+162,	+108,	+ 81,	+ 54.			
Add +108,	+ 90,	+ 81,	+ 72,	+ 54,	+ 27,	0,	− 54,
	+270,	+216,	+189,	+162.			
Quotients,	*,	*,	+ 8,	+ 9,	*,	0,	− 27,
	−135,	− 72,	*,	*.			
Add +45,	. .	. .	+ 53,	+ 54,		+ 45,	+ 18,
	− 90,	− 27.					
Quotients,	. .	. .	*,	+ 9,		+ 15,	+ 9,
	+ 45,	+ 9.					
Add −18,	. .	. .		− 9,		− 3,	− 9,
	+ 27,	− 9.					
Quotients,	. .	. .	. .	*,		− 1,	*,
	*,	+ 3.					
Add +1,	. .	+ 4,				0.	

Therefore, $+3$ is a root of the transformed equation.

The first derived polynomial of the transformed equation is $4y^3-54y^2+90y+108$; now, we shall find that $y-3$ is a divisor of this as well as the transformed equation; therefore, +3 and +3 are two roots of the transformed equation (Art. 414), and if we divide it by $(y-3)(y-3)$, the quotient is $y^2-12y-36$; hence $y^2-12y-36=0$, and $y=6\pm6\sqrt{2}$.

$$\text{Therefore, } y=+3,\ +3,\ +6+6\sqrt{2},\ +6-6\sqrt{2}.$$

$$x=\frac{y}{2}=+\tfrac{3}{2},\ +\tfrac{3}{2},\ +3+3\sqrt{2},\ +3-3\sqrt{2}.$$

NOTE.—This example may be solved by Art. 414, but the above is the shortest method.

HORNER'S METHOD OF APPROXIMATION.

Article 434.

(1) $x^2+5x \quad -12.24=0.$

1	+5	−12.24	$(1.8=x.$ (r)
	+1	+ 6	
	+6	− 6.24	
	+1	+ 6.24	
1	+7*		
	.8		$r=\frac{V'}{T'}=\frac{6.24}{7}=.8+.$
	+7.8		

It is readily found that x is greater than 1, and less than 2; hence, 1 is the integral part of the root.

(2) $x^2+12x \quad -35.4025=0.$

1	+12	−35.4025	$\lvert 2.45=x$ ($r\ s$)
	+ 2	+28	
	+14	− 7.4025*	
	+ 2	+ 6.56	
1	+16*	− .8425*	
	.4	+ .8425	
	+16.4	.0	
	.4		$r=\frac{7.4}{16}=4+.$
1	+16.8*		
	.05		$s=\frac{.84}{16.8}=.05.$
	+16.85		

When the operation gives a remainder zero, we know from Art. 395, Cor., that the exact root is obtained.

NOTE.—In the solution of the succeeding problems, we shall merely present the operation, without exhibiting the work by which the successive figures of the root are obtained, since they can generally be determined mentally, as in Long Division.

(3) $4x^2-28x-61.25=0.$

4	-28	-61.25	$8.75=x.$
	$+32$	$+32$	
	$+4$	-29.25^*	
	32	$+27.16$	
4	$+36^*$	-2.09	
	2.8	$+2.09$	
	$+38.8$	0	
	2.8		
4	$+41.6^*$		
	$.2=.05\times4$		
	$+41.8$		

(4) $8x^2-120x+394.875=0.$

8	-120	$+394.875$	$10.125=x.$
	$+80$	-400	
	-40	-5.125^*	
	$+80$	$+4.08$	
8	$+40^*$	-1.045	
	$.8$	$+.8352$	
	$+40.8$	$-.2098$	
	$.8$	$+.2098$	
8	$+41.6^*$	0	
	$.16$		
	$+41.76$		
	$.16$		
8	$+41.92^*$		
	$.04=.005\times8$		
	$+41.96$		

(5) $5x^2-7.4x-16.08=0.$

5	-7.4	-16.08	$2.68=x.$
	$+10$	$+5.2$	
	$+2.6$	-10.88	

	+10	+ 9.36
5	+12.6*	− 1.52
	3	+ 1.52
	+15.6	0
	3	
5	+18.6*	
	.4=.08×5	
	19.0.	

(6) $x^2-6x+6=0.$

1	−6	+6	4.73205=x
	+4	−8	
	−2	−2	
	+4	+1.89	
1	+2*	− .11	
	.7	+ .1029	
	+2.7	− .0071	
	.7		
1	+3.4*	$\frac{.0071}{3.46}$=.00205.	
	.03		
	+3.43		
	.03		
1	3.46*.		

(7) $x^3+4x^2-9x-57.623625=0.$

1	+4	− 9	−57.623625	3.45=x.
	+3	+21	+36	
	+7	+12	−21.623625*	
	+3	+30	18.944	
	+10	+42*	− 2.679625	
	3	5.36	+ 2.679625	
1	+13*	+47.36	0	
	.4	5.52		
	+13.4	+52.88*		
	.4	.7125		
	+13.8	+53.5925		
	.4			
1	+14.2*			
	.05			
	+14.25.			

(8) $2x^3-50x+32.994306=0.$

2	±0	—50	+32.994306	4.68 = x
	+8	32	—72	
	+8	—18	—39.005694*	
	+8	+64	+36.672	
	+16	+46*	— 2.333694*	
	8	+15.12	+ 2.333694	
2	+24*	+61.12	0	
	+ 1.2	15.84		
	+25.2	+76.96*		
	1.2	.8298		
	+26.4	+77.7898		
	1.2			
2	+27.6*			
	.06			
	+27.66.			

(9) $x^3+4x^2-5x-20=0.$

1	+4	—5	—20	2.23608
	+2	+12	+14	
	+6	+7	—6*	
	+2	+16	+5.008	
	+8	+23*	— .992	
	2	2.04	+ .823167	
	+10*	+25.04	— .168833	
	.2	2.08		
	+10.2	+27.12*		
	.2	.3189		
	+10.4	+27.4389		
	.2	.3198		
1	+10.6*	27.7587*		
	.03			
	+10.63			
	.03			
	+10.66			

$\frac{.168833}{27.76}=.00608.$

Note.—In the solution of the remaining examples, we shall use the abridged method employed in example 3, page 392, of the Algebra. The learner, however, who chooses to carry out the decimals fully will find no difficulty in so doing.

(10) $x^3-2x-5=0$.

1	0	—2	—5	2.0945515=x.
	+2	4	+4	
	2	+2	—1*	
	2	8	+0.949329	
	4	+10*	— .050671*	
	2	.5481	+ .04451752	
1	+6*	+10.5481	— .00615348*	
	.09	.5562	557875	
	6.09	+11.1043*	57473*	
	.09	.02508	55800	
	6.18	11.12938	1673*	
	.09	.02508	1116	
1	6.27*	+11.15446*	557*	
		.0031	558	
		11.1575		
		.003		
		+11.16*		

In finding the result true to 7 places, it is not necessary to add more figures to 6.27, as it will not alter the result.

This example is found in the work of M. Fourier, "*Analyse des Equations*," where the result is given to 32 places of decimals: the result to 40 places, as given by Gregory is,

$$x=2.0945514815423265914823865405793029638576.$$

The other two values of x are imaginary.

(11) $x^3+10x^2-24x-240=0$.

1	+10	— 24	—240	4.8989795=x.
	+ 4	+ 56	+128	
	+14	+ 32	—112*	
	+ 4	+ 72	+ 97.792	
	+18	+104*	— 14.208*	
	+ 4	18.24	+ 12.899169	
1	+22*	122.24	— 1.308831*	
	.8	18.88	1.165869792	
	22.8	+141.12*	— .142961208	
	.8	2.2041	.131358087	
	23.6	143.3241	11603121	

	.8	2.2122	10218295
1	+24.4*	+145.5363*	1384826
	.09	.197424	1313781
	24.49	145.733724	71045
	.09	.197488	72988
	24.58	+145.931212*	
	.09	.02222	
1	+24.67*	145.95343	
	.008	.02222	
	24.678	+145.97565*	
	.008		
	24.686		
	.008		
1	+24.694*		

(12) $x^4-8x^3+20x^2-15x+.5=0.$

1	−8	+20	−15	+ .5	1.284724=x
	+1	− 7	+13	−2.0	
	−7	+13	− 2	−1.5*	
	+1	− 6	+ 7	+1.0496	
	−6	+ 7	+ 5*	− .4504*	
	+1	− 5	.248	.4255385	
	−5	+ 2*	+ 5.248	248615*	
	+1	− .76	.104	210536	
1	−4*	1.24	5.352*	38079*	
	.2	− .72	− .032768	36820	
	−3.8	.52	5.319232	1259*	
	.2	− .68	− .0522	1052	
	−3.6	− .16*	+ 5.2670*	207	
	.2	− .2496	− .0036	210	
	−3.4	− .4096	5.2634		
	.2	− .2432	− .0036		
1	−3.2*	− .6528	+ 5.2598*		
	.08	− .24	.0006		
	−3.12	− .89*	5.26		

	.08	— .01
	—3.04	— .90
	.08	— .01
	—2.96	— .91
	.08	
1	—2.88*	

(13) $x^4-59x^2+840=0$.

Note.—This is a trinomial equation and may be solved as a quadratic (Art. 242), but it is placed here to be solved by Horner's method.

1	0	—59	0	+840 (4.8989795
	4	16	—172	—688
	+ 4	—43	—172	+152*
	4	32	— 44	—140.5184
	8	—11	—216*	+ 11.4816
	4	48	40.352	— 10.50697359
	12	+37*	—175.648	+ .97462641
	4	13.44	51.616	— .868978336
1	+16*	50.44	—124.032*	.105648074
	0.8	14.08	7.287849	97080804
	16.8	64.52	—116.744151	8567270
	.8	14.72	7.444827	7544964
	17.6	+79.24*	—109.299324*	1022306
	.8	1.7361	.677032	970011
	18.4	80.9761	—108.622292	52295
	.8	1.7442	.678280	53885
1	+19.2*	82.7203	—107.944012*	
	.09	1.7523	.07645	
	19.29	+84.4726*	—107.86756	
	.09	.1564	.07645	
	19.38	84.629	—107.79111*	
	.09	.156	.0059	
	19.47	84.785	—107.7852	
	.09	.156	.0059	
1	+19.56*	+84.941*	—107.7793	

(14) $2x^4+5x^3+4x^2+3x=8002.$

2	+ 5	+ 4	+ 3	—8002 (7.33555
	14	133	959	+6734 (40314
	19	137	962	—1268*
	14	231	2576	1125.7932
	33	368	3538*	— 142.2068*
	14	329	214.644	119.86597542
	47	697*	3752.644	—22.34082458*
	14	18.48	220.242	20.11015620
2	+61*	715.48	3972.886*	— 2.23066838*
	.6	18.66	22.646514	2.01310385
	61.6	734.14	3995.532514	— .21756453
	.6	18.84	22.703682	.20133125
	62.2	752.98*	4018.236196*	402666) 1623328(
	.6	1.9038	3.79505	1610665
	62.8	754.8838	4022.03124	12663
	.6	1.9056	3.79665	12080
2	+63.4*	756.7894	4025.82789*	583
	.06	1.9074	.3798	403
	63.46	758.6968*	4026.2077	180
	.06	.32	.3798	161
	63.52	759.01	4026.5875*	19
	.95	.32	.038	
	63.58	759.33	4026.625	
	.06	.32	.038	
2	+63.94*	759.65*	4026.663*	$x=7.3355540314.$

Remark.—It is sometimes convenient by drawing lines, as in the preceding solution, to render separate and distinct the operation for finding each successive figure.

(15) $x^5+2x^4+3x^3+4x^2+5x=54321.$

1	+ 2	+ 3	+ 4	+ 5	—54321 (8.414
	8	80	664	5344	42792 (455
	10	83	668	5349	—11529*
	8	144	1816	19872	11088.97344
	18	227	2484	25221*	—440.02656
	8	208	3480	2501.4336	304.1105122
	26	435	5964*	27722.4336	—135.9160478
	8	272	289.584	2620.0064	122.0290372
	34	+707*	6253.584	30342.4400*	— 13.8870106

	8	16.96	296.432	68.61122	12.2150180	
1	+42*	723.96	6550.016	30411.05122	— 1.6719926	
	0.4	17.12	303.344	68.68888	1.5270320	
	42.4	741.08	6853.360*	30479.74010*	— .1449606	
	.4	17.28	7.762	27.5192	.1527032	
	42.8	758.36	6861.122	30507.2593		
	.4	17.44	7.766	27.5316		
	43.2	+775.80*	6868.888	30534.7909*		
	.4	.4	7.770	2.754		
	43.6	776.2	6876.658*	30537.545		
	.4	.4	3.1	2.754		
1	+44.0*	776.6	6879.8	20540.299*		$x=8.414455$
		.4	3.1	.34		
		777.0	6882.9	30540.64		
		.4	3.1			
		777.4*	6886.0*			

Article 435.

TO EXTRACT THE ROOTS OF NUMBERS BY HORNER'S METHOD.

(2) To find the cube root of 34012224.

1	0	0	34012224	(324. *Ans.*
	3	9	27	
	3	9	7012	
	3	18	5768	
	6	27*	1244224	
	3	184		
1	9*	2884		
	2	188		
	92	3072*		
	2	3856		
	94	311056		
	2			
	96			
	4			
	964			

(3) To find the cube root of 9.

1	0	0	9	2.080084, *Ans*
	2	4	8	
	2	4	1*	
	2	8	.998912	
	4	12*	.001088	
	2	.4864	.001038	
	6*	12.4864	50	
	.08	.4928	51	
	6.08	12.9792*		
	.08			
	6.16			
	.08			
	6.24*			

(4) To find the cube root of 30.

1	0	0	30	3.107233, *Ans.*
	3	9	27	
	3	9	3*	
	3	18	2.791	
	6	27*	.209	
	3	.91	.20223	
1	9*	27.91	.00677	
	.1	.92	579	
	9.1	28.83*	98	
	.1	.06	87	
	9.2	28.89	11	
	.1	.06	9	
	9.3*	28.95*		

(5) To find the fifth root of 68641485507.

1	0	0	0	0	68641485507 (147, *Ans.*
	1	1	1	1	1
	1	1	1	1	586414
	1	2	3	4	437824
	2	3	4	5*	14859085507
	1	3	6	59456	14859085507
	3	6	10*	109456	
	1	4	4864	82624	
	4	10*	14864	192080*	

	1	216	5792	201926501
1	5*	1216	20656	2122726501
	4	232	6784	
	54	1448	27440*	
	4	248	1406643	
	58	1696	28846643	
	4	264		
	62	1960*		
	4	4949		
	66	200949		
	4			
1	70*			
	7			
	707			

APPROXIMATION BY DOUBLE POSITION.

Article 436.

(2) $x^3+30x=420$.

6	x	7
216	x^3	343
180	$30x$	210
396	results	553
553	7	420
396	6	396
157 :	1 ::	24 : 0.1

6.1	x	6.2
226.981	x^3	238.328
183.0	$30x$	186.0
409.981	results	424.328
14.347 :	.1 ::	10.019 : 0.163

By trial x is found to be greater than 6.17; therefore, let $x=6.17$ and 6.18.

6.17	x	6.18
234.885	x^3	236.029
185.10	$30x$	185.40
419.985	results	421.429
1.444 :	.01 ::	.015 :.000103

Therefore, $x=6.17+.000103=6.170103$ nearly.

(3) $144x^3-973x=319$.

2	x	3
1152	$144x^3$	3888
−1946	$-973x$	−2919
− 794	results	+ 969
	3	
+ 969	2	319
1763 :	1 ::	650 : .3

$$x=3-.3=2.7.$$

2.7	x	2.8
2834.352	$144x^3$	3161.088
−2627.1	$-973x$	−2724.4
+ 207.252	results	+ 436.688
229.436 :	.1 ::	111.748 : .048

Therefore, $x=2.7+.048=2.748$, and by trial 2.75 is found to verify the equation exactly; hence, $x=2.75$.

In the application of the rule of Double Position to the solution of equations, the first correction is generally too small, as in the two preceding solutions, and, as may be seen more particularly, in the solution of example 5.

To see the reason of this, it must be noticed that the sums, or the differences, of the higher powers of numbers, increase very rapidly as the numbers increase. Hence, if two numbers equally distant from the true number, are substituted in any equation containing the second or higher powers of the unknown quantity, the result arising from the substitution of the greater number, will be further from the true result than that obtained by the substitution of the smaller. And hence, by the operation of the rule, the correction will give for the true number a number too small. To illustrate this by an example, suppose we have the equation

$x^3-x=24$, of which the root is 3.

Let us notice the results obtained by the substitution of 2 and 4 for x.

2	x	4
8	x^3	64
− 2	$-x$	− 4
6	results	60
−18	errors	+36

Difference of the errors $=36-(-18)=54$.

then, $54:2::18:\frac{2}{3}$.

Now, the true correction is 1, but we obtained $\frac{3}{5}$, because although the suppositions, 2 and 4, are *equally* distant from the true number, yet the corresponding results are *unequally* distant from it. Now, the rule proceeds on the hypothesis that the errors of the results are proportional to the errors of the suppositions. But this is never exactly true, and is only nearly so when each of the suppositions is very near the true number. Attention to this principle will often guide the pupil in selecting trial numbers for the second operation.

(4) $x^3+10x^2+5x=2600$.

By trial, we find that 11 is so near the true number that we may at once make a trial of 11 and 11.1.

11	x	11.1
1831	x^3	1367.631
1210	$10x^2$	1232.1
55	$5x$	55.5
2596	results	2655.231
—4	errors	+55.231
59.231 :	.1 ::	4 : .006

Therefore, $x=11+.006=11.006$ nearly.

11.006	x	11.007
1333.179188	x^3	1333.542617
1211.32036	$10x^2$	1211.54049
55.030	$5x$	55.035
2599.529548	results	2600.118107
.470452	errors	+.118107
.588559 :	.001 :	.470452 : .00079

Therefore, $x=11.006+.00079=11.00679$.

(5) $2x^3+3x^2-4x=10$.

1	x	2
2	$2x^3$	16
3	$+3x^2$	12
—4	$-4x$	— 8
+1	results	+20
—9	errors	+10
19 : 1	::	1 : .5 nearly.

Therefore, $x=1+.5=1.5$ nearly.

By trial, however, we find that 1.6 is too small, and 1.7 too great. Let these, therefore, be the next two assumed numbers.

1.6	x	1.7
+8.192	$2x^3$	+ 9.826
+7.68	$+3x^2$	+ 8.67
—6.4	$-4x$	— 6.8
+9.472	results	+11.696
— .528	errors	+ 1.696

2.224 : .1 :: .528 : .024 nearly.

Therefore, $x=1.6+.024=1.624$.

By trial, we find 1.624 is too small, and 1.625 too great; using these as the next two assumed numbers, we readily find the next two figures of the root.

(6) $x^4-x^3+2x^2+x=4$.

It is easily seen by inspection, that x is a little more than 1, and by trial it is found greater than 1.1, and less than 1.2; let these, therefore, be the two assumed numbers.

1.1	x	1.2
+1.4641	$+x^4$	+2.0736
—1.331	$-x^3$	—1.728
+2.42	$+2x^2$	+2.88
+1.1	$+x$	+1.2
+3.6531	results	+4.4256
— .3469	errors	+ .4256

.7725 : .1 :: .3469 : .045 nearly.

By trial, x is found greater than 1.146, and less than 1.147. By repeating the operation with these numbers, we readily find the next two figures of the root.

(7) $\sqrt[3]{7x^3+4x^2}+\sqrt{10x(2x-1)}=28$.

By trial, we readily find that x lies between 4 and 5; we, therefore, take these as the first two assumed numbers.

4	x	5
+ 8	$\sqrt[3]{7x^3+4x^2}$	9.91
+16.73	$+\sqrt{10x(2x-1)}$	21.21
—28	—28	—28
— 3.27	errors	+ 3.12

6.39 : 1 :: 3.27 : .51.

Therefore, $x=4+.51=4.51$ nearly.

By trial, we find x greater than 4.51, and less than 4.52; therefore, let these be the next two assumed numbers.

4.51	x	4.52
$+8.9773$	$\sqrt[3]{7x^3+4x^2}$	8.9965
$+19.0185$	$+\sqrt{10x(2x-1)}$	$+19.0633$
$-28.$	-28	$-28.$
$-.0042$	errors	$+.0598$

.064 : .01 :: .0042 . .00066 nearly.

Therefore, $x=4.51+.00066=4.51066$ nearly

Article 437.

NEWTON'S METHOD OF APPROXIMATION.

Observe that A is what the proposed equation becomes when $x=a$, and that A′ is what the first derived polynomial, or first derived function (Art. 411), becomes when $x=a$.

Proposed equation $X=x^3-2x-5=0$.
First derived function $X'=3x^2-2$.

When 2 is substituted for x, the result is -1, and when 3 is substituted the result is $+16$; therefore (Art. 403), one real root of the equation lies between 2 and 3, and is not much greater than 2. By trial we find that 2.1 gives a positive result; therefore, the root lies between 2.0 and 2.1.

Therefore, let $x=a+y=2+y$;
then, $A=(2)^3-2(2)-5$, and $A'=3(2)^2-2$;

$$y=-\frac{A}{A'}=-\frac{8-4-5}{12-2}=+.1.$$

$$\text{Therefore, } x=a+y=2+\left(-\frac{A}{A'}\right)=2+.1=2.1.$$

Next, let $x=b+z=2.1+z$;
then, $B=(2.1)^3-2(2.1)-5$, and $B'=3(2.1)^2-2$.

$$z=-\frac{B}{B'}=-\frac{(2.1)^3-2(2.1)-5}{3(2.1)^2-2}=-\frac{.061}{11.23}=-.0054;$$

Therefore, $x=b+z=2.1+(-.0054)=2.0946$.
Next, let $x=c+z'=2.0946+z'$;
then, $C=(2.0946)^3-2(2.0946)-5=.000541550536$
$C'=3(2.0946)^2-2=11.16204748$;

$$z=-\frac{C}{C'}=\frac{.000541550536}{11.16204748}=-.00004851.$$

Therefore, $x = C + z' = 2.0946 + (-.00004851) = 2.09455149$, which is true to the seventh place of decimals.

By proceeding in a similar manner, the value of x may be found to any required degree of accuracy.

REMARK.—The great objection to Newton's Method of Approximation is, that we are obliged after each operation to commence with the entire approximate value of x in the same manner as at first, and no assistance is derived from the previous calculations, except in having found a nearer value of the root. But in Horner's method, we approximate continuously to the true value of the root by the evolution of single figures, as in Long Division, and the Extraction of the square root in arithmetic; and each previous figure is of use in finding the next. Newton's method is now rarely used, and may be classed among the scientific curiosities of a past age.

Articles 438—441.

CARDAN'S SOLUTION OF CUBIC EQUATIONS.

Formulæ, $x^3+3qx+2r=0$.

$x=\sqrt[3]{(-r+\sqrt{r^2+q^3})}+\sqrt[3]{(-r-\sqrt{r^2+q^3})}$.

(2) $x^3-9x+28=0$. Here, $q=-3$, and $r=+14$.

$x=\sqrt[3]{(-14+\sqrt{196-27})}+\sqrt[3]{(-14-\sqrt{196-27})}$

$=\sqrt[3]{(-14+13)}+\sqrt[3]{(-14-13)}=\sqrt[3]{-1}+\sqrt[3]{-27}=-1$

$-3=-4$.

Dividing the given equation by $x-(-4)=x+4$, the quotient is x^2-4x+7; hence, $x^2-4x+7=0$, and

$x=2\pm\sqrt{-3}$.

(3) $x^3+6x-2=0$. Here, $q=+2$, and $r=-1$.

$x=\sqrt[3]{(+1+\sqrt{1+8})}+\sqrt[3]{(+1-\sqrt{1+8})}=\sqrt[3]{4}+\sqrt[3]{-2}$

$=\sqrt[3]{4}-\sqrt[3]{2}=1.58740-1.25992=.32748$.

(4) $x^3-6x^2+13x-10=0$.

To remove the second term (see Art. 407, Cor.),

$r=-\frac{A}{n}=-\frac{-6}{3}=+2$.

Therefore, $x=y+2$, and the transformed equation is

$(y+2)^3-6(y+2)^2+13(y+2)-10=0$

$y^3+y=0$, or $y(y^2+1)=0$;

whence, $y=0$, and $y^2+1=0$; or $y=\pm\sqrt{-1}$.
Therefore, $x=y+2=2$; or $2\pm\sqrt{-1}$.

(5) $x^3-9x^2+6x-2=0$.
Let $x=y+\frac{9}{3}=y+3$; then,
$(y+3)^3-9(y+3)^2+6(y+3)-2=0$;
or $y^3-21y-38=0$.
Here, $q=-7$, and $r=-19$.

$$x=\sqrt[3]{(19+\sqrt{361-343})}+\sqrt[3]{(19-\sqrt{361-343})}$$
$$=\sqrt[3]{(19+3\sqrt{2})}+\sqrt[3]{(19-3\sqrt{2})}$$
$$=\sqrt[3]{(19+3\times1.414213562373095048\text{8})}$$
$$+\sqrt[3]{(19-3\times1.4142135623730950488)}$$
$$=\sqrt[3]{(23.2426406871192851\text{46})}$$
$$+\sqrt[3]{(14.757359312880714854)}$$
$$=2.8538325+2.4528418=5.306674+.$$

Therefore, $x=y+3=5.306674+3=8.306674+$.

REMARK.—In the solution to the last example, the extraction of the square root is carried to 18 places of decimals, but this is further than is necessary to insure accuracy in extracting the cube root to 7 places. For this purpose 10 places, or even less, are quite sufficient.

After the pupil has faithfully performed all the operations in the 5th example, let him solve the same by Horner's method (Art. 434), and he will then appreciate its superiority. To obtain the result true to 6 places of decimals requires about one-fourth as much labor by Horner's Method as by Cardan's Rule, and the difference increases rapidly with the increase in the number of places of decimals.

Article 442.

RECIPROCAL OR RECURRING EQUATIONS.

(1) $x^4-10x^3+26x^2-10x+1=0$.

$x^2-10x+26-\frac{10}{x}+\frac{1}{x^2}=0$, by dividing by x^2;

or $x^2+\frac{1}{x^2}-10\left(x+\frac{1}{x}\right)=-26$,

Let $x+\frac{1}{x}=z$; then, $x^2+\frac{1}{x^2}=z^2-2$, and

$z^2-2-10z=-26$,

$z^2-10z=-24$, and $z=6$ or 4.

Therefore, $x+\frac{1}{x}=6$ or 4;

whence, $x=3\pm2\sqrt{2}$, or $2\pm\sqrt{3}$.

(2) $x^4-\frac{5}{2}x^3+2x^2-\frac{5}{2}x+1=0$.

$x^2-\frac{5}{2}x+2-\frac{5}{2x}+\frac{1}{x^2}=0$, by dividing by x^2;

$x^2+\frac{1}{x^2}-\frac{5}{2}\left(x+\frac{1}{x}\right)=-2$.

Let $x+\frac{1}{x}=z$; then, $x^2+\frac{1}{x^2}=z^2-2$, and

$z^2-\frac{5}{2}z=0$; whence, $z=0$, or $+\frac{5}{2}$.

Therefore, $x+\frac{1}{x}=0$, or $+\frac{5}{2}$;

whence, $x=\pm\sqrt{-1}$, or 2, or $\frac{1}{2}$.

(3) $x^4-3x^3+3x-1=0$.

It is proved in Art. 442, Prop. III, that this equation is divisible by x^2-1; therefore, $x^2-1=0$, and $x=\pm1$.

Dividing the given equation by x^2-1, the quotient is x^2-3x+1; therefore, $x^2-3x+1=0$; whence, $x=\frac{1}{2}(3\pm\sqrt{5})$.

(4) $x^5-11x^4+17x^3+17x^2-11x+1=0$.

It follows from Art. 442, Prop. II, that -1 is a root of this equation; therefore, it is divisible by $x+1$ (Art. 395).

$$\begin{array}{r} 1-11+17+17-11+1 \quad (-1 \\ -\ 1+12-29+12-1 \\ \hline 1-12+29-12+\ 1 \quad 0 \end{array}$$

Therefore, $x^4-12x^3+29x^2-12x+1=0$.

$x^2-12x+29-\frac{12}{x}+\frac{1}{x^2}=0$, by dividing by x^2;

$x^2+\frac{1}{x^2}-12\left(x+\frac{1}{x}\right)=-29$.

Let $x+\frac{1}{x}=z$; then, $x^2+\frac{1}{x^2}=z^2-2$, and

$z^2-12z=-27$; whence, $z=9$ or 3.

Therefore, $x+\frac{1}{x}=9$ or 3;

whence, $x=\frac{9\pm\sqrt{77}}{2}$, or $\frac{3\pm\sqrt{5}}{2}$.

(5) $4x^6-24x^5+57x^4-73x^3+57x^2-24x+4=0$

$4x^3-24x^2+57x-73+\frac{57}{x}-\frac{24}{x^2}+\frac{4}{x^3}=0$, by dividing by x^3;

$4\left(x^3+\frac{1}{x^3}\right)-24\left(x^2+\frac{1}{x^2}\right)+57\left(x+\frac{1}{x}\right)=73.$

Let $x+\frac{1}{x}=z$; then, $x^2+\frac{1}{x^2}=z^2-2$, and $x^3+\frac{1}{x^3}=z^3-3z$

Therefore, $4(z^3-3z)-24(z^2-2)+57z=73$,

$z^3-6z^2+\frac{45}{4}z=+\frac{25}{4}$.

To solve this equation by Cardan's Rule, Art. 441,

let $z=y+2$; then, $y^3-\frac{3}{4}y+\frac{1}{4}=0$,

$y=\sqrt[3]{\left(-\frac{1}{8}+\sqrt{\frac{1}{64}-\frac{1}{64}}\right)}+\sqrt[3]{\left(-\frac{1}{8}-\sqrt{\frac{1}{64}-\frac{1}{64}}\right)}$

$=-\frac{1}{2}-\frac{1}{2}=-1$.

Dividing $y^3-\frac{3}{4}y+\frac{1}{4}$ by $y+1$, the quotient is $y^2-y+\frac{1}{4}$;

therefore, $y^2-y+\frac{1}{4}=0$, and $y=+\frac{1}{2}$, and $+\frac{1}{2}$.

Therefore, $z=y+2=-1+2=1$, or $\frac{1}{2}+2=\frac{5}{2}$, and $\frac{5}{2}$.

Therefore, $x+\frac{1}{x}=1$; whence, $x=\frac{1\pm\sqrt{-3}}{2}$;

or $x+\frac{1}{x}=\frac{5}{2}$; whence, $x=2$, or $\frac{1}{2}$.

Therefore, the six roots are $2, \frac{1}{2}, 2, \frac{1}{2}, \frac{1+\sqrt{-3}}{2}$

and $\frac{1-\sqrt{-3}}{2}$.

Article 444.

BINOMIAL EQUATIONS.

(1) Let $x^4=1$, then, $x^4-1=0$, and $(x^2-1)(x^2+1)=0$.

$\therefore$ $x^2-1=0$; whence, $x^2=1$, and $x=+1$ or -1.

Also, $x^2+1=0$; whence, $x^2=-1$, and $x=+\sqrt{-1}$,

or, $-\sqrt{-1}$.

(2) Let $x^5=1$; then, $x^5-1=0$, and the equation is divisible by $x-1$; $\therefore$ $x-1=0$, and $x=+1$.

Dividing x^5-1 by $x-1$, and placing the quotient equal to zero, we have

$x^4+x^3+x^2+x+1=0$;

$x^2+x+1+\frac{1}{x}+\frac{1}{x^2}=0$, by dividing by x^2,

$x^2+\frac{1}{x^2}+x+\frac{1}{x}=-1$.

Let $x+\frac{1}{x}=z$; then, $x^2+\frac{1}{x^2}=z^2-2$, and

$z^2+z=1$; whence, $z=\frac{-1\pm\sqrt{5}}{2}=a$.

$\therefore$ $x+\frac{1}{x}=a$; whence, $x=\frac{a}{2}+\frac{1}{2}\sqrt{a^2-4}$, or $\frac{a}{2}-\frac{1}{2}\sqrt{a^2-4}$

and since a has two values, x will have four values.

$$a^2=\frac{(-1\pm\sqrt{5})^2}{4}=\frac{6-2\sqrt{5}}{4}, \text{ or } \frac{6+2\sqrt{5}}{4}.$$

$$x=\frac{a}{2}+\frac{1}{2}\sqrt{a^2-4}=\frac{-1+\sqrt{5}}{4}+\frac{1}{4}\sqrt{-10-2\sqrt{5}}$$
$$=\tfrac{1}{4}\{\sqrt{5}-1+\sqrt{(-10-2\sqrt{5})}\};$$
$$x=\frac{a}{2}-\frac{1}{2}\sqrt{a^2-4}=\frac{-1+\sqrt{5}}{4}-\frac{1}{4}\sqrt{-10-2\sqrt{5}}$$
$$=\tfrac{1}{4}\{\sqrt{5}-1-\sqrt{(-10-2\sqrt{5})}\};$$
$$x=-\frac{a}{2}+\frac{1}{2}\sqrt{a^2-4}=\frac{-1-\sqrt{5}}{4}+\frac{1}{4}\sqrt{-10+2\sqrt{5}}$$
$$=-\tfrac{1}{4}\{\sqrt{5}+1-\sqrt{(-10+2\sqrt{5})}\};$$
$$x=\frac{a}{2}-\frac{1}{2}\sqrt{a^2-4}=\frac{-1-\sqrt{5}}{4}-\frac{1}{4}\sqrt{-10+2\sqrt{5}}$$
$$=-\tfrac{1}{4}\{\sqrt{5}+1+\sqrt{(-10+2\sqrt{5})}\}.$$